Menu

ACKNOWLEDGEMENTS

Many thanks to the hundred or so CAMRA members who surveyed pubs and supplied information, particularly Simon Fyffe, Mike & Gill Harvey, Mr. Towler, Anne Radley, Derek Wisdom, Margaret & Del Ryan and Will Morley.

TRADING STANDARDS

If you believe that you have received short measure, or that the prices of beers, etc. are not correctly displayed, you are advised to contact the Trading Standards Department of the local Council. Essex Headquarters General Enquiries are on (01245) 341800.

Copyright CAMRA Ltd.

MILD
MARKETING
BOARD

9th ESSEX BEER GUIDE

WELCOME to the ninth Essex beer guide. Firstly a word about the scope of this guide - it is a comprehensive and non-selective guide to the pubs in the county of Essex. In other words we aim to include every pub in the county, and we take the word "pub" in its widest sense to mean any establishment which sells beer of any sort dispensed from a bulk container into a glass for consumption on the premises, without the requirement to have a meal. You will find that those pubs selling cask-conditioned beer (real ale) at the time of the survey have a full entry with plenty of useful information and those which do not just have a briefer entry.

How do we get our information? Every pub in Essex has been surveyed (that is visited) by CAMRA members who will if possible speak to the licensee himself or herself to obtain accurate information for the guide.

THE CHANGING SCENE

As you can imagine surveying is a fairly large task and takes some time. This issue of the guide has taken longer to produce than previous editions due to the great increase in the rate of change in the pub scene over the last few years. Pubs now frequently change ownership or management, many pubs sadly have closed particularly in rural areas and numerous new pubs have opened (also sadly in some cases) in urban areas. We have done our best to keep up with the changes by updating as much information as we can prior to publication but it is inevitable that by the time you have bought the guide, further changes will have occurred and there will be inaccuracies. In spite of this you do hold in your hand the most comprehensive guide available to the drinking establishments of Essex.

Beers, facilities and pub opening hours are liable to change without notice, so if you have any particular requirements, we strongly advise you to contact the pub concerned before travelling.

The opinions expressed in the pub comments are those of the individual surveyor and not necessarily those of the Essex branches of CAMRA or the editorial team. All trademarks are acknowledged.

WHO ARE WE?

The guide is produced by the members of the Essex branches of CAMRA, all of whom give their time free (and pay for their own beer!). CAMRA was founded in 1971 and now has around 55,000 members. It has been described as the most successful consumer association ever and succeeded in stemming the flow of keg beer which threatened to engulf the country in the 60s and 70s by showing that there is a demand for tasty traditional beer and that not everyone is prepared to accept second best just because the brewers tell us we should. Or in other words we are a large group of ordinary people who enjoy drinking good beer and are prepared to take steps to ensure that it continues to be available. To this end we support and promote the brewers and retailers of real ale, organise beer festivals, produce beer guides and generally have a good time while doing so. We also ensure that the voice of the beer drinker is heard, be it at local level such as a threat to a local pub, industry level such as brewery closures, national level as in the iniquitous rates of duty imposed on the British beer drinker, and at international level as in our successful representations to the E.C. over the threat to the right of publicans to stock a guest cask-conditioned ale. If you are not already a member then please come and join us - you will find a membership application form and details of the Essex branches at the back of this book.

ABOUT BEER

What is real ale? Real ale is a living beer. Having been produced by the brewer from the finest ingredients - malt, hops, yeast and water - it is racked into casks, finings are added to help clear the beer, additional hops may be added to give extra flavour and aroma and priming sugar may be added. The beer still contains living yeast which continues to act (secondary fermentation) to develop the full flavour and condition of the beer. The optimum time over which the secondary fermentation takes place varies from beer to beer and the skilled publican or cellarman will be able to judge when a cask of beer is right for serving. So the quality of the beer in your glass depends not only on the skill of the brewer but also on the skill and care taken in the pub cellar.

Draught real ale is usually dispensed via a beer engine (hand pump) or sometimes by gravity (straight from the cask). In some parts of the country electric pumps are used, but this is rare in Essex.

Real ale is pleasantly cool and clear in appearance. It should not be too warm or cold - ideally 12C (54F) to 14C (57F) in the cellar. Neither should it be flat or cloudy (a slight haze which does not affect the flavour may be acceptable), nor is real ale necessarily strong - most are of ordinary drinking strength, 3.5-4.5% alcohol by volume.

When is real ale not real ale? The secondary fermentation produces carbon dioxide and sufficient of this will dissolve in the beer to produce the right amount of sparkle (condition) and head on the beer. Beer should not have any gas applied to it from any extraneous source. **Top pressure** is a method of applying gas to the cask at sufficient pressure to force the beer to the bar when a tap is opened, the beer can be served through a small tap similar to a keg dispenser or through a fake handpump where there is no pumping action but the beer continues to flow as the handle is held down. This can prevent the beer from developing its full flavour and also causes excessive gas to dissolve in the beer giving an unpleasant gassy feel in the mouth and often unpleasant after effects. What left the brewery as a perfectly good beer is ruined by the time it gets to your glass.

When beer is served in the correct manner air is drawn into the cask to replace the volume of liquid drawn off. If the cask is not kept in cool, clean surroundings or takes an excessive time to sell (more than three or four days) then problems can arise - the beer will lose condition and go flat, start to taste stale and eventually turn sour. In order to counteract this some publicans use a device called a **cask breather** or **aspirator** which applies gas (CO_2 or a nitrogen/CO_2 mixture) to the cask at about atmospheric pressure thus preventing air from entering the cask, delaying the effects of oxidation and effectively prolonging the life of the beer - although it is unlikely to prevent loss of condition. In circumstances where a pub has a very low or erratic turnover of beer then use of a cask breather may be the only way to keep a cask-conditioned ale in drinkable condition and most CAMRA members would prefer to drink real ale served with a cask breather than to have no real ale at all. However in reality the number of pubs in which this situation applies is fairly small and the cask breather is all too often used as a cover up for poor cellar management, to allow beer to be stocked in too large a size of cask or to allow the pub to stock a larger range of beers than its turnover warrants. For these reasons CAMRA does not recommend any such system and pubs using them are unlikely to be included in the Good Beer Guide.(In exceptional circumstances a pub may be included if it serves some beers without breather, but those beers or ciders served with will be excluded).

What is keg beer then? Keg beers are not living beers. They have been well and truly killed off in the brewery by pasteurisation and filtration and put into sealed kegs from which the only way to serve them is by gas pressure. Keg beers have nothing like the character and flavour of a decent real ale and are usually served chilled to mask the unpleasant taste imparted by pasteurisation.

Brewers (particularly the big ones) became very keen on keg beers because they are easier to mass produce, have a longer shelf life than real ales and require no skill to keep and serve, and a consistent product can be served by anyone with little or no training. You may be old enough to remember the notorious Watney's Red Barrel and such other delights as Ben Truman, Double Diamond , Younger's Tartan and many more, which were replacing cask conditioned beers all over the country - heavy advertising persuading many drinkers that these were actually better than the traditional beers. CAMRA was formed in response to this threat to our traditional beers and after much campaigning the big brewers (and those smaller brewers who had joined the keg revolution) realised that there is a big market for real ale. Handpumps reappeared on bars, the range of real ales increased, and the number of keg beers diminished. Things are looking good.

But wait a minute! What are these new beers that have appeared recently? They are heavily advertised, generally more expensive than real ales and often served via a device that resembles a miniature handpump so they must be good surely? Sorry but the answer is NO - they are just keg beers all over again but under a different guise. Known as **nitrokeg** beers, they are served using a mixture of nitrogen and CO2 which makes them less obviously fizzy than the old keg beers but produces many tiny bubbles which settle to form a thick foamy head. They are usually called creamflow or cream (surely cream goes better with strawberries than with beer) or smooth (meaning no lumps or no flavour?) and should be avoided as they are no substitute for good cask conditioned beer.

THE STRENGTH OF BEER

This is expressed in two different ways, the traditional method is in terms of "ORIGINAL GRAVITY" (OG), which is dependent upon the quantity of fermentable material added to the brewing liquor (water) to produce the beer. For example, a beer with an OG of 1040 degrees would have 40 parts of fermentable material to every 1000 parts of water. The newer method is to consider the percentage of alcohol by volume (ABV) in the final product. The 1040 beer (above), would have an ABV of roughly 4%. Similarly a beer of 1080 OG would have 80 parts per 1000 and would be twice as strong with an ABV of around 8%.

The strength of beer can vary considerably, but generally falls into the following approximate OG bands:

Beer style	OG	Approx. ABV
Milds (and many lagers!)	1030 to 1036	3.0 to 3.6%
Bitters	1034 to 1040	3.4 to 4.0%
Best Bitters	1040 to 1045	4.0 to 4.5%
Premium Bitters & Winter Ales	1045 to 1055	4.5 to 5.5%
Extra Strong Beers	1055 to 1070	5.5 to 7.0%
Barley Wines	1070 to 1100	7.0 to 10.0%
Kamikazi Brews!	1100 upwards	10.0% upwards

SWAN NECKS AND SPARKLERS

Have you noticed a change in the beer in your glass lately? Using the traditional handpump dispense in the Southern half of the country, bar staff should be able with two steady pulls plus a little extra to perfectly fill a pint glass with a pint of beer with a small head on. All too often you will find the bar staff flexing their muscles for numerous pulls on the pump against some resistance to present you with a glass of swirling liquid which eventually settles to have at least half an inch of thick foam on top. When you get through the foam to reach the beer you find it is disappointingly bland and undistinguished - your beer has been served through a tight sparkler, usually attached to a swan neck (a long metal tube which is inserted to the bottom of the glass as the beer is dispensed). This type of dispense has three disadvantages:

1. Use of the sparkler forces bitterness into the head and leaves the body of the beer blander. This is traditional in the North and some Northern beers are brewed to withstand this treatment. Most Southern beers are not and will have their flavour ruined.

2. The space taken up by the foam makes it impossible to get a full pint into a brim measure glass, and so you are getting short measure unless the pub uses oversized glasses (not very common around here).

3. A tube coated with dried beer and probably visited by flies and bits of drifting cigarette ash, and possibly other peoples saliva if a fresh glass is not used each time is being dipped into your beer!

WHY DO THEY DO IT? Two reasons, firstly, many pub companies think that you're so dim you drink with your eyes and won't drink anything unless it has a thick head as in the Boddington's adverts. Secondly many pubs see it as a good way of giving you short measure and so increasing profits.

SO WHAT CAN I DO? Glance over the bar before you order and if you see a plastic sparkler fitted to the end of the spout ask politely for it to be removed (it only takes a few seconds). If you have been served short measure ask politely for it to be topped up. If either of these requests is refused then the best option is to walk out and find another pub - one which cares about its beer and its customers.

BEER FESTIVALS

CAMRA organises many beer festivals throughout the year and all over the country, ranging in size from the humblest local event to the highlight of the year the Great British Beer Festival held every August at Olympia. These events are where we show that we are not just theorists telling everyone else how to serve beer, but we can actually do the job ourselves. Festivals also allow us to provide a wide selection of different beers at one event, many of them not usually available in the locality.

All CAMRA festivals are open to both members and non-members, and members also have the opportunity to help to run them. If you are a member and you haven't worked at a festival before, why not give it a try?

You can start gently by volunteering for just one session and one day you may end up on the organising committee!

The exact dates and details of festivals are published in What's Brewing, and are advertised in local newsletters, pubs, etc. Here is a list of the festivals normally held in Essex with their approximate dates:

HARLOW	JANUARY
ONGAR	MAY
COLCHESTER	MAY
THURROCK	MAY/JUNE
CHELMSFORD	JULY
CLACTON	AUGUST
CHAPPEL	SEPTEMBER
SAFFRON WALDEN	OCTOBER
ROCHFORD	NOVEMBER

There are also many beer festivals which are not organised by CAMRA. For example, numerous pubs organise festivals from time to time, also Round Table groups and even local authorities such as Castle Point. These events all provide an excellent opportunity to sample a wide range of ales.

ESSEX BREWERIES

Essex once had many breweries, indeed almost every village had a brewery at some time and some 27 have been recorded in Chelmsford alone, but sadly the numbers have declined dramatically during this century. For a full and detailed history Ian Peaty's excellent book "Essex Brewers" published by the brewery history society is recommended. We just mention here some recent history:

1974 was a bad year for brewing in Essex as two old established berweries closed down - G.E. Cook & Sons of Halstead and Gray & Sons of Chelmsford. Both companies still continue in business, Cooks as a wine merchant, and Grays still run their estate of excellent pubs. Gray & Sons brewery stood forlornly disused in Springfield Road for a number of years until becoming part of a retail development - some of the buildings are still recognisable. These closures reduced the number of breweries in Essex to two: T.D.Ridley & Sons of Hartford End, Chelmsford and the Ind Coope brewery in Romford, the latter having been in its heyday a huge concern with its own railway sidings.

1981 saw the number of Essex breweries double with the opening of the Pheasant brewery at Gestingthorpe and Crouch Vale brewery at South Woodham Ferrers. The former only lasted three years, closing in 1984 and the latter is still with us. In 1992 the Romford brewery closed, once more reducing the numbers to two and there has been a welcome boost recently with the opening of the Mighty Oak brewery, Hutton in 1996.

There are currently two "pub breweries" known to be operating in the county: The Original Brewing Company at the Hollywood Bowl, Basildon - owned by Bass- and the Ford and Firkin in Romford - owned by Carlsberg-Tetley.

CIDER

The situation with traditional Cider today is similar to that of Real Ale in the 1970's, with the vast majority of cider produced being in keg form.

Real Cider is made by fermenting the juice of cider and dessert apples with, sometimes, a little sugar - sadly many cider manufacturers use only concentrate! Real Cider must not be filtered or pasteurised, nor must it be stored or served under pressure - unfortunately, certain manufacturers are using the traditional handpump which has strong associations with Real Beer to dispense keg cider - so beware!

Scrumpy Jack and *Cidermaster* are examples of keg ciders often sold through handpumps, this method of dispense appears to have been chosen with the aim of conning the public into believing that it is the 'Real' thing. Also, *Addlestone's* is often stored under carbon dioxide (top or blanket pressure).

Most of the market is controlled by a couple of large producers. However, a few smal! independent producers still survive, and with the revival in popularity of 'Real' Cider (Scrumpy) it is now becoming widely available throughout Essex.

WHAT ARE CAMRA'S PRIORITIES NOW?

1. **Quality**: As you can see from this guide real ale is very widely available now and you can find it in almost any part of the county, but it is no good having real ale if the quality is not up to scratch. We must continue to push the message that all licensees must pay proper attention to hygeine, temperature, cask-handling and stock control so that their customers can enjoy a good pint. It is far better to sell a small range of beers with a fast turnover than a large range some of which sell slowly and turn to vinegar.

2. **Choice:** The introduction of the guest beer laws requiring all large brewers to allow their tenants to stock a guest beer was hailed as a resounding success. Unfortunately they soon found a loophole - the law applies only to brewers - so they have been busy offloading most of their pubs to non-brewing subsidiaries. The tenants lose their guest beer rights, customers lose choice and small brewers lose their outlets. The law must be changed to include non-brewing pub chains.

3. **Duty:** Most European countries enjoy a lower rate of duty than we do. This results in large quantities of beer being brought across the channel for home consumption, leading to a huge loss of trade for British pubs and breweries CAMRA demands that duty be lowered to the European average, this would safeguard jobs and pubs and in the end lead to no loss to the exchequer. Smaller breweries are hit particularly hard as the levels of duty levied cause cash flow problems and lack of money for investment. This could be solved if we had a sliding rate of tax - the smaller the production, the lower the rate of duty charged. This system is used in most of Europe and the U.S. The British Government must take urgent action on these matters.

Abberton & Langenhoe E3

11-2.30; 7-11 (12-3; 7-10.30 Sun)

Langenhoe Lion
Mersea Road (B1025)
Tel: (01206) 735263
Greene King - No Real Ale.

Abridge A4

Retains its charm, despite its proximity to London.

12-11 (10.30 Sun)

Blue Boar Hungry Man
Market Place, London Road
(by A113)
Tel: (01992) 812110
S&N Courage Best Bitter **H**
Directors **G; Whitbread**
Flowers Original **G**

🍺 🍻 🌙 🍴 📻 🏮 ♿
Large Greenall's pub-restaurant, with interesting old photographs and prints. The drinking area is split into several cosy sections. Beers on gravity dispense are a regular feature.

11-3.30; 6.30-11
(12-4; 7-10.30 Sun)

Maltster's Arms
London Road (A113)
Tel: (01992) 813404
Greene King IPA, Abbot Ale **H**
🍺 🍴 📻 🌸
Unspoilt 16th Century pub, with a friendly atmosphere. Original beams and open fires - a place to relax in. Parking difficult.

11-11 (12-10.30 Sun)

White Hart
Market Place (A113/B172)
Tel: (01992) 813104
S&N Courage Best Bitter,
Directors, John Smiths Bitter,
Youngers No 3, Websters
Yorkshire Bitter; **Whitbread**
Boddingtons Bitter **H**
🍺 🍻 🍴 🌙 📻
Large traditional pub by the River Roding. Live music - jazz on Wednesday, other on Fridays. Quizzes on Thursdays.

Aingers Green (Gt Bentley) E3

11-2.30 (3.30 Sat); 5.30-11
(12-4; 7-10.30 Sun)

Royal Fusilier
Aingers Green Road
OS: TM119204
Tel: (01206) 250001
Adnams Bitter; **Guest Beers H**
Real Cider (Summer) **G**
🏮 🌙 🌸
Friendly, 200 year old pub with a colourful landlord, who has many a story to tell.
The pub is a regular entry in the Good Beer Guide. Two guest beers each week. The MG Club meets here on Mondays.

Aldborough Hatch (Newbury Park) A4

11-11 (12-10.30 Sun)

Dick Turpin
Aldborough Road North (H mile North of A12)
Tel: (0181) 590 1281
Whitbread Boddingtons Bitter,
Flowers Original **H**
🍺 🍻 🍴 📻
Refurbished Beefeater.

Alresford E2

11.30-2.30 (3 Sat); 5.30 (6 Sat)-11
(12-3; 7-10.30 Sun)

Pointer
Wivenhoe Road (nr B1027)
Tel: (01206) 822866
Tetley Imperial; **Tolly** Original **H**
🏮 🌸 ⚓
Two-bar village pub with good beer garden, aviary and fish pond, near the railway station. Pool played. Beware 'sparklers' on the Tolly beer.

Rose & Crown
St Osyth Road (B1027)
OS: TM064225
Free-house - Pub closed and converted to a 'B&B'.

Althorne D4

Fine views of Crouch estuary.

11.30-3; 6.30-11 (12-10.30 Sun)

Black Lion
Burnham Road (B1018)
OS: TQ909999
Tel: (01621) 740241
Greene King IPA; **Ridleys** IPA **H**
🍺 🍻 🏮 📻 ♿
Attractive country pub, in the same hands for 10 years. Food-oriented, plush and comfortable with well-maintained gardens. No fruit machines.

12-3; 5-11 (12-11 Sat: 12-10.30 Sun)

Huntsman & Hounds
Green Lane (off B1018)
OS: TL906004
Tel: (01621) 740387
Greene King IPA, Abbot Ale;
Marstons Pedigree (guest) **H**
Addlestones Cider **H**
🍺 🍻 📻 ♿
Picturesque, 16th century, partly-thatched Grays pub with well-kept garden & pond. Interesting bank note collection. Large (6 acre) field at rear is available for functions. Camping and caravanning available. No food Sun, Mon or Tue evening.

12-3; 7-11 (12-10.30 Sun)

Three Horse Shoes
Burnham Road (B1010)
Tel: (01621) 740307
Greene King IPA **H**
🍺 🍻 🍴 🌸 📻
Gray & Sons outlet set back from the road. Mini zoo and children's room in garden in summer. Excellent menu.

Andrewsfield (Stebbing) C2

11 (12 Sun) - Dusk or later
(closed Mondays)

Milli-Bar & Marauder Restaurant
Saling Airfield, Saling Road
OS: TL689248
Tel: (01371) 856744
Adnams Bitter; **Greene King** IPA **H**
🍺 🍻 🍴 📻
Former WW2 air base, now used for light aircraft. Watch the planes take off from the viewing terrace.
Bar may stay open after dusk, if there are customers to serve.

Ardleigh E2

Sprawling village with pleasant church and large reservoir nearby. The home of Mary Whitehouse and 'Notcutts' nursery.

11-11 (12-10.30 Sun)

Butterfly Hotel (Walts Bar)
Old Ipswich Road
(by A12/A1232/A120)
OS: TM021290
Tel: (01206) 230900
Greene King IPA, Abbot **H**
🍺 🍻 🍴 📻 🌙 🌸 🏮 ♿
Plush, sumptuous, new hotel, that caters for non-residents.

11-3 (4 Sat); 7-11 (12-5; 7-10.30 Sun)

Lion
The Street (B1029, by A137)
Tel: (01206) 230083
Greene King IPA; **Tolly**
Cobbold Mild **H**
🍺 🍻 🏮
Village locals boozer, dating from the 14th century, with strong darts and pool following.

12-11 (10.30 Sun)

Old Crown Inn
Old Ipswich Road (nrA1232/A12)
OS: TM022293
Tel: (01206) 231102
Bass Hancocks HB,
Worthingtons BB,
Draught Bass **H**
🍺 🍻 🍴 📻
Nicely refurbished, and vastly-extended early 1997, with flagstone floors and old timbers. Lots of character, but lacking atmosphere. Could become very food-oriented.
Located two miles west of the village.

11-3; 6-11 (12-3; 7-10.30 Sun)

Wooden Fender Inn
Harwich Road (A137)
OS: TM044290
Tel: (01206) 230466
Adnams Bitter; **Greene King** IPA,
Abbot Ale; **Marstons** Pedigree;
Morlands Old Speckled Hen **H**
🍺🍺🍺🅁🍴🐾♿
Pleasant 14th century roadside
inn. Frequented by Witchfinder
Matthew Hopkins in the 1640's.
Regular guest beers. Good
range of vegetarian meals.

Arkesden
A1

*Picturesque village with
thatched cottages by a small
stream.*

12-2.30; 6-11 (12-2.30; 7-10.30
Sun)

Axe & Compasses
2 miles North of B1038
OS: TL483344
Tel: (01799) 550272
Greene King IPA, Abbot Ale **H**
🍺🍺🍺🅁🍴🐾♿
Superb, partly-thatched, 17th
Century, village local with a
thriving food trade. Listed in
CAMRA's 'Classic Country Pubs'.

Ashdon
B1

*Scene of an agricultural work-
ers' strike in 1912, which led to
farming reform.*

Bonnet
Steventon End
OS: TL598428
Free-house - Pub closed and
converted to a private house.

Bricklayers Arms
Bartlow Road
Greene King - Pub closed and
converted to a private house.

11-11 (12-10.30 Sun)

Rose & Crown
(Crown Hill)
Tel: (01799) 584337
Greene King IPA; **Ind Coope**
Burton Ale **H**
🍺🍺🍺🍺 (Not Mon) 🅁🍺🐾
Very friendly, cosy listed build-
ing, dating from the 15th to 17th
centuries. Has a wood-burning
stove in the old inglenook.
Occasional Guest beers. Friday
is 'fresh fish' day!

Ashingdon
D4

Quiet, but expanding village.

11-11 (12-10.30 Sun)

Victory
485 Ashingdon Road
Tel: (01702) 548440
S&N Courage Best Bitter,
Directors **H**
🍺🍺🍺🐾
Spacious local, refurbished as a
'Steak & Ale' outlet.
Accommodating darts and Sky
sports. Children welcome.
Sunday roasts a speciality. 32oz
steaks. Beware all beers are
served through 'sparklers'!

Aveley
B5

*Unusually, this small friendly
Thurrock town has a High Street
full of pubs. It also includes
Belhus Woods Country Park, a
golf course and swimming pool.*

11-5; 7-11 (Not Mon) (11-11 Sat:
12-5 Sun)

Capability Brown
Park Lane, Belhus Park (off
B1335)
OS: TQ573811
Tel: (01708) 852248
Free-house - No Real Ale.

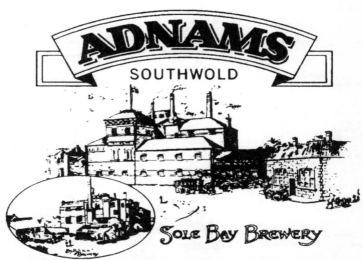

9

11-3; 6-11 (11-11 Sat: 12-10.30 Sun)

Crown & Anchor
43 High Street (nr B1335)
Tel: (01708) 890424
Ind Coope 'House' Bitter;
Tetley Bitter **H**
◖D ◖ ▶ ❀

Comfortable and friendly pub with one bar and adjoining dining area. Enthusiastic landlord may introduce a separate restaurant in the future. The food is particularly recommended.

11-11 (12-10.30 Sun)

Marisco
Romford Road (nr B1335)
Tel: (01708) 890379
Bass - No Real Ale.

11-3; 6-11 (11-11 Sat: 12-10.30 Sun)

Old Ship
58 High Street (nr B1335)
Tel: (01708) 865647
Ind Coope Burton Ale;
Tetley Bitter **H**
◖D ⊞

Traditionally-styled local with three bars and a friendly, quiet atmosphere. Parking difficult. Formerly the "Ship".

11-11 (12-10.30 Sun)

Prince Albert
35 High Street (nr B1335)
Tel: (01708) 890671
S&N Courage Best Bitter (or) Directors Winter Warmer **H**
⊞

Atmospheric drinkers pub, with a lively crowd and very cheap Real Ale! Popular with older drinkers at lunchtimes. Children also welcome.
Weekend sea-food stall, limited parking.

12-11 (10.30 Sun)

Sir Henry Gurnett
Romford Road (nr B1335)
OS: TQ563818
Tel: (01708) 864042
Greene King Abbot Ale; **S&N** Theakstons XB; **Ushers** Gibbs Mew Salisbury BB, Bishops Tipple; **Wadworths** 6X **H**
◖D ◖ ▶ R ❀ ♿

Impressive, 800 year old half-timbered farmhouse with stream, and resident swans in the pond and garden. Internally rebuilt with upstairs restaurant. Children's playground. Beware 'tight sparklers' used.

12-11 (10.30 Sun)

Top House
14 Purfleet Road (nr B1335)
Tel: (01708) 864614
Free-house - No Real Ale at present, but may change.

Aythorpe Roding   B3

Scattered community.

11.30-2; 6.30-11 (11-11 Sat: Hours vary Sun)

Axe & Compasses
Dunmow Road (B184)
OS: TL594154
Tel: (01279) 876647
Whitbread Boddingtons Bitter; Flowers IPA;
Guest Beer H
◖D ◖ ▶ ▬ ❀ ♿

Interesting, steep-roofed, low-roomed, 16th century building.

Ballards Gore (Stambridge)   D4

12-3; 7-11 (10.30 Sun)

Shepherd & Dog
Gore Road
OS: TQ906928
Tel: (01702) 258279
S&N Courage Directors; **Guest Beers H**
◖D ◖ ▶ R (book!) ⊞ ❀

Log fires in winter. Extensive menu, including 'A la Carte' and traditional pub fare.

Bannister Green (Felsted)   C2

12-2.30 (3 Sat); 6 (7 Sat)-11 (12-3; 7-10.30 Sun)

Three Horseshoes
Bannister Green (nr B1417)
OS: TL696206
Tel: (01371) 820467
Ridleys IPA, ESX, Rumpus, seasonal beers **H**
◖D ◖ ⊞ ❀

Unspoilt, picturesque, low-beamed, 15th century pub on the village green. 'Ring the Bull' in public bar. Well-run and friendly, with home-cooking and a welcoming atmosphere.

Bardfield End Green   B2

Butchers Arms
Bardfield Road
1 mile East of B184 at Thaxted
OS: TL628305
Greene King - Pub closed and converted to a private house. A sad loss!

Barking   A5

Once a fishing port, where captain Cook was married in 1762. Now urbanised, and generally a poor drinking town, with a couple of notable exceptions.

11-11 (12-10.30 Sun)

Barge Aground   1
15 Broadway (near A124/A123)
Tel: (0181) 591 0341
S&N Courage Best Bitter;
Guest Beer (occasional) **H**
◖D ◖ ▶ ▬ ⇌ ⊖

Youngsters pub, with little character. Real Ale not always available. Pool played. DJ at weekends. Back as the "Barge Aground" after a few years as the "Ferret & Trouserleg".

11-11 (12-10.30 Sun)

Barking Dog   2
61 Station Parade
(near A124/A123)
Tel: (0181) 507 9109
Fullers London Pride; **S&N** Courage Directors, Scotch Bitter, Theakstons BB; **Guest Beers H**
◖D ◖ ▶ ▬ ♿ ☂ ✗ ⊖

Huge, new 'Wetherspoon' conversion of former supermarket and a welcome addition to the local pub scene. Good value food. Guest beers usually available, with beer festivals in April and November.

11-11 (12.30 Thu-Sat) (12-10.30 Sun)

Brewery Tap   3
2 Linton Road (near A124)
Tel: (0181) 594 4296
Saxon Inns - No Real Ale (Handpump disused!). Back as the "Brewery Tap", after a period as the "James Figg".

11-3; 5-11 (11-11 Sat: 12-3; 7-10.30 Sun. 12-10.30 Sun when live football on TV)

Britannia   4
1 Church Road (near A123)
Tel: (0181) 594 1305
Youngs Bitter, Special, Winter Warmer (Winter only) **H**
◖D ◖ ▶ ⊞ ▬ ⇌ ⊖

Young's only tied house in 'Essex', with traditional, games-oriented public bar and comfy lounge. Charity quiz nights. A regular 'Good Beer Guide' entry. SW Essex branch (London Area) 'Pub-of-the-Year' for 1995 & 1996. Note the 'caryatids' on the exterior.

11-11 (12-10.30 Sun)

Bull   5
2 North Street (nr A124)
Tel: (0181) 591 3662
Bass Draught Bass **H**
◖D ◖ ▶ ⊞ ▬ ⇌ ⊖

Spacious and comfortable with distinct drinking areas. Plenty of wood-panelling. A recent convert to Real Ale (good value), although not always available. Darts and pool. Live music / DJ at weekends. Limited parking. Beware keg 'Cidermaster' on fake handpump.

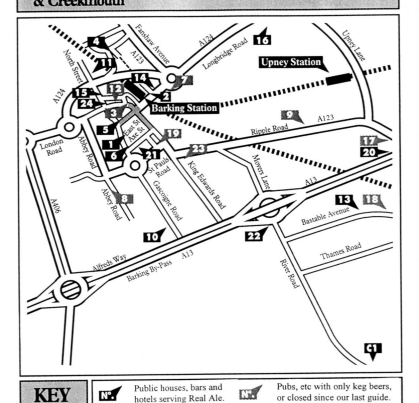

BARKING
& Creekmouth

KEY — Public houses, bars and hotels serving Real Ale. — Pubs, etc with only keg beers, or closed since our last guide.

Errata

Unfortunately, an older version of the **BARKING & Creekmouth** town map was included in error. After that version had been produced three pubs were renamed, resulting in most of the pubs appearing in the wrong places. The correct version is shown above.

The following errors have been discovered in other town maps:-

HARLOW - The positions of Pubs **21** & **23** have been reversed.
HARWICH - The positions of Pubs **11** & **12** have been reversed.

BARKING
& Creekmouth

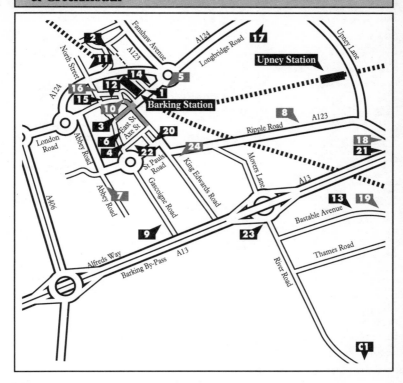

11-11 (12-10.30 Sun)

Captain Cook 6
Axe Street (nr A123)
Tel: (0181) 594 2539
Ind Coope Burton Ale; **Tetley**
Bitter; **Youngs** Bitter; **Guest**
Beer H

◑ ◖ ⛁ 🚃 ≷ ⊖
Comfortable, modern, split-level
pub with a pleasant atmosphere,
and mixed clientele. Good value
food at lunchtimes, plus fish &
chips night on Thursdays. Guest
beer changes fortnightly.

Chains 7
36-38 Longbridge Road
(nr A124/A123)
Tel: (0181) 591 4767
Free-house - Now closed and
converted to the "Box" night-
club. Formerly "Chains-a-Gain".

11-11 (12-10.30 Sun)

Fishing Smack 8
92 Abbey Road (nr A123)
Tel: (0181) 594 8320
Allied Domecq - No Real Ale.

12(11 Fri/Sat)-11 (12-10.30 Sun)

Harrow 9
373-397 Ripple Road (A123)
Tel: (0181) 591 4138
Bass - No Real Ale.

11-11 (12-10.30 Sun)

Hope 10
170 Gascoigne Road (nr
A123/A13)
Tel: (0181) 594 2694
Ruddles Best Bitter **H**
◑ ◖ 🏠 ❀
Spacious, two-bar estate pub. A
popular local, with quiz nights,
occasional pool tournaments
and various function nights.
Real Ale not always available.

11-11 (12-10.30 Sun)

Jolly Fisherman 11
108 North Street (nr A124)
Tel: (0181) 591 4649
S&N John Smiths Bitter **H**
◑ 🏠 ❀ 🚃 ≷ ⊖
Built in the 1860s, this small,
friendly, family pub was once a
coaching inn. Real Ale not
always available. Darts, pool and
jukebox. Limited parking.

12-3; 5-11 (12-3 only Sun)

Legends 12
20-22 London Road (nr A124)
Tel: (0181) 594 3051
Free-house / night-club - No
Real Ale. Formerly "Connolly's
Wine Bar".

11-11 (12-10.30 Sun)

Lighterman 13
109 Bastable Avenue, Thames
View Estate
Tel: (0181) 594 8492
Greene King IPA; **Tetley**
Bitter **H**
🏠 ❀
Estate pub with separate bars,
Sky TV in saloon. Garden has
swings. Beware 'tight sparkler'
on the IPA!

11

11.30-3.30 (4 Sat); 5 (7 Sat)-11
(12-3.30; 7-10.30 Sun)

Original Spotted Dog 14
15 Longbridge Road
(nr A124/A123)
Tel: (0181) 594 0228
S&N Courage Best Bitter, "Old
Wallop" **H**
Ⓓ Ⓓ Ⓓ **R** Ⓓ ▰ ⇌ ⊖
A Davy & Co. house with an
abundance of wood panelling,
and sawdust strewn across the
floor. The 'Signal Box' Bar has
been incorporated into the front
bar and there is a 'Dog House'
area to the rear.
A new 'Colonel Jaspers' bar and
restaurant has been built downstairs in the former cellars, but it
is not open all sessions.
Interesting food menu. Port and
many wines available.
Note that the 'Old Wallop' is
believed to be 'Courage
Directors' still. Ask for the
'sparkler' to be removed when
ordering your beer. New pavement patio at the front. Worth a
visit. Parking difficult.
Formerly the "Spotted Dog".

11-11 (12.30 Fri/Sat)
(12-10.30 Sun)

Red Lion 15
66 North Street / George Street
(nr A124)
Tel: (0181) 594 4809
Ind Coope 'House' Beer **H**
Ⓓ Ⓓ **R** Ⓓ ⇌ ⊖
Street-corner pub, that has started to sell Real Ale again, but not
all the time! Pool and live music.

11-11 (12-3; 7-10.30 Sun)

Royal Oak 16
203 Longbridge Road (A124)
Tel: (0181) 507 1600
Marstons Pedigree; **Youngs**
Bitter; **Guest Beer H**
Ⓓ Ⓓ ✿ ♿
Single 'U'-shaped bar with
framed prints of old Barking.
Regular live music on
Wednesdays, DJs on Mondays,
Thursdays and Sundays. Other
functions also held. Regularly
changing guest beer.

11-11 (12-10.30 Sun)

Ship & Shovel 17
Ripple Road (A13)
Tel: (0181) 592 1243
S&N - No Real Ale.

11-11 (12-10.30 Sun)

Short Blue 18
207 Bastable Avenue, Thames
View Estate
Tel: (0181) 594 1457
Labbatts - No Real Ale.

11-11 (12-10.30 Sun)

Stag 19
82 Ripple Road (A123)
Tel: (0181) 591 3186
Allied - No Real Ale (Handpump
disused!).

11-3.30; 5-11 (11-11 Fri/Sat:
12-10.30 Sun)

Thatched House 20
632 Ripple Road (by A13)
Tel: (0181) 591 2721
Ind Coope 'House' Bitter **H**
Ⓓ Ⓓ Ⓓ Ⓓ ⊖
A "Mr Qs", with one large, comfortable bar and distinct drinking
areas (part of which can be parti-
tioned-off for private functions).
Food all day. Pool played.

11-11 (12-5; 7-10.30 Sun)

Victoria 21
86 Axe Street (nr A123)
Tel: (0181) 594 2143
Bass Worthington BB **H**
Ⓓ Ⓓ ▰ ⇌ ⊖
Pleasant two-bar pub, close to
the town hall. Quiet background
music. Real Ale not always available.

11-11 (12-10.30 Sun)

Volunteer 22
Alfreds Way/River Road (by A13)
Tel: (0181) 591 3208
Bass Draught Bass **H**
Ⓓ Ⓓ Ⓓ **R** ┗ ▰
Large pub with restaurant area
and large TV screen for sports,
games machines and recorded
music. Beware 'tight sparkler' on
the 'Bass'.

11-11 (12-10.30 Sun)

Westbury Arms 23
174 Ripple Road (A123)
Tel: (0181) 594 3195
Inntrepreneur - No Real Ale.

11-11 (12-10.30 Sun)

White Horse
(Pickled Newt) 24
London Road / North Street
(nr A124)
Tel: (0181) 594 0167
Bass Draught Bass; **Greene
King** Martha Greene's, IPA;
S&N Courage Best Bitter,
Directors **H**
Ⓓ Ⓓ Ⓓ Ⓓ Ⓓ ┗ ▰ ⇌ ⊖
A mainly young crowd with 'Sky
Sports' on the large screen,
many sporting photos adorn the
walls.
Good value food and drink avail-
able all day. Not all the beers are
'on' all of the time. Pool played.

Barkingside A4

11-11 (12-10.30 Sun)

Doctor Johnson
175 Longwood Gardens (nr
A406)
Tel: (0181) 550 0497
S&N Courage Best Bitter,
Directors **H**
Ⓓ Ⓓ Ⓓ Ⓓ ┗ ✿
Large inter-war pub of character
with revolving door. Three sepa-
rate bars, including a large snug.
Occasional live music in the
function room.

11-11 (12-10.30 Sun)

Fairlop Waters
Forest Road
Tel: (0181) 500 9911
Free-house (Daltons) - No Real Ale.

11-11 (12-10.30 Sun)

Horns Tavern
134 Horns Road (nr A12)
Tel: (0181) 554 1939
S&N Courage Best Bitter **H**
Ⓓ Ⓓ Ⓓ ✿ ⊖
Pleasant & friendly, locals pub,
near Newbury Park. Separate
area for pool. Loud music.
Pleasant garden area, suitable
for children.

11-11 (12-10.30 Sun)

New Fairlop Oak
Fencepiece Road, Fulwell Cross
(A123)
Tel: (0181) 500 2217
S&N Courage Directors,
Theakstons BB; **Guest Beers H**
Westons Old Rosie **H**
Ⓓ Ⓓ Ⓓ Ⓓ ▰ Ⓓ ✂ ⊖
Pleasant 'Wetherspoon' in
former 'Berni Inn' - smaller than
most, but still in the typical
house-style. Can get busy with
good, reasonably-priced food
and beer. Four or five guest
beers usually available.

12-3; 5.30-11 (12-11 Fri/Sat: 12-3;
7-10.30 Sun)

Old Maypole
105 Fencepiece Road (A123)
Tel: (0181) 501 4483
Allied - No Real Ale (Handpump
disused).

11-11 (12-10.30 Sun)

Ye Olde Investigator
2 High Street (A123)
Tel: (0181) 550 6259
S&N - No Real Ale. Formerly the
"Chequers".

Barnston B2

11-3; 6-11 (12-3; 7-10.30 Sun)

Bushel & Sack
Chelmsford Road (A130)
Tel: (01371) 872726 / 874442
Greene King IPA, Abbot Ale;
Ridleys ESX **H**
Ⓓ Ⓓ Ⓓ (not Sun eve)
Ⓓ **R** ┗ ⛷ ✿
Unusual, purpose-built country
pub with restaurant and accom-
modation. Comfortable bar with
sofas and wood-burning stove.
Home-prepared food.

Basildon C4

Large post war new-town, with
surprisingly few pubs in the
town centre itself, and fewer of
merit.
The huge, new, multi-million
pound development of the
'Festival Leisure Park', north of
the town centre, has already
added three new 'pubs', and
new "Jaks" and "Bonds" bars
were due to open in late July
1998.

BASILDON Fobbing, Laindon, Langdon Hills, Lee Chapel, Nevendon, Pitsea & Vange

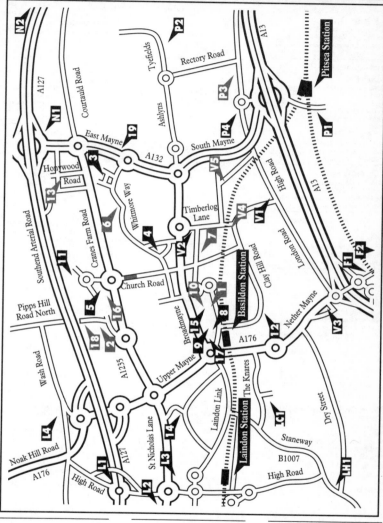

Buzz Bar   **1**
23 Market Pavement (Raquel's Corner)
Tel: (01268) 293116
Free-house - No Real Ale.
Formerly "Strings Piano Bar".

11-11 (12-2.30; 7-10.30 Sun)
Conservatory Bar
(Forte Posthouse)   **2**
Cranes Farm Road, Pipps Hill Road (off A1235)
Tel: (01268) 553955
Free-house - No Real Ale.
Previous bar here was the "Fat Sams Grand Slam Bar".

11-11 (12-10.30 Sun)
Crane   **3**
Denys Drive / Pendle Drive
Tel: (01268) 520418
Marstons Pedigree **H**
◖ ◖ D ✿
A community pub serving local housing area, with Saturday evening olde-time singalong. Limited snacks, good beer. Guinness advertising merchandise in abundance.

11-11 (12-10.30 Sun)

Double Six 4
Whitmore Way (off A132)
Tel: (01268) 288877
Greene King IPA; **Morlands** Old
Speckled Hen; **S&N** Courage
Directors, Websters Green Label **H**

◑ ◀ Ⓡ ⌂ ⛥ ⚄ ⚲
Beer variable. Newish landlord
would like to develop Real Ale
trade, but the new-town clientele
do not seem to share his vision.

11-11 (12-10.30 Sun)

Honey Pot 5
Pipps Hill South, Cranes Farm
Road (nr A1235)
Tel:
Wadworths 6X; **Whitbread**
Boddingtons Bitter, Fuggles
Imperial **H**

◑ ◑ ◀ Ⓡ ⛢
New 'Brewers Fayre', by the
Festival Leisure Park, with
children's play area.

11-3; 6 (7 Sat)-11 (11-11 Some
Sat: 12-3; 7-10.30 Sun)

Jolly Friar 6
Whitmore Way (off A132)
Tel: (01268) 520531
S&N - Not so jolly, as there is no
Real Ale (Handpumps disused).

11-3; 6 (7 Sat)-11 (11-11 Some
Sat: 12-3; 7-10.30 Sun)

Long Riding 7
301 Long Riding (off A1321)
Tel: (01268) 523559
Allied Domecq - No Real Ale.

11-11 (12-10.30 Sun)

Market Tavern 8
Southernhay (nr A176/A1321)
Tel: (01268) 522686
Bass Cask Toby, Draught Bass,
seasonal beers; **Fullers**
London Pride **H**

◑ ◑ ◀ Ⓡ ⍾ ⌂ ⌸ ⛢ ⚲
Greatly improved by recent
refurbishment. Handy for the rail
and bus stations. Jazz Sunday
lunchtimes, discos Thursday to
Saturday evenings. Parking
difficult. Formerly the "Bullseye".

11-11 (12-10.30 Sun)

Moon On The Square 9
1/15 Market Square / Fodderwick
(nr A176/A1321)
Tel: (01268) 520360
Marstons Pedigree; **S&N**
Courage Directors, Theakstons
BB, XB, **Guest Beers H**

◑ ◑ ◀ ◑ ⚄ ⌇ ⍁ ⚲
Early 1996 'Wetherspoon' on the
site of a former bakery. Regular
guest beers.

11-11 (12-10.30 Sun)

Oasis 10
Block PQ, Great Oaks (Town
Centre)
Tel: (01268) 527321
Labbatts - No Real Ale. Back as
the "Oasis", after a period as the
Waggoner".

11-11 (12-10.30 Sun)

Original Brew Bar 11
Hollywood Bowl, Festival
Leisure Park,
Cranes Farm Road (nr A1235)
Tel: (01268) 531122
Original Best Bitter, Glenn's
Special, seasonal specials **H**

◑ ◑ ◀ ◑ Ⓡ
The latest in Bass's new
'Hollywood Bowl' chain of bowling alleys with a built-in brewery. The beers are believed to be
stored in tanks under pressure.

11-11 (12-10.30 Sun)

Owl & Pussycat 12
164 Clay Hill Road (nr A1321)
Tel: -
S&N Courage Best Bitter,
Directors **H**

◑ ◑ ◀ ◑ Ⓡ ⍈ ⛢ ⚲
An estate pub, with a comfortable lounge. Juke box and Sky
TV, karaoke and discos. Good
value food, including all-day
breakfasts. Formerly "Lears".

12-2.30 (Not Sat/Sun.
Discos/night-club only in the
evenings)

Piccadillys 13
1 Paycocke Road / Honywood
Road (off A132)
Tel: (01268) 533512
Free-house - No Real Ale.
Formerly "Hats" and the
"Factory".

11-11 (12-10.30 Sun)

Plough & Tractor 14
Great Knightleys (Nr B1036)
Tel: (01268) 543496
S&N Courage Directors **H**

◑ ◑ ⍈ ⛢
Comfortable new-town community pub. Ask for the sparkler to
be removed. Formerly "Stores".

11-11 (7 Mon, 2 Thu-Sat, closed
Sun)

Roof Garden 15
6-8 High Pavement (Town
Square)
Tel: (01268) 524205 / 529397
Ruddles County; **S&N** Courage
Directors; **Whitbread**
Boddingtons Bitter **H**

◑ ◑ ◀ ◑ ⚲
Comfortable, modern pub at top
of the escalators, with live bands
Saturday night, and disco music
Tuesdays to Fridays.
Parking difficult - disabled
access from multi-storey car
park only. Formerly the "New
Yorker".

11-11 (12-10.30 Sun)

T.G.I. Friday's 16
Pipps Hill South, Cranes Farm
Road (nr A1235)
Tel: (01268) 534222
Whitbread (T.G.I. Friday's) - No
Real Ale.

12-5 (5.30 Sat); 6 (6.30 Sat)-11
(12 Fri/Sat) (12-3; 7-10.30 Sun)

Towngate Theatre 17
Pagel Mead (Off Roundacre
roundabout, A176/A1321)
Tel: (01268) 531343
Greene King IPA, Abbot Ale,
seasonal ales **E**; **Guest Beers E/G**

◑ ◀ Ⓡ ⌂ ⚄
Town-centre theatre complex,
with live jazz Sunday lunch and
Tuesday evenings, folk music
Sunday evenings, live 'pop'
Fridays and Saturdays, and
acoustic music Wednesday
evenings.
Upstairs bar open 9pm to mid-
night Fridays and Saturdays.
Handpump-activated electric dispense. Large range of changing
guest beers.

12-3; 6-11 (12-3; 7-10.30 Sun)

Treble Chance 18
Pipps Hill Road (nr A1235)
Tel: (01268) 523456
Free-house - No Real Ale.
Formerly the "Golfers Arms"
and "Lakeside", now back to its
original name.

11-11 (12-10.30 Sun)

Watermill 19
Felmores, East Mayne (nr A132)
Tel: (01268) 522227
Marstons Pedigree;
Morlands Old Speckled Hen;
Wadworths 6X; **Whitbread**
Boddingtons Bitter, Flowers
Original; **Guest Beers H**

◑ ◑ ◀ Ⓡ ⍈ ⌂ ⚄ ⚄
Modern, weather-boarded
'Beefeater' with large conserva-
tory and motel attached.
Enthusiastic landlord, keen on
guest beers.

Battlesbridge C4

*Tidal limit of the Crouch and first
inland river crossing. Now a
popular antiques centre. On the
Wickford to Southminster
railway line.*

11-11 (closed 3-5 Mon/Tue in
Winter: 12-10.30 Sun)

Barge Inn
Hawk Hill (nr A130)
OS: TQ781947
Tel: (01268) 732622
Hardys Pope's Bitter; **Ind**
Coope Burton Ale; **Marstons**
Pedigree; **Tetley** Bitter;
Guest Beer H

◑ ◑ ◀ ◑ Ⓡ ⌂ ⚄ ⍈ ⚲
Refurbished, weather-boarded
inn, with mini-beer festivals in
Spring and Autumn. Beware
pressurised Addlestones Cider
served on handpump.

11-11 (12-10.30 Sun)

Hawk
Hawk Hill (nr A130)
Tel: (01268) 733264
Bass Hancocks HB, Worthington
BB; **Crouch Vale** Best Bitter **H**
◑ ▯ ◑ ▶ ⛺ 🐕 ⇌

After a 'Tardis-like' conversion
the pub now appears three
times bigger inside. In its new
guise as a Fork & Pitcher, it has a
new 'old' flagstone floor and
many new 'old' beams.
The atmosphere is very pleasant, but geared more to diners
than drinkers. Real fires. Handy
for the station. Beware keg
'Cidermaster' on handpump!

11-11 (12-3; 6-11 Mon-Thu
(Winter); 12-11 Fri/Sat (Winter):
12-10.30 Sun)

Lodge Hotel
Hayes Chase, Woodham Road
(between A132 & B1012)
OS: TQ787961
Tel: (01268) 320060
Crouch Vale Best Bitter;
Guest Beer H
◑ ▯ ◑ ▶ ℝ 🛏 ⛺ 🐕 🏺

Free-house - restored after fire,
with six double rooms (en-suite).
Live music on Friday evenings.
Special menus from time-to-
time.
Over 50s luncheon club cards
give 20% discount.

Baythorne End C1
Swan
(A1017, was A604 / A1092)
Greene King - Pub closed, now
an antiques shop!

Beaumont-
Cum-Moze F2
*Agricultural region, deep in the
Tendring Hundred.*

Swan Inn
Chapel Road (between B1035 &
B1414)
OS: TM168249
Free-house - Pub closed.

Beazley End C2
(Wethersfield)
*The only 3 Oast houses in Essex
are in this area.*

12-3; 6.30-11 (12-3; 7-10.30 Sun)

Cock
Beazley End (nr B1053)
OS: TL742289
Tel: (01371) 850566
Greene King IPA; **Whitbread**
Boddingtons Bitter **H**
◑ ▯ ◑ ▶ ℝ 🍺 🐕

Spacious, country free-house,
with real fires in the inglenooks,
amongst the beams. Extensive
and varying menu, including
Vegetarian, in the 28 seat restaurant.

Belchamp
Otten D1
The smallest of the Belchamps.

12-3 (not Mon-Fri in Winter);
7-11 (10.30 Sun)

Red Lion Inn
Fowes Lane
OS: TL799415
Tel: (01787) 277537
Greene King IPA; **Guest Beer H**
◑ ▯ ◑ ▶ 🐕 ⛝

Small, quiet, country pub, well-
worth finding. Walkers, cyclists
and children tolerated. Home-
made pies a speciality. Food
served Tuesday to Saturday
evenings (Thursday advance
booking only), also Saturday
and Sunday lunchtimes.

Windmill
Otten Road
OS: TL798417
Free-house - Pub closed and
delicensed.

Belchamp
St Paul D1
*Largest and prettiest of the
Belchamps, with wide grass
verge and village green.*

11.30-2.30; 7-11 (12-3; 7-10.30
Sun)

Half Moon Inn
Cole Green
OS: TL792423
Tel: (01787) 277402
Greene King IPA; **Nethergate**
Bitter; **Guest Beer H**
◑ ▯ ◑ ▶ 🍺 🐕

Beautiful thatched pub dating
from 1685, opposite village
green.

Plough
Gage's Road
OS: TL790421
Greene King - Pub closed and
converted to a private house.

Bicknacre C4

11-2.30; 6-11 (12-3; 7-10.30 Sun)

Brewers Arms
Main Road (B1418)
OS: TL788021
Tel: (01245) 224061
Greene King IPA, Abbot Ale;
Guest Beer H
◑ ▯ 🐕

Popular, three-bar village local
with children's garden and
'Tapsters' Choice' range of guest
beers. Pool table and darts.

11-11 (12-10.30 Sun)

White Swan
Main Road (B1418)
OS: TL788021
Tel: (01245) 222826
Marstons Pedigree; **Whitbread**
Flowers IPA, Original **H**
◑ ▯ ◑ ▶ 🐕

Popular, 400 year-old, one-bar
village pub with pool table and
mug collection. Food available
all day.

Billericay C4
*Commuter town with many old
buildings despite developers.
Frequent appearance of the
name 'Mayflower' is because
some of the Pilgrim Fathers
were from the town.*

Charles III Cocktail Bar
5 Holly Court (nr B1007)
Free-house - Closed and converted to an Indian restaurant.

12-11 (12-3; 7-10.30 Sun)

Chequers
44 High Street (B1007)
Tel: (01277) 651804
Marstons Pedigree; **Tetley**
Bitter; **Guest Beer** (occasional) **H**
🛏 ⇌

Pleasant, mid-town pub, built in
1544, with two drinking areas.
Popular with the younger clientele. Live bands on Saturday
evenings. Sky TV, discos, etc.

10-11 (12-3.30; 7-10.30 Sun)

Coach & Horses
36 Chapel Street (nr B1007)
Tel: (01277) 622873
Greene King IPA, Abbot Ale;
Shepherd Neame Masterbrew
Bitter; **Guest Beer H**
◑ ▯ ◑ 🐕 ⇌

Excellent, well-maintained, one-
bar Grays local with patio - a
regular Good Beer Guide entry.
Original 1700s pub on the site
was known as the 'Crown Tap',
until replaced by current
building in 1935.
Friendly, long-standing landlord
encourages convivial atmosphere. Darts, dominoes and crib.
Impressive collection of jugs and
elephants. No food on Sundays.

11-11 (12-10.30 Sun)

Crown
2 High Road (B1007)
Tel: (01277) 650279
Fullers London Pride; **Greene
King** IPA **H**
◑ ▯ ◑ ▶ ℝ 🍺 🏺 🍴 ⇌

Refurbished, popular 'social cen-
tre', with public bar, opposite the
'Railway'. Pool, Satellite TV,
darts and live 'Indy Pop Rock' on
Thursdays.
Separate restaurant upstairs.
Sunday lunch carvery.

12-11 (10.30 Sun)

Mayflower
61 Jacksons Lane
OS: TQ682947
Tel: (01277) 654224
Inntrepreneur - No Real Ale.

15

12-3; 6-11 (12-11 Fri/Sat: 12-10.30
Sun)

Pickled Newt
1 The Pantiles, Queens Park
Avenue
Tel: (01277) 626505
Greene King Martha Greene's,
IPA, Abbot Ale; **S&N** Courage
Best Bitter **H**
◖◗ ◐◑ 📇
'Ye olde beamed' interior, con-
trasts with the modern exterior.
Mixed clientele. Children
allowed in bar. Live sporting
events on big screen TV.
Formerly the "Forge" - a shame
that the name was changed!

11-11 (12-10.30 Sun)

Pilgrim
44 Mountnessing Road
Tel: (01277) 658998
S&N - No Real Ale.

12-3 (Not Sat); 7-11 (12-10.30
Sun)

Quilters
66-68 Laindon Road (Nr A129)
Tel: (01277) 632378
Free-house - No Real Ale.

11-11 (12-10.30 Sun)

Railway
1 High Street (B1007)
Tel: (01277) 652173
Greene King IPA, Abbot Ale **H**
Guest Beer (occasional) **G**
◖◗ ❀ ♿ ⇌
Busy 'Grays' house, near railway
station, built circa 1885 and
since extended. A comfortable
drinkers pub with pool, gaming
machines and large juke box.
Occasional live bands. Parking
difficult.

11-11 (12-10.30 Sun)

Red Lion
113 High Street (B1007)
Tel: (01277) 623031
Bass M&B Brew XI, Draught
Bass; **Guest Beer H**
◖◗ ◐◑ ❀ ⇌
A busy town pub, one of the oldest buildings in Billericay, but
sadly lacking in olde-world
charm. Evening meals Monday
to Thursday only. Parking difficult.

11-11 (12-10.30 Sun)

Rising Sun
2 Sun Street (A129/B1007)
Tel: (01277) 624850
Greene King IPA; **Guest Beer**
(occasional) **H**
◖◗ ◖▙ ❀ ⇌
Cosy pub and a nice local, with
original stained-glass windows
remaining. Hall (for 100)
separate from pub.

11-11 (12-10.30 Sun)

White Hart
138 High Street (B1007)
Tel: (01277) 652323
Bass Draught Bass; **Greene
King** IPA; **Guest Beer H**
◖◗ ◐ R ◖▙ ❀ ⇌
Family-run, single bar pub with
children and dogs welcome in
the dining area at rear. Three
darts teams and a golf society.
No food on Sundays.

Birchanger   B2

*Pleasant village, near junction 8
of M11 motorway.*

12-3; 6-11 (12-3; 7-10.30 Sun)

Three Willows
Birchanger Lane, Duck End (nr
A120, off M11 at Jcn 8)
OS: TL513224
Tel: (01279) 815913
Greene King IPA, Rayments
Special Bitter, Abbot Ale **H**
◖◗ ◐ ♿ ❀
Excellent, welcoming village
pub, with basic public bar and
comfortable lounge. Noted for
its good food and extensive gar-
dens. No food Sunday evenings.

Birdbrook   C1

*Former wartime U.S.A.F. base,
and had a station on the Colne
Valley Line until 1962.*

12-3; 6-11 (12-3; 7-10.30 Sun)

Plough
The Street (1 mile off B1054)
OS: TL706411
Tel: (01440) 785336
Adnams Bitter; **Fullers** London
Pride; **Greene King** IPA; **Guest
Beers H**
◖◗ ◐◑ R ♿ ◖▙ ❀
Traditional, 16th century,
thatched village local, enjoying a
friendly atmosphere. Shove
ha'penny played. Cosy dining
area doubles as a meeting
room. Worth a visit.

Bishops Green
(Gt Dunmow)   B3

11-3; 6-11 (11-11 Sat: 12-10.30
Sun)

Spotted Dog
High Easter Road
OS: TL631179
Tel: (01245) 231598
Greene King IPA; **Morlands**
Old Speckled Hen; **Guest Beer H**
◖◗ ◐◑ R ♿ ❀
Picturesque, cosy, country pub
in quiet hamlet, with a garden
that is well-equipped for
children.
Beware 'sparklers' used.

Black Notley   C2

12-3; 5.30-11 (12-11 Sat: 12-5;
7-10.30 Sun)

Reindeer
111 The Street / Notley Road
Tel: (01376) 320238
Greene King - No Real Ale.

12-2.30 (4 Sat/Sun); 6-11 (10.30
Sun)

Vine Inn
105 The Street
Tel: (01376) 324269
Adnams Bitter; **Ridleys** IPA;
Guest Beers H
◖◗ ◐◑ R
Small, friendly, country pub dating back to 1640. Enthusiastic
owners keen on quality beer and
food - try the home-made pies
and 'huffers'.
Restaurant in converted barn,
with minstrels gallery.

Blackheath
(Colchester)   E2

*(See Colchester map for location
of pub)*

11-3 (4 Sat);5 (5.30 Sat)-11
(12-10.30 Sun)

Cherry Tree   B1
Mersea Road (B1025)
Tel: (01206) 564018
Ruddles Bitter **H**
◖◗ ◖▙ ❀
Extended roadside pub on the
road to Mersea.

Blackmore   B3

*Attractive village centred on a
green with stocks and pond. The
church with its timber tower,
Jericho Priory and several
buildings are noteworthy.*

11.30-3; 6.30-11 (12-3; 7-10.30
Sun)

Bull
Church Street
Tel: (01277) 821208
Ind Coope Burton Ale;
Morlands Old Speckled Hen;
Whitbread Flowers IPA;
Guest Beers H
◖◗ ◐◑ ♿ ◖▙ ❀ ❀
Original Tudor pub with a quiet
and friendly atmosphere. See
the daily food specials board.

11.30-11 (12-10.30 Sun)

Leather Bottle
The Green
OS: TL603009
Tel: (01277) 821891
Ridleys IPA; **Whitbread** Castle
Eden Ale; **Guest Beers** (week-
ends) **H**
◖◗ ◐◑ ❀
Friendly, family pub, with large
garden and roofed patio. Guest
beers may include a mild, in
Summer. Easter Beer Festivals.
Live music on Fridays.

11-2.30; 6-11 (11-11 Sat: 12-10.30
Sun)

Prince Albert
Blackmore Road / The Green
Tel: (01277) 821705
Bass Hancocks HB, **Draught**
Bass; **Guest Beers H**
◖◗ ◐◑ ❀
Food-oriented, family pub. Busy
with diners early evening.

"The Cock", Boreham

Blackmore End C2

12-3; 6.30-11 (closed Mondays - except Bank Holidays: 12-3; 7-10.30 Sun)

Bull Inn
Blackmore End
OS: TL737310
Tel: (01371) 851037
Adnams Bitter; **Greene King** IPA; **Mauldons** White Adder; **Guest Beers H**

◧◨ ◧◨ R ⛵ 🌺 (Booking advisable) 🐾
Attractive village local with two bar areas, one leading to the restaurant. A-la-Carte meals and bar snacks available.

Red Cow
Blackmore End
OS: TL738310
Ridleys - Pub closed in 1991, and is now delicensed.

Blake End (Gt Saling) C2

11-11 (12-10.30 Sun) (may close early if quiet)

Saling Oak
Rayne Road (A120)
Tel: (01376) 322623
Ridleys IPA, ESX, Rumpus **H**

◧◨ R 🐾 🌺 ♿
Large Restaurant with regular cabaret. Popular children's play area.

Bocking C2

Bradford Street is one of the finest Elizabethan streets in the country.

(See Braintree map for location of pubs)

11-3; 5.30-11 (12-10.30 Sun)
Angel Inn B1
36 Bocking End (B1053)
Tel: (01376) 321549
Guest Beers H

◧◨ ◧◨ 🌺
15th century pub, in a conservation area, with a lively atmosphere, and a beer club. Sports-oriented, with live football matches shown.

11-3; 6-11 (11-11 Sat & some Fri: 12-10.30 Sun)
Kings Head B2
52 Bradford Street (B1053)
Tel: (01376) 322582
Greene King - No Real Ale.

11-3; 6-11 (12-3; 7-10.30 Sun)
Old Court Hotel B3
31 Bradford Street (B1053)
Tel: (01376) 321444
Free-house - No Real Ale.

11-3 (or later some Sat); 6.30-11 (12-3; 7-10.30 Sun)
Spread Eagle B4
111 Coldnailhurst Avenue
Tel: (01376) 343890
Greene King IPA, Abbot Ale **H**

◧◨ 🚗
Large, one-bar estate pub, catering for all ages.

12-3; 6-11 (12-3; 7-10.30 Sun)
Tabor Arms B5
94 Panfield Lane
OS: TL752236
Tel: (01376) 321188
Greene King IPA **H**
1930s estate pub, canned music, pool and darts. Formerly the "Panfield Way".

Bocking Churchstreet C2

11 (12 Sat)-3; 6-11 (12-3; 7-10.30 Sun)

King William
82 Church Street (nr B1053)
Tel: (01376) 324737
Whitbread - No Real Ale.

12-3; 7-11 (10.30 Sun)

Retreat
42 Church Street (nr B1053)
Tel: (01376) 347947
Ridleys IPA; **Guest Beers H/G**

◧◨ ◧◨ 🚗 ♿
Comfortable free-house, with enthusiastic landlord who usually has 6 to 8 beers available. Occasional beer festivals. Limited parking. Converted from three cottages in 1910. Formerly the "Black Boy".

11-11 (12-10.30 Sun)

Rose & Crown
94 Church Street (nr B1053)
Tel: (01376) 324661
Greene King IPA **H**

◧◨ 🍺
Old pub with two small bars. Real outside Gents!

Boreham C3

Almost a suburb of Chelmsford. New Hall & Boreham House are notable.

12-3; 6-11 (12-10.30 Sun)

Cock Inn
Main Road (B1137, nr A12)
Tel: (01245) 467284
Ridleys IPA, ESX, Rumpus **H**

◧◨ ◧◨ R 🌺
Friendly one-bar pub with separate pool room. Limited parking.

17

10.30 (10 Sat)-3; 5 (6 Sat)-11
(12-4; 7-10.30 Sun)

Queens Head
Church Road (Behind church, nr
B1137)
Tel: (01245) 467298
Greene King IPA, Abbot Ale **H**
◖D ◖D ◖Ⱥ ❁
Excellent, friendly and tradition-
al, 16th century Gray & Sons
pub, with darts, crib and domi-
noes teams; a good example of
what CAMRA stands for. Good
value Sunday lunches.

11-3; 6-11 (11-11 Fri/Sat: 12-10.30
Sun)

Red Lion
Main Road (B1137)
Tel: (01245) 464336
S&N Courage Best Bitter,
Directors **H**
◖D ◖❶ ⊫ ⋟ ❁
Pub with attractions for children
in garden. Car rally club, walking
stick making club! Occasional
live music.

11.30-3; 6-11 (12-3; 7-10.30 Sun)

Six Bells
Main Road (B1137)
Tel: (01245) 467232
Greene King IPA, Rayments SB,
Abbot Ale, seasonal beers **H**
◖D ◖❶ R ❁
Well-appointed and comfortable
pub, with golf society.

Bournes Green (Gt Wakering)   D5

11-11 (12-10.30 Sun)

Rose Inn Tavern
Wakering Road (nr A13)
Tel: (01702) 588008
Greene King IPA; **S&N** Courage
Directors, Theakstons BB, Old
Peculier **H**
◖D ◖❶ R ⋟ ❁ Ⱥ
Large, well-tended garden.
'Sparklers' removed on request.

Bowers Gifford   C5

*Land held by William Gifford in
1243. 'Bura' (cottage) listed in
the Domesday Book.*

11.30-11 (12-3; 7-10.30 Sun)

Bull
London Road (B1464)
OS: TQ747883
Tel: (01268) 551083
Bass - No Real Ale. Formerly the
"Prohibition" & "Beanos".

11-11 (12-10.30 Sun)

Cornhusker
London Road (B1464)
OS: TQ751882
Tel: (01268) 552202
S&N Courage Directors; **Guest
Beers H**
◖D ◖❶ R ⊫ ⋟ ❁ Ⱥ
Strong American theme and
ample facilities for kids. Three
regular guest beers. Bar food all
day. Better inside than the silly
name would indicate. Formerly
"Aunt Fanny's Cabin" and the
"Gun Inn".

Boxted   E2

Cross Inn
Boxted Cross / Straight Road (3
miles off A134)
OS: TM006325
Free-house - Pub closed and
converted to a private house.

11-2.30; 6-11 (12-3; 7-10.30 Sun)

Wig & Fidgett
Straight Road
OS: TM001317
Tel: (01206) 272227
Greene King IPA; **Guest Beer H**
◖D ◖❶ (not Sun or Tue eve)
Ⱥ ⊫ ❁
Popular lunchtime local, with
large garden. Beware keg
'Scrumpy Jack' cider on fake
handpump.

Boyton Cross (Roxwell)   B3

11.30-11 (12-3; 7-10.30 Sun)

Cross Keys
Boyton Cross (A1060)
Tel: (01245) 248201
Fullers London Pride;
Greene King IPA; **Guest
Beer** (occasional) **H**
◖D ◖ R Ⱥ ⋟ ❁
Welcoming, roadside pub offer-
ing good beer and food.
Attractive restaurant area and
garden with summer barbecues.
No food Sunday & Monday
evenings.

Bradfield   F2

11-3; 7-11 (11-11 Summer: 12-3;
7-10.30 Sun)

Strangers Home Inn
The Street (B1352)
Tel: (01255) 870304
Whitbread Boddingtons Bitter,
Flowers Original **H**
◖D ◖❶ R Ⱥ ⊫ ❁
Large camping site at the rear,
for caravans and tents. Excellent
play area for children.

"The Green Man", Bradwell-on-Sea

11-3; 5.30-11 (12-3; 7-10.30 Sun)
Village Maid
Heath Road / The Street
OS: TM142302
Tel: (01255) 870329
Greene King IPA, Abbot Ale,
Seasonal Beers **H**
🍷 🍴 ◀ ▶ **R** 🍺 ❀
Snug, many-beamed, traditional
local with large open fire. No
darts or juke box, but shove
ha'penny and crib played.

Bradfield
Heath   E2

11-3; 6.30-11 (12-3; 7-10.30 Sun)
Ram & Hoggett
Heath Road (nr B1035)
Tel: (01255) 870640
Pubmaster - No Real Ale.

Bradwell   D2

11-3; 6-11 (12-3;7-10.30 Sun)
Swan Inn
Coggeshall Road / The Street,
Bradwell Village (A120)
Tel: (01376) 562111
Greene King IPA, Abbot Ale **H**
🍷 🍴 ◀ ▶ **R** ┗ ❀
Large 16th century, village pub
by main road, with open fires
and cricketing theme.
Note that the handpumps oper-
ate electric pumps due to the
length of the beerpipe run to the
cellar.

Bradwell-
on-Sea   E3

*Yachting centre famous for the
7th century Chapel of St. Peter's
on the Wall which was built near
the Saxon fort of Othona. The
area is dominated by a nuclear
power station, which now has a
visitor centre.*

11-3; 6-11 (12-3; 7-10.30 Sun)
Cricketers
East End Road
OS: TL011073
Tel: (01621) 776013
Greene King IPA **H**
🍷 ◀ ▶ 🛒
Isolated pub on the road to St
Peter's chapel and the Roman
fort.

11-11 (12-10.30 Sun)
Green Man Inn
Waterside (B1021)
OS: TL995078
Tel: (01621) 776226
Adnams Bitter; **Ridleys** IPA,
Spectacular; **Tetley** Bitter **H**
🍷 🍴 ◀ ▶ **R** 🍽 ┗ 🍺 ❀
Busy on summer weekends with
sailing and caravanning fraternity.
An old cast iron fireplace
(chestnuts in winter), flagstone
floor and home-cooking add to
the homely atmosphere.
An old notice above the 500 year
old fireplace reads:
'More shall trust score I sent

For what I my and has
Do beer if pay clerk brewer
I my and must his the'
Can you solve the riddle?

11-3; 6-11 (12-2.30; 7-10.30 Sun)
Kings Head
High Street/South Street
(off B1021)
Tel: (01621) 776224
Ruddles Best Bitter, County;
Guest Beers H
🍷 🍴 ◀ ▶ 🍺 ☕ ❀
Thriving village pub with good
food. Darts and dominoes in
public bar. Children allowed in
the conservatory, and children's
menu available.

Queens Head
Maldon Road (B1021)
OS: TL991058
Tel: (01621) 776342
Free-house - Pub closed.
Formerly the "Blackwater Inn".

Braintree   C2

*Unspoilt former Market Town,
sadly this can't be said for many
of the pubs!*

*Braintree lace was used in
Queen's wedding dress.
Relieved of much through traffic
by the Southern and Eastern
bypasses.*

11-3; 6-11 (11-11 Fri/Sat: 12-10.30
Sun)
Angel   1
33 Notley Road
Tel: (01376) 320122
Free-house - No Real Ale.

6-11 only Mon-Thu (11-11
Fri/Sat: 12-10.30 Sun)
Bird in Hand   2
272 Coggeshall Road (B1256)
Tel: (01376) 321126
Tetley Bitter **H**
🍷 🍴 🍺 ❀
Locals pub with regular discos.
Darts and pool played.

11-11 (12-10.30 Sun)
Boar's Head   3
85 High Street (nr B1256)
Tel: (01376) 320119
Ridleys IPA, ESX, Spectacular **H**
🍷 🍴 ◀ ▶ ❀ ☕
The first of the new food-oriented 'Ridley Inns'. Beware some
of the attractive timber-work is
plastic!

Bow & Arrow   4
191 South Street (B1256)
Free-house - Pub closed.

11-11 (12-10.30 Sun)
Bull   5
Market Place (nr B1256)
Tel: (01376) 320551
Greene King IPA, Abbot Ale **H**
🍷 🍴 ◀ 🍺 ⬆ ☕
Market square pub, popular with
the younger set. Loud video
jukebox. Parking difficult at
lunchtime.

11-3; 6.30-11 (12-3; 7-10.30 Sun)
Eagle   6
192/198 Coggeshall Road
(B1256)
Tel: (01376) 322828
Greene King - No Real Ale.

11-1am (2am Thu-Sat) (12-10.30
Sun)
Flack's Hotel   7
101-103 High Street (B1256)
Tel: (01376) 346918
Greene King IPA, Abbot Ale **H**
🍷 🍴 🍺 🍽 ❀ ☕
Old pub, much-renovated, dark,
noisy and popular with a young
clientele. Regular discos and live
groups. Includes wine bar, bistro
and night club. Sparklers used.
Parking difficult. Formerly the
"Fountain".

12-11 (10.30 Sun)
Golden Lion   8
69-71 Manor Street
Tel: (01376) 321515
Greene King - No Real Ale.

11-3; 5.30-11 (11-11 Wed-Sat:
12-3; 7-10.30 Sun)
Horse & Groom   9
20 Rayne Road (B1256)
Tel: (01376) 347569
Greene King IPA, Abbot Ale **H**
🍷 🍴 ❀
Two-bar pub, close to the new
shopping precinct. Limited
parking.

International   10
Railway Street (B1256)
Free-house - Closed and con-
verted to a Chinese Restaurant.
Formerly the "New Sun".

11-3; 6-11 (12-11 Sat: 12-3; 7-
10.30 Sun)
King William IV   11
114 London Road (B1053, by
A120 jcn)
OS: TL749217
Tel: (01376) 330088
Ridleys IPA **G**
🍺 ❀
Small two-bar local, with a very
friendly atmosphere. Darts and
quizzes. Award-winning flower
displays in summer. Local produce sold. Worth a visit, for the
only regular gravity-dispensed
beer in Braintree.
One mile south of the town
centre, near the bypass.

11-3; 7-11 (11-11 Sat: 12-10.30
Sun)
Kings Head   12
242 Coggeshall Road (B1256)
Tel: (01376) 550381
Ridleys IPA **H**
🍷 ◀ 🍺 ❀
Small two-bar pub on the main
road. Can be noisy at weekends
with regular karaoke, quieter
mid-week. 'Sky Sports.'

19

BRAINTREE
& Bocking

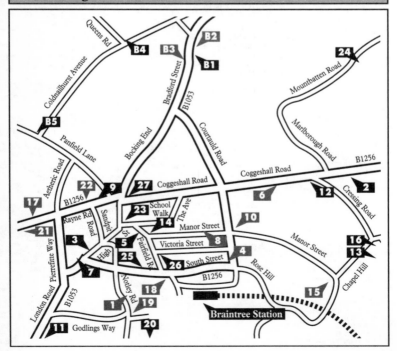

11-11 (12-10.30 Sun)

Mulberry Tree　13
Galleys Corner, Cressing Road
(A120/B1018)
Tel: (01376) 340690
Whitbread Boddingtons Bitter,
Flowers Original;
Wadworths 6X H

◖D ◖ R ⛟ ❀

Spacious, new "Brewers Fayre"
restaurant-cum-pub, with panelled walls and raised dining
area. A 'kids' paradise with outdoor and indoor play areas and
a children's certificate. The
beer's not bad either - though a
little too cold.

10.30-3; 7-11 (12-3; 7-10.30 Sun)

Nag's Head　14
8 Market Place (nr B1256)
Tel: (01376) 323348
Greene King IPA; **Tetley** Bitter H

◖D ◖ R ◖ 🍴 ⛟ ⇌

Busy multi-roomed marketplace
pub. Public bar is popular with
younger drinkers, the saloon is
quieter. Parking difficult at lunchtime.

Oak　15
Chapel Hill (nr B1018)
Greene King - Pub closed and
converted to offices.

**11-3; 6.30-11 (11-11 Fri/Sat:
12-10.30 Sun)**

Orange Tree　16
Cressing Road, Three Rivers
(B1018)
Tel: (01376) 344013
Greene King IPA, Abbot Ale H

◖D ◖ ◖ ◖ ⛟

1930s pub with large saloon bar
and an emphasis on food - now
a 'Hungry Horse'. A good selection of board games is available.

**11-3 (or later Sat); 6.30-11 (12-3;
7-10.30 Sun)**

Queen's Head　17
140 Rayne Road (B1256)
Tel: (01376) 323310
Greene King IPA, seasonal beers H

◖D ◖

Tiny Victorian front room with a
small extension. Near the hospital.

11-11 (12-10.30 Sun)

Railway Tavern　18
South Street (B1256)
Tel: (01376) 324081
Free-house - No Real Ale.

**11-3 (later some Sat); 6.30-11
(12-3; 7-10.30 Sun)**

Rifleman　19
Rifle Hill
Tel: (01376) 323382
Greene King IPA H

◖ ◖ ❀ ⛾

Estate pub catering for the local
community.

11 (12 Sat)-11 (12-10.30 Sun)

Rose & Crown　20
Betjeman Close / Masefield
Road (nr B1256)
Tel: (01376) 324830
Ridleys IPA H

◖

Isolated estate pub with limited
parking.

Stable (Essex Barn)　21
Rayne Road (B1256)
Free-house - Pub closed and
demolished, new housing built
on the site.

Star　22
38 Rayne Road (B1256)
Greene King - Pub closed and
converted to Solicitors Offices.

11-11 (12-10.30 Sun)

Swan　23
24 Bank Street (nr B1256)
Tel: (01376) 324056
Ind Coope Friary Meux Bitter;
Greene King Abbot Ale; **Tetley**
Bitter H

◖ ◖ ❀ ⛾ ⇌

Recently-extended town centre
pub with a wealth of timbers.
Watch out for the very low
handle on the front door!

**11-3; 6-11 (11-11 Fri/Sat: 12-10.30
Sun)**

Swiss Bell　24
Mountbatten Road
Tel: (01376) 322078
Tetley Bitter H

◖ ⛉ 🚗

Barn-like estate pub with regular
live entertainment.

**11-3 (4 Sat); 5.30 (6 Sat)-11 (12-3;
7-10.30 Sun)**

Wagon & Horses　25
53 South Street (B1256)
Tel: (01376) 553356
Greene King IPA, Abbot Ale,
seasonal beers H

◖D ◖ ◖ R ❀ ⇌

Beautifully refurbished 17th
Century inn, with two distinct
drinking areas. The only regular
Good Beer Guide pub in the
town centre. Darts, doms and
crib played. No meals
Wednesday or Sunday
evenings.

11-11 (12-10.30 Sun)

Wetherspoons　26
Fairfield Road / Victoria Street
(nr B1256)
Tel:
Greene King IPA; **S&N**
Theakstons BB; **Guest Beers** H

◖D ◖ ⛾ 🚗 ✂ ⇌

New JD Wetherspoon conversion of the former Embassy
Cinema, opened in late July
1998. Ask for the 'sparkler' to be
removed when ordering.

10.30-3; 6-11 (12-3; 7-10.30 Sun)

White Hart Hotel　27
Bocking End (B1256)
Tel: (01376) 321401
Greene King IPA; **S&N** Courage
Best Bitter H

◖D ◖ ◖ R ⛉ 🍴 ⛟ ⛟ 🚗

Former 16th century coaching
inn in the town centre, with
several bars. Now a Four
Crowns hotel (35 en-suite
rooms). Comfortable and
relaxing.

Brentwood　B4

*Once a coaching town with an
attractive High Street which has
now given way to modern shopping facilities. The Roman
Catholic Cathedral and the
Grammar School are impressive. Two country parks nearby.*

*Named on TV, a few years ago,
as Britain's most boring town -
even its name is an anagram of
'bored town'.*

*Hoardings around the former
'Fads' store, at 82 High Street,
were advertising a forthcoming
'Global Netcafe' for many
months with little sign of any
progress. Another operator will
probably now develop the site.*

*'Fullers' and 'Surrey Free Trade
Inns' are also believed to be
interested in developing new
pubs in the town.*

**11.30-2.30; 5.30-11 (12-10.30
Sun)**

Artichoke　1
Shenfield Common (by A128)
Tel: (01277) 210401
Bass Hancocks HB, Draught
Bass H

◖D ◖ ◖ R ⛉ ❀ ⛾

A Toby Restaurant and carving
room that has a small public bar
area with cheaper beer.

**11-3; 5-11 (11-11 Sat: 12-10.30
Sun)**

Brewery Tap　2
28 Primrose Hill/Kings Road (by
B185)
Tel: (01277) 218431
Greene King IPA; **Morlands** Old
Speckled Hen; **Wadworths** 6X;
Guest Beer H

◖ ◖ ❀ ⇌

Cosy, busy, one-bar pub with a
sporting theme - especially West
Ham United. Sports on TV.
Large patio garden.

11-11 (12-10.30 Sun)

Bull　3
13 Brook Street (A1023)
Tel: (01277) 210445
S&N Courage Directors Bitter,
Theakstons BB, XB; **Guest Beers**
H

◖D ◖ ◖ ❀ ⛾

Suburban roadside local with a
rather olde-worlde 'feel' and a
secluded garden.

11-11 (12-10.30 Sun)

Castle (Mr Q's)　4
17 Ongar Road (A128)
Tel: (01277) 212676
Allied Domecq - No Real Ale.

Cheers　5
67a High Street (nr A1023)
Free-house - Pub closed and
converted to the "Boardwalk"
restaurant. Formerly "Maxine's"

BRENTWOOD
Shenfield & Warley

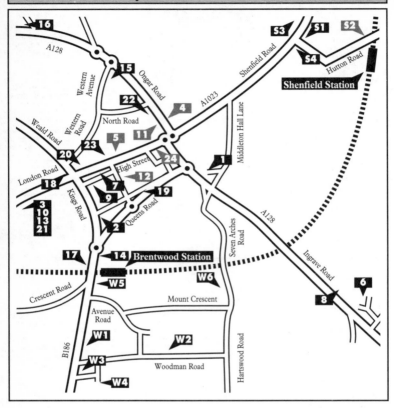

11-11 (12-3.30;7-10.30 Sun)

Chough 6
East Ham Crescent (nr A128)
Tel: (01277) 212618
Whitbread Flowers IPA **H**
🍺 🍽 🌣 ✿ ⛄
Friendly estate local with games
bar.

11-11 (12-10.30 Sun)

Fire & Firkin 7
86 High Street (A1023)
Tel:
Ford & Firkin Flamin' Ale,
Fire, Pyromani' Ale, Dogbolter
H
🍸🍺 ◑ ❚ ⮑
Loud, boisterous, 'Firkin' pub - a
recent shop conversion. Popular
with the younger crowd. The
'Firkin' beers are brewed at the
"Ford & Firkin" in Romford.

11-11 (12-10.30 Sun)

Fountain Head 8
153/157 Ingrave Road (A128)
Tel: (01277) 212151
Crouch Vale IPA, **Conkeror; S&N**
Websters Yorkshire Bitter;
Guest Beers H
🍸 ◑ ✿
Deceptively-large beamed pub
with real fire. Collection of brass
and jugs on display. Beer festivals twice a year. Live music
once a month.

11-3; 7-11 (11-11 Thu-Sat: 12-3;
7-10.30 Sun)

Gardeners Arms 9
27 Hart Street (nr A1023/B185)
Tel: (01277) 210430
Greene King IPA; **Ind Coope**
Burton Ale **H**
❚ ✿ ⮑
Improved back-street local with
darts teams.

11-3; 5-11 (11-11 Sat: 12-10.30
Sun)

Golden Fleece 10
101 London Road (A1023)
Tel: (01277) 224511
Bass Hancocks HB, Draught
Bass **H**
🍸🍺 ◑ ❚ R ⮑ ✿ ⛄ (not bar)
A 'Harvester' restaurant with
small garden and patio.

Good Intent 11
33 High Street (A1023)
Inntrepreneur - Pub closed in
1996, and converted to a restaurant.

12 (7 Sat)-11 (3 Mon, 12 Thu-Sat)
(Closed Sun)

Latinos Bar Brasserie 12
60 Crown Street (nr A1023)
Tel:(01277) 210135
Free-house - No Real Ale.
Formerly the "Gallery Bar &
Brasserie" & "Swints".

11.30-3; 5.30-11 (11.30-11 Fri: 12-4; 7-10.30 Sun)

Nag's Head 13
44 Brook Street (A1023, nr M25/A12)
Tel: (01277) 213487
Greene King Abbot Ale; **Ind Coope** Burton Ale; **Morlands** Old Speckled Hen; **Tetley** Bitter **H**

◑ D ◑ ▶ ⊞ 🍴
Comfortable pub with sofas and bookshelves. Terraced open garden and elevated patio. Discos on Sunday evenings, quiz night Monday.

12-3 (Not Sat); 5-11 (12 Thu-Sat) Closed Sun.

Parkers Wine Bar 14
110/112 Kings Road (B186)
Tel: (01277) 217450
Adnams Bitter **H**
🚉
Attracts the office lunchtime trade, and the disco crowd Thur to Sat evenings. Good beer. Formerly "Odells" & "Bradleys Wine Bar".

11-11 (12-10.30 Sun)

Rising Sun 15
144 Ongar Road (A128)
Tel: (01277) 213749
Greene King IPA **H**
◑ ⊞ 🍴
Street-corner local, with patio and pool table. No food Sundays.

11-11 (12-10.30 Sun)

Robin Hood & Little John 16
Ongar Road (A128)
Tel: (01277) 213982
Tetley Bitter; **Guest Beer H**
◑ D ⊞ ❀ &
Inviting local with darts, pool and quizzes. May suffer conversion to a 'Big Steak'.

11-11 (12-10.30 Sun)

Scruffy Murphys 17
161 Kings Road / St James' Road (B186)
Tel: (01277) 212860
Tetley Bitter **H**
◑ ◀ & 🚉
Pseudo-Irish themed bar, with lots of wooden partitions. Quiz night Tuesday. Parking difficult. Formerly the "Railway Tavern"

11.30-11 (12-10.30 Sun)

Sir Charles Napier 18
141 High Street (A1023)
Tel: (01277) 219039
S&N Courage Directors, Websters Yorkshire Bitter **H**
◑ D ◑ ▶ ❀ 🚉
Compact pub by traffic lights, with biannual fun day. Real Ale not always available. Beware 'Scrumpy Jack' keg cider on Handpump. No food Sundays. Parking difficult.

11-3; 6-11 (11-11 Sat: 12-10.30 Sun)

Spread Eagle 19
88 Queens Road (B186, nr A128)
Tel: (01277) 221556
Tetley Bitter; **Whitbread** Flowers IPA; **Guest Beer H**
◑ ◀ 🚉
Splendid, tiny, triangular local, with quiz nights and darts teams. No meals Sundays. Parking can be difficult.

11-11 (12-10.30 Sun)

Swan (Hogshead) 20
123 High Street (A1023)
Tel: (01277) 211848
Mighty Oak Burntwood Bitter; **Whitbread** Boddingtons Bitter, Flowers IPA, Original, Abroad Cooper; **Guest Beers H**
Bulmers Old Hazy **H**
◑ ◀ ⊞ ◳ ▶ 🍴 & 🚉
High Street pub dating from the 15th century, with flagstone floors and a real fire. Now a Whitbread 'Hogshead', much-altered, but retaining some traditional panelling.
Guest beers include two to four on gravity dispense. New garden bar area. Parking available evenings and Sundays only.

11-11 (12-10.30 Sun)

Traders Bar (Forte Post House) 21
Brook Street (A1023, nr M25/A12)
Tel: (01277) 260260
Bass Hancocks HB **H**
◑ D ◑ R ⊞ ▶ &
Much-improved hotel bar, which could benefit from a wider range of Real Ales. Formerly the "Oak" bar.

11-11 (12-10.30 Sun)

Victoria Arms 22
50 Ongar Road (A128)
Tel: (01277) 223371
Greene King IPA, Abbot Ale; **Shepherd Neame** Spitfire; **Guest Beers H**
◑ ◀ ❀
A drinkers pub, with a wide range of malt whiskies. Patio and TV, no loud music. Beer variable. Parking difficult.

11-11 (12-10.30 Sun)

White Hart Inn 23
93 High Street (A1023)
Tel: (01277) 200885
Bass Draught Bass; **Greene King** Abbot Ale; **S&N** Courage Directors **H**
◑ D ◑ ▶ R ⊞ ▶ ❀ &
Renovated coaching house, with windowed-gallery and courtyard, now serving a sadly much-reduced range of Real Ales. Board games played. Rather expensive.
The 'Alebar' closes from 3 to 7 on Sundays, but the other bar stays open.

High Street (A1023)
Bass Charrington - Pub closed and converted to a 'KFC' (Kentucky Fried Chicken).

Brick End (Broxted) B2

12-3; 6-11 (12-3; 7-10.30 Sun)

Prince of Wales
Brick End (1 Mile off B1051)
OS: TL573259
Tel: (01279) 850256
Ind Coope Friary Meux BB; **Guest Beer H**
◑ D ◑ R ⊞ ☕ ❀ ✕
Large pub on a quiet, triangular traffic island, which has an emphasis on food. The conservatory doubles as a meeting room and family room.

Brightlingsea E3

Quaint riverside yachting centre once renowned for shipbuilding, and latterly for animal export protesters.

11-11 (12-10.30 Sun)

Anchor Hotel
Waterside (nr B1029)
Tel: (01206) 302035
Free-house - Pub closed.

11.30 (12 Sun)-3; 7-11 (10.30 Sun)

Brewers Arms
1 Victoria Place / New Street (B1029)
Tel: (01206) 302028
Ridleys IPA; **Guest Beers H**
◑ ◀ R ▶ 🍴 & 🍺
17th century pub with many exposed beams and a massive cellar that was used as air-raid shelter in last war. Beer served through sparklers.

11.30-3; 7-11 (11-11 Sat: 12-10.30 Sun)

Cherry Tree
29 Church Road/Dean Street (B1029)
Tel: (01206) 302713
Greene King IPA, Abbot Ale **H**
◑ D ◑ ⊞
Pleasant pub.

11-11 (12-10.30 Sun)

Freemasons Arms
8 Sydney Street / New Street (B1029)
Tel: (01206) 302529
S&N Theakstons BB; **Guest Beers H**
◑ D ◑ ⊞ ❀
Two Guest Ales.

11-3; 7-11 (12-3; 7-10.30 Sun)

Kings Head
41 Victoria Place (B1029)
Tel: (01206) 304323
Allied Domecq - No Real Ale.

New Brightlingsea
Hall Hotel
Church Road (B1029)
OS: TM078187
Free-house - Hotel/Pub closed.

12 (5 Mon-Thu)-11 (12-3; 7-10.30 Sun)

Railway Tavern
58 Station Road (nr B1029)
Tel: (01206) 302581
Mauldons Best Bitter; **Guest Beers H**
Guest Cider G
🍺 ❀

Two-bar pub popular with early evening drinkers. Railway memorabilia adorns the walls. Three guest beers and a mild normally available.

11-11 (12-10.30 Sun)

Rosebud
66 Hurst Green
Tel: (01206) 304571
Mauldons Best Bitter; **S&N** Theakstons BB; **Guest Beer H**
❀

Large, sporting pub, close to public green and overlooking Brightlingsea creek. Popular with locals, has an 'L'-shaped bar.

11-11 (12-10.30 Sun)

Smugglers Inn
82 Sydney Street / Francis Street (nr B1029)
Tel: (01206) 304520
Greene King IPA **H**
🍺 ♿

Occasional Guest Ales. Formerly the "Hanging Basket", the "Evening Star" & the "Martello".

11-11 (12-10.30 Sun)

Sun Inn
128 New Street (nr B1029)
Tel: (01206) 302179
Greene King IPA **H**
◖◗ 🍺 🚗

Fine, olde-worlde, weatherboarded building. Pool played. Parking difficult.

12-3; 7-11 (10.30 Sun)

Victoria
55 Spring Road (nr B1029)
Tel: (01206) 302088
Free-house - No Real Ale.

11-3; 6-11 (11-11 Sat & Summer: 12-10.30 Sun)

Yachtsman's Arms
35 Waterside (B1029) / Sydney Street
Tel: (01206) 302342
Greene King IPA, Abbot Ale **H**
◖◗ ◖◗ 🍺 ❀ ♿

Local sailing resort pub, close to the waterside. Excellent Sunday roasts. Pool, darts and other pub games played. Sparklers used.

12-3; 7-11 (10.30 Sun)

Ye Olde Swan
15 High Street
Tel: (01206) 302024
Whitbread Flowers IPA, Original **H**
◖◗ ◖◗ 🅁 🍴 ⬅ 🐾 🚗

One of the oldest buildings in Brightlingsea, and a friendly, characterful local.

Broad Green (Gt Tey) D2

Main road village, between Coggeshall and Marks Tey.

11.30-11 (12-3; 7-10.30 Sun)

Kings Arms
Coggeshall Road (A120)
Tel: (01376) 561581
Greene King IPA, Abbot Ale **H**
◖◗ ◖◗ ❀

Small and friendly, pub games a feature. Good range of food at reasonable prices.

Broadley Common A3

11-3; 5.30-11 (12-3; 7-10.30 Sun)

Black Swan
Common Road (nr B181)
OS: TL422072
Tel: (01992) 892123
Ind Coope Ansells Bitter; **Tetley** Bitter; **Whitbread** Flowers IPA **H**
◖◗ 🍺 ❀

Typical, timbered, Essex village pub, with parts believed to date back to the 11th century. Its huge potential has not yet been fully realised.

Broads Green (Gt Waltham) C3

11.30-2.30; 6.15-11 (12-2.30; 7-10.30 Sun)

Walnut Tree
Broads Green (1 Mile West of B1008)
OS: TL694125
Tel: (01245) 360222
Ridleys IPA, seasonal beers **G/H**
◖◗ ◖◗ 🍺 ❀

Splendid, traditional, Victorian pub facing village green, with comfortable lounge and unspoilt public bar, both accessed through a central snug. A warm welcome awaits. No food Thursday evenings.

Broomfield C3

11-11 (12-10.30 Sun)

Angel Inn
160 Main Road (B1008)
Tel: (01245) 440310
Ind Coope Benskins BB; **Marstons** Pedigree; **Tetley** Bitter; **Guest Beer H**
◖◗ ◖◗ 🅁 ❀ ♿

A many-beamed 'Big Steak' pub. Guest beers from the 'Tapsters Choice' range.

11.30-2.30; 6.30-11 (12-3; 7-10.30 Sun)

Kings Arms
295 Main Road (B1008)
Tel: (01245) 440258
Mauldons Bitter; **Whitbread** Flowers IPA, Original **H**
◖◗ ◖◗ 🅁 🚗

15th century oak-beamed pub with separate dining area, no meals Sunday or Monday evenings.

Buckhurst Hill A4

Posh suburb on fringe of Epping Forest.

12-3; 5.30-11 (12-11 Sat: 12-10.30 Sun)

Colorado Exchange
66 Epping New Road (A104)
Tel: (0181) 504 9886
Morlands (Exchange) - No Real Ale.

11-11 (12-10.30 Sun)

Jeffersons
High Road (A121)
Tel: (0181) 559 0909
Free-house (Jeffersons)
- No Real Ale. Formerly the "Bald Faced Stag".

11-11 (12-10.30 Sun)

Monarch's
24 Lower Queens Road (nr B170)
Tel: (0181) 504 3458
Free-house - No Real Ale. Formerly "B52s" and the "Prince of Wales".

11-11 (12-10.30 Sun)

Monkhams
Station Way / Buckhurst Way
Tel: (0181) 504 4525
Whitbread Boddingtons Bitter, Flowers Original **H**
◖◗ ◖◗ 🅁 🐾 ❀ ♿ ⊖

Large food-oriented pub near Roding Valley tube station. Large outdoor areas.

1-11 (12-10.30 Sun)

Queens
63 Queens Road (nr B170)
Tel: (0181) 504 4796
Allied Domecq - No Real Ale.

11-11 (12-10.30 Sun)

Railway Tavern
5 Queens Road (nr B170)
Tel: (0181) 504 2881
Whitbread Flowers IPA **H**

Smart, refurbished pub, but with little character, by the underground station. Pool room and function suite.

11-11 (12-10.30 Sun)

Roebuck Inn
Roebuck Lane / North End (nr A121)
OS: TQ412945
Tel: (0181) 505 4636
Free-house hotel - No Real Ale.

11-11 (12-10.30 Sun)

Three Colts Ale House
54 Princes Road / Kings Place
Tel: (0181) 504 0335
S&N Courage Directors, Theakstons BB, Old Peculier **H**

Fairly basic, pleasant, back-street pub, partially covered with ivy. Limited parking.

11-11 (12-10.30 Sun)

Warren Wood
Epping New Road (A104)
Tel: (0181) 504 0244
Fullers London Pride; **Ridleys** IPA; **S&N** Courage Best Bitter, Directors; **Guest beers** (occasional) **H**

Refurbished in bare wood style, but fairly smart. Close to Epping Forest with fine views at the rear. Loud obtrusive music. Expensive.

Bulmer D1

Hand-made bricks have been produced at the kiln here for several hundred years.

12-2 (3 Sun); 7-11 (10.30 Sun)

Cock & Blackbirds
Bulmer Street
OS: TL842403
Tel: (01787) 373039
Adnams Bitter; **Greene King** IPA **H**

Small, friendly, family-run, village pub. A short detour gives a welcome rest from the A131.

Bulmer Tye D1

11-11 (12-10.30 Sun)

Fox
Bulmer Tye (A131)
Tel: (01787) 377505
Greene King IPA; **Mauldons** Bitter **H**

Typical, large, modernised roadside pub. Small, but friendly bar for 'non-diners'.

Bulphan B5

11-3; 6-11 (12-3; 7-10.30 Sun)

Harrow Inn
Harrow Road, Fen Lane
OS: TQ623852
Tel: (01375) 891269
Free-house - No Real Ale.

11-11 (12-10.30 Sun)

Langdon Hills Golf Centre
Lower Dunton Road (nr B1007)
OS: TQ662856
Tel: (01268) 548444
Greene King IPA, Abbot Ale **H**

New Greene King Golf Club and Hotel. Pleasant, clean bar area, with friendly staff.

Bures Hamlet D1

Straddles the River Stour which is the Essex/Suffolk county border.

11-3; 6-11 (12-3; 7-10.30 Sun)

Eight Bells
Colchester Road (B1508)
Tel: (01787) 227354
Greene King IPA; **Tetley** Bitter **H**

Pleasant and well-established village local, with long-serving landlord.

11-11 (12-10.30 Sun)

Swan Inn
1 Station Hill (nr B1508)
Tel: (01787) 228121
Greene King IPA, Abbot Ale **H**

Built in 1490, with a basic homely, public bar, plush lounge, open fires. Good value beer.

Burnham-on Crouch D4

Picturesque tidal riverside town, still retaining its cinema. The old school with its unusual clock-tower dominates the high street. Now a lively yachting centre, with marina, and lots of eating establishments.

11-11 (12-10.30 Sun)

Anchor Hotel
The Quay / Shore Road (nr B1010)
Tel: (01621) 782117
Adnams Bitter; **Crouch Vale** Millennium Gold; **Greene King** IPA **H**
Guest Cider (Summer) **G**

Popular, 16th century inn, overlooking the River Crouch, with low ceilings and a nautical flavour. Separate pool room. Well-kept beer.

11-11 (12-10.30 Sun)

New Welcome Sailor
74 Station Road (B1010)
Tel: (01621) 784778
Greene King IPA **H**

A true local Grays pub with no frills, where time has stood still - an icon to the 1960s.
Stop here for darts, dominoes, crib, shove-halfpenny, 'Devil Amongst the Tailors' and a piano.

11-3; 6-11 (12-3; 7-10.30 Sun)

Ostend George
16 Maldon Road, Ostend (B1010)
Tel: (01621) 784552
Mauldons White Adder; **Ridleys** IPA; **Wadworths** Farmers Glory; **Guest Beers H**

Smart, modern free-house with a constantly-changing range of Guest Beers. Darts and pool played.

11-3; 6-11 (12-3; 7-10.30 Sun)

Oyster Smack
112 Station Road (B1010)
Tel: (01621) 782141
Greene King IPA, Abbot; **Whitbread** Flowers IPA, Original; **Guest Beers H**

Much-improved town pub with single bar and horseshoe-servery. Good selection of Guest beers (Whitbread portfolio) See the stained-glass saucy post-cards over the bar!

11-3 (4 Sat); 6-11 (12-10.30 Sun, hours may vary)

Queen's Head
26 Providence (nr B1010)
Tel: (01621) 784825
Greene King IPA, Abbot Ale; **Guest Beers H**
Basic, popular, back-street Grays watering hole, with pool table. Hours may vary.

11-11 (12-10.30 Sun)

Railway Hotel
12 Station Road (B1010)
Tel: (01621) 783002
Inntrepreneur Pub - No Real Ale. Formerly the "Railway Arms".

11-3; 7-11 (12-3; 7-10.30 Sun)

Ship
52 High Street (B1010)
Tel: (01621) 785057
Adnams Bitter, Broadside, seasonal beers **H**

Pleasant local with excellent nautical collection. Good food and friendly service. Limited parking.

11-11 (12-10.30 Sun)

Star Inn
29/31 High Street (B1010)
Tel: (01621) 782010
Adnams Bitter; **Youngs** Bitter **H**

Beer variable, limited parking.

11-11 (12-10.30 Sun)

Victoria Inn
1 Belvedere Road / High St
(B1010)
Tel: (01621) 783585
Greene King IPA, Abbot Ale **H**
◑ ⅅ ◖ ⊞
Friendly, Gray's local with rare
'tiled' pub sign. Pool table and
dart board in pubic bar. Food all
day. Limited Parking.

11-11 (12-10.30 Sun)

Ye Olde White Harte
The Quay / Shore Road (nr
B1010)
Tel: (01621) 782106
Adnams Bitter; **Tolly Cobbold**
Bitter **H**
◑ ⅅ ◖ ℝ ◳ ⊫ ❀
Charming old red-brick inn with
superb views of river and private
jetty. Excellent food, beer vari-
able.

Burton End (Stansted)　B2

*Pleasant rural hamlet near
Stansted Airport.*

11-11 (12-10.30 Sun)

Ash
Burton End
OS: TL532237
Tel: (01279) 814841
Greene King IPA, Abbot Ale,
seasonal ale **H**
◑ ⅅ ◖ ℝ ⊞ ❀
Thatched 17th century cottage
pub, which has been refurbished
and extended to create a new
restaurant.
Still retains some of its
character, despite its proximity
to the increasingly busy airport.
Accommodation may be
available in the future.
Photos of Stansted as the home
of the WW2 American 344th
Bomber Group adorn the walls.

Canewdon　D4

*Quiet village 'witch' comes alive
at Halloween.*

11.30-3; 5-11 (12-3 (later if busy);
7-10.30 Sun)

Anchor
High Street
Tel: (01702) 258213
Greene King IPA; **Whitbread**
Flowers IPA; **Guest Beers H**
◑ ⅅ ◖ ℝ ◳ ❀ ⅋
Cosy, low-beamed, 500 year old
pub, with large enclosed garden,
that has children's facilities and
aviary. Near the village stocks.

12 (11.30 Sat)-3 (4 Sat); 7-11
(12-4; 7-10.30 Sun)

Chequers Inn
High Street
Tel: (01702) 258251
Fullers London Pride; **Greene
King** IPA, Abbot Ale; **Guest
Beer H**
◑ ⅅ ◖ ℝ ◳ ❀ ⅋
Friendly, village free-house,
saved from demolition by locals
and CAMRA. Carriage lamp col-
lection.

Canfield End (Lt Canfield)　B2

11-2.30; 6-11 (12-3; 7-10.30 Sun)

Lion & Lamb
Stortford Road (A120)
Tel: (01279) 870257
Ridleys IPA, ESX **H**
◑ ⅅ ◖ ℝ ⊫ ❀
Friendly roadside pub, with
extensive menu. Wood-theme
decor, spinning bar stools. Won
the Ridley's 1993/94 Pub of the
Year award.

Canvey Island　C5

*Once a holiday resort for
Eastenders. Flooded in 1953, but
now a developing residential
and industrial area.*

11-11 (12-3; 7-10.30 Sun)

1066 Tavern (Paddocks)
Long Road (A130)
Tel: (01268) 695055
Free-house - No Real Ale.

12-11 (12-4; 7-10.30 Sun)

Admiral Jellicoe
283 High Street, Leigh Beck
(B1014)
Tel: (01268) 660011
Bass Draught Bass **H**
◑ ◖ ⅋ ◳ ⊫ ⅀ ❀
Long, lounge bar area, with loud
music.

Dr Feelgood Music Bar
21 Knightswick Road (B1014)
Free-house - Closed and demolished, but see the 'Oysterfleet'
entry.

12-12 (12-3; 7-10.30 Sun)

Emily's
1/3 Eastern Esplanade
Tel: (01268) 683026
Free-house - No Real Ale.
Formerly the "Monico"

10.30-12.30am (12-4; 7-10.30
Sun)

Haystack
56 Furtherwick Road (A130)
Tel: (01268) 680454
S&N Theakstons BB, XB; **Guest
Beer H**
◑ ⅅ ◖ ℝ ⊫ ⅀ ❀ ⅋
Refurbished, multi-bar pub with
American cafe-bar, in the town
centre, near the Knightswick
shopping centre. Formerly
"Tropics".

11-11 (12-10.30 Sun)

King Canute
Long Road / Canvey Road (A130)
Tel: (01268) 683115
Bass - No Real Ale.

Kings Piano Bar
Kings Holiday Park, Newlands
Camp
Tel: (01268) 684572
Free-house - No Real Ale.

11-11 (12-10.30 Sun)

Lobster Smack
Haven Road, Hole Haven
OS: TQ782822
Tel: (01268) 660021
Bass Hancocks HB, Draught
Bass; **Guest Beer H**
◑ ◖ ❀
18th century local, full of charm,
character and history from a
bygone age, with Dickensian
connections.
Good view of the shipping on
the Thames (and the oil termi-
nals!) from the sea wall. Guest
beers from the 'Cask Masters
Guest Ales'. Worth a visit.

Olympic Bar
Waterside Sports Centre,
Somnes Avenue (B1014)
Tel: (01268) 693935
Free-house - No Real Ale.

11-11 (12-10.30 Sun)

Oysterfleet
21 Knightswick Road (B1014)
Tel: (01268) 510111
Morlands Old Speckled Hen;
Whitbread Boddingtons Bitter,
Flowers Original; **Guest Beers H**
◑ ⅅ ◖ ℝ ◳ ❀ ⅋
A purpose-built complex, that
opened in October 1995, on the
site of the old "Dr Feelgood
Music Bar" (previously known
as the "Oyster Fleet").
Family-oriented pub, restaurant
and hotel with a large lake at the
rear and conference facilities for
200. Wedding receptions catered
for - wedding licence held.

11-3; 5-11 (11-11 Fri/Sat: 12-6;
7-10.30 Sun)

Silver Jubilee
Link Road / Hilton Road (nr
B1014)
Tel: (Ex-Directory)
Ind Coope 'House' Bitter **H**
◑ ⅅ ◖ ◗ (not Sun) ⅀ ❀
Modern family pub, with a regal
theme. Safe indoor play area for
children. Live music Friday and
Saturday evenings. 'L'-shaped
pool table.

Two Flights Up
Western Esplanade
Free-house - Pub closed and
converted to flats. Formerly the
"Waters Edge".

11-11 (12 Fri/Sat: 12-4.30; 7-10.30 Sun)
Windjammer
Eastern Esplanade
Tel: (01268) 695389
Adnams Bitter; **Guest Bitter H**

◑ ◖ ❀

Overlooking the Thames, with good value beer. No food at weekends. Beware! 'Scrumpy Jack' keg cider on handpump.

Castle Hedingham   C1

Beautiful village with 12th century Norman keep. Silk mills and Colne Valley Railway nearby.

11.30-3; 6-11 (12-3; 7-10.30 Sun)
Bell Inn
10 St James Street (B1058)
Tel: (01787) 460350
Greene King IPA, Abbot Ale **G**

◑ ◗ ◖ ◐ **R** 日 ┗ ➳ ❀ 🍺

Excellent, genuine, timbered, multi-roomed pub with casks behind bar. Good value food, not available Monday evenings, except Bank Holidays. No smoking room.

Memories Cafe Bar
Nunnery Road, Crouch Green (by A1017, was A604)
Free-house - Pub closed and converted to a Chinese restaurant.

11-2.30; 7-11 (12-3; 7-10.30 Sun)
Rising Sun
71 Nunnery Street (nr B1058 & A1017 - A604)
Tel: (01787) 460355
Greene King IPA, Abbot Ale **H**

◑ ◗ ◖ **R** 日 ❀

Small, friendly, basic, locals pub with pool table.

11-3; 7-11 (11-11 Sat: 12-10.30 Sun)
Wheatsheaf
2 Queen Street (B1058)
Tel: (01787) 460555
Greene King - No Real Ale.

Chadwell Heath   A4

Separated from Romford by the Open Crown lands.

11-11 (12-10.30 Sun)
Big Hand Mo's
1149 High Road (A118)
Tel: (0181) 590 3294
S&N - No Real Ale. Formerly the "Chadwell Arms" & "Chads".

11-11 (12-10.30 Sun)
Coopers Arms
2 High Road (A118) / Station Road
Tel: (0181) 590 1216
S&N Courage Best Bitter, Directors **H**

◑ ◗ ◖ ◐ ┗ ➳

Lively pub with a 'U'-shaped bar, attracting a mixed crowd. Regular entertainment include bands, discos, karaoke and quizzes. Can get busy and noisy at times.
Beware 'Courage Best' served on a 'sparkler' - ask for it to be removed when ordering. Beer variable.

11-11 (12-10.30 Sun)
Eva Hart
1128 High Road (A118) / Station Road
Tel:
Greene King Abbot Ale; **S&N** Courage Directors, Theakstons BB; **Guest Beers H**

◑ ◗ ◖ ◐ 🍴 ♿ ✂ 日 ➳

New 'Wetherspoon' converted from a former police station and opened in July 1998. Gallery bar and toilets upstairs. Named after a survivor of the 'Titanic', who lived locally.

11-11 (12-10.30 Sun)
Greyhound
900 High Road (A118)
Tel: (0181) 599 1533
Bass Hancocks HB **H**

◑ ◗ ◖ ◐ ➳ ➳

Comfortable, 'mock-Tudor Olde Worlde' pub, recently converted to a 'Harvester'. Obviously food-oriented, but serves Real Ale - ask for the 'sparkler' to be removed when ordering.

11-11 (12-10.30 Sun)
Moby Dick
Eastern Avenue West / Whalebone Lane North (A12/A1112)
Tel: (0181) 590 9524
S&N John Smiths Bitter **H**

◑ ◗ ◖ **R** 日 ┗ ➳ ❀ ♿

Large 'Country Carvery' pub/restaurant by main road junction. Public 'Games' bar open all day, but the saloon by the restaurant closes 3-5pm.

11.30-11 (12-10.30 Sun)
Tollgate
High Road / Whalebone Lane North (A118/A1112)
Tel: (0181) 599 1095
Bass Toby Cask, Draught Bass; **Fullers** London Pride **H**

◑ ◗ ◖ ◐ 日 ❀

Recently-refurbished, with a 'brand-new' feel. Large central pine bar surrounded by three distinct drinking areas - including a no smoking area. Offers cheap beer for OAPs.

11-11 (12-3; 7-10.30 Sun)
White Horse
118 High Road (A118)
Tel: (0181) 597 0229
Ind Coope Burton Ale; **Tetley** Bitter; **Youngs** Bitter, Winter Warmer **H**

◑ ◖ ❀

Large, one-bar pub with friendly and helpful bar staff. Beware 'Addlestones' cider served under CO2 on handpump. Car park has its own traffic lights. Large garden.

Chadwell St Mary   B5

Once the home of Daniel Defoe, now a rather dull district sandwiched between Tilbury and Orsett.

11-11 (12-10.30 Sun)
Cross Keys
2 River View (nr A126/B149)
Tel: (01375) 842252
Phoenix Pub Co - No Real Ale.

11-11 (12-10.30 Sun)
Daniels
Longhouse Road
Tel: (01375) 843918
S&N - No Real Ale. Formerly the "Robinson Crusoe".

Chafford Hundred   B5

New town near the vast Lakeside shopping complex, with its own railway station.

11-11 (12-10.30 Sun)
Chafford Hundred
Fleming Road / Howard Road (by B186)
Tel: (01375) 481153
Fullers London Pride; **Gales** HSB; **Whitbread** Boddingtons Bitter, Castle Eden Ale, Flowers Original **H**

◑ ◗ ◖ ◐ **R** ➳ ❀ ♿ ➳

Large new 'Brewers Fayre' with children's play area, near the Lakeside Shopping Centre.

11-3; 5.30-11 (12-10.30 Sun)
Sandmartin
Drake Road / Clifford Road (nr A1012)
Tel: (01375) 481056
Greene King IPA, Abbot Ale, Seasonal Beers **H**

◑ ◗ ◖ ◐ ❀ ♿

Large pub in new development, with varied menu and children's certificate.

27

11-11 (12-10.30 Sun)

Treacle Mine
Lodge Lane / Elizabeth Rd
(A1306/A1012)
Tel: (01375) 390701
Bass Hancocks HB, Draught
Bass;
Crouch Vale Woodham IPA;
Guest Beer H
Westons Old Rosie H
◖D ◖▶ R ✿ ♿
'Foody' pub for families, suppos-
edly named after a nearby local
feature.

Chappel   D2

*Charming riverside village with
magnificent railway viaduct - the
largest in East Anglia, with 32
arches - each of 30' span, and
dating from 1849, it was built
with 7,500,000 bricks!*

*The home of the East Anglian
Railway Museum, with its regular steam days, which also hosts
the Chappel Beer Festival - in
association with the Essex
Branches of CAMRA - in the
week following the first Sunday
each September.*

11-3; 6-11 (12-3; 7-10.30 Sun)

Swan Inn
The Street (nr A1124, was A604)
Tel: (01787) 222353
Greene King IPA, Rayments
Special, Abbot Ale;
Whitbread Castle Eden Ale H
◖D ◖▶ R ⌂ ✿ ♿ ⇌
Lovely 14th century inn and
restaurant by the River Colne, in
the shadow of Chappel viaduct.

Chatham Green   C3

12-3; 6-11 (12-11 Sat: 12-10.30
Sun)

Windmill Motel
Chatham Green (nr A131)
OS: TL716151
Tel: (01245) 361188
Ridleys IPA; **Guest Beer** H
◖D ◖▶ 🛏 🚗
Rural local, recently re-opened
after a sympathetic restoration,
following several years of closure.
Ridleys, had wanted to sell it off
as a private house, but permis-
sion was refused after a campaign involving the local branch
of CAMRA.
Accommodation has now been
built into the base of the old
windmill, and there are seven
double rooms.
Varying guest beers.

Chelmer Village   C3

11-11 (12-3;7-10.30 Sun)

Barnes Farm
Barnes Mill Road, Chelmer
Village Way (nr A138)
Tel: (01245) 495336
Fullers London Pride; **Greene
King** IPA, Abbot Ale;
Whitbread Boddingtons
Bitter, Flowers Original;
Guest Beers H
◖D ◖▶ R ✿ ♿
Typical 'Beefeater' restaurant,
but with comfortable bar area.
Beer quality better than one
might expect, but you'll have to
ask for the sparklers to be
removed, to appreciate it!

12-3; 6-11 (11-11 Sat; 12-7 Sun)

Chelmer Inn
Village Square, Village Gate
OS: TL732072
Tel: (01245) 469700
Bass Hancocks HB H
◖ ◖ ✿
Wonderful, scenic pub by the
river - but that's enough about
the pub-sign! Perhaps designed
by someone with a sense of
humour, or very wishful think-
ing!?
In reality an uninspiring, typical,
modern estate pub, near the
ASDA superstore.

11-11 (12-10.30 Sun)

'Chelmer Tavern'
New Dukes Way (by A138)
Tel: (01245) 450695
Whitbread Boddingtons Bitter,
Flowers Original H
◖D ◖▶ R ✿ ♿
More emphasis on food, than
beer for the discerning drinker
following refurbishment.
Comfortable bar - beer quality
still adequate. Formerly the
"Berni Inn".

12-11 (10.30 Sun)

Fox & Raven
Barnes Mill Road, Chelmer
Village Way (nr A138)
Tel: (01245) 252390
Bass Hancocks HB, Worthington
BB, Draught Bass H
◖D ◖▶ R ⛏ ✿ ♿
Old farm house, converted by
Bass to a 'Fork and Pitcher'.
Mainly unspoilt with hanging
baskets, spacious interior, bare
floors and wooden furniture.
'Chintzy' and catering for mainly
a restaurant clientele.
Subdued 'piped' music. Beware
the beer is served cold, and the
Cider on handpump is under
CO_2 pressure.

"The Red Lion", Chelmsford

Chelmsford   C3

County town of Essex. An agri-cultural centre with cattle and produce markets. Few ancient buildings have survived a period of desecration in the sixties. The Shire Hall, the cathedral and Moulsham Bridge are excep-tions.

Marconi set up his first wireless station here and the town was the first to have electric light. Gray's Brewery was behind Debenhams.

11-11 (12-3; 7-10.30 Sun)
Alma   1
33 Arbour Lane, Springfield (nr B1137)
Tel: (01245) 256783
Greene King IPA, seasonal ales; **Ridleys** IPA **H**
◖D ◖ ⊞ ⊫ ❀
Lively, enlarged pub with sepa-rate pool room/function room, and a friendly atmosphere. Varied live entertainment. Beware 'tight sparklers' used.

11-11 (12-10.30 Sun)
Anchor   2
151 Moulsham Street
Tel: (01245) 250865
Bass Draught Bass; **Tetley** Bitter **H**
Large, uninspiring, one-bar pub, with established local clientele. Beer variable. Limited parking.

11-11 (12-10.30 Sun)
Army & Navy   3
138 Parkway (A138) / Van Diemans Road (A414)
Tel: (01245) 354155
Tetley Bitter; **Guest Beer** (occasional) **H**
❀ ♿
Chelmsford's foremost music venue. The pub gave its name to the adjacent roundabout.

11-12 (2am Fri/Sat) (12-10.30 Sun)
Basement   4
16 Wells Street
Tel: (01245) 358480
Bass Draught Bass; **S&N** Courage Directors; **Wadworths** 6X **H**
◖D ◖ ◗ ⇌
Live music venue for the younger set. Parking difficult. Formerly "Snifters Wine Bar".

11-11 (12-10.30 Sun)
Bay Horse Tavern   5
189 Moulsham Street
Tel: (01245) 352066
S&N Courage Directors, John Smiths Bitter, Websters Yorkshire Bitter **H**
◖D ◖ ⊓
17th century pub, popular with young people. No food Sundays. Beware 'tight sparklers'

Billy Rays   6
Unit 7, Riverside Retail Park, Victoria Road
Tel: (01245) 348465
Free-house - Temporarily closed.

12-3; 6-11 (12-11 Fri/Sat: 12-10.30 Sun)
Bird in Hand   7
New Writtle Street (nr B1007)
Tel: (01245) 600002
Ridleys IPA, Rumpus **H**
◖D ◖ ◗ ⊞ ⊓ ⇌
Large, friendly, sports-oriented pub near cricket and football grounds. No meals Sunday lunchtimes.

11-3; 7-11 (12-3; 7-10.30 Sun)
Black Bull   8
244 Rainsford Road (A1060)
Tel: (01245) 496252
Whitbread Flowers Original **H** ⊓
Unassuming pub with regular discos and limited parking.

11-11 (12-10.30 Sun)
Black Horse   9
165 Moulsham Street
Tel: (01245) 251611
Fullers London Pride; **Greene King** IPA **H**
◖D ❀
Comfortable, sport-oriented, one-bar locals pub.

Chicago's   10
122 Springfield Road (A1090, jcn with B1137)
Tel: (01245) 250753
Free-house - Pub closed.
Formerly the "Three Cups".

12-3; 6-11 (11-4; 7-11 Sat: 12-3; 7-10.30 Sun)
Clay Pigeon   11
26 Robin Way (off Linnet Drive), Tile Kiln Estate (nr B1007)
Tel: (01245) 268589
Greene King IPA; **S&N** Courage Best Bitter **H**
◖D ❀
Circular estate pub, with a friendly, family atmosphere.

12-3; 6-11 (11-11 Fri/Sat: 12-3; 7-10.30 Sun)
Clockhouse   12
271 Broomfield Road (B1008)
Tel: (01245) 346115
Bass Draught Bass **H**
◖D ❀
Quiet pub with pool tables. Karaoke night - Friday.

11-2.30 (3 Fri/Sat); 6-11 (12-3; 7-10.30 Sun)
Compasses   13
141 Broomfield Road (B1008)
Tel: (01245) 257867
Bass Hancocks HB **H**
◖D ◖ ◗ ⊞ ◗ ❀
Basic public bar and comfortable lounge. Limited parking.

Corks Wine Bar   14
34a Moulsham Street (nr A138)
Tel: (01245) 258733
Free-house - No Real Ale.

12-3; 6-11 (10.30 Sun)
County Hotel   15
Rainsford Road (nr A138/A1016)
Tel: (01245) 491911
Adnams Bitter; **Greene King** IPA **H**
◖D ◖ ◗ ⊠ ⌂ ⊫ ⊓ ⇌
Comfortable hotel lounge bar. Beware 'sparklers'

11-11 (12-10.30 Sun)
Cricketers Inn   16
143 Moulsham Street / Queens Street (nr B1007)
Tel: (01245) 261157
Greene King IPA **H**
◖D ◖ ⊞ ⊓
Refurbished Grays house on a corner in Chelmsford's most (or only!) historic street. Parking difficult.

11-11 (12-10.30 Sun)
Flyer (Hungry Horse)   17
Dickens Place, Copperfield Road, Newland Spring, North Melbourne
OS: TL689092
Tel: (01245) 441242
Bass Draught Bass, Toby Cask; **S&N** Courage Directors **H**
◖D ◖ ❀ ♿
Magic Pub company local incor-porating a no-smoking area. Beware 'tight sparklers'. Formerly the "Flyer".

11-3; 6-11 (12-3.30; 7-10.30 Sun)
Fox & Hounds   18
89 Wood Street (B1007)
OS: TL691049
Tel: (01245) 355864
Greene King IPA; **Shepherd Neame** Masterbrew **H**
◖D ◖ ◗ ⊞ ❀
Modernised two-bar Grays pub opposite maternity hospital. Good quiz team.

11-11 (12-10.30 Sun)
Globe   19
Rainsford Road (A1060)
Tel: (01245) 261263
Marstons Sundance; **Ridleys** IPA; **S&N** Courage Directors, Theakstons BB; **Shepherd Neame** Spitfire Guest Beer **H**; **Westons** Cider **H**
◖D ◖ ◗ ⊓ ⊁ ⇌ ⊖
A former 'Harvester', that was actually owned by Ridleys. Now a large, attractive 'Wetherspoon' that reopened in July 1998. A much improved beer range. Beware some beers on 'sparkler'. 'Quiet' fruit machines!

11-3; 5-11 (12-3; 7-10.30 Sun)
Greenlands   20
1 Cherry Garden Lane / Writtle Road (B1007)
Tel: (01245) 250661
Tetley Bitter, Imperial **H**
◖D ◖ ◗ ❀
Large, renovated pub with a range of flavoured vodkas. Hopefully a different a different range of beers will be intro-duced. Formerly the "Cherry Tree".

CHELMSFORD
Great Baddow

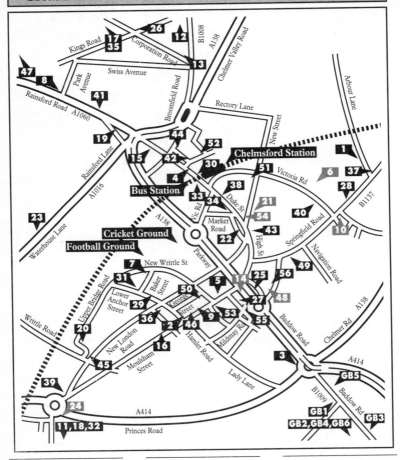

12-3; 5-11 (12-11 Fri/Sat)

Hot House Bar & Bistro **21**
57 New Street / Waterloo Lane
(nr A1099)
Tel: (01245) 491248
Free-house - No Real Ale. In old
police station cells. Formerly
"Peelers Wine Bar".

11-11 (closed Sun)

Judge Tindals Tavern **22**
6 Tindal Street (nr A1099)
Tel: (01245) 252241
Ridleys IPA, ESX **H**
◖ ◖ ⇌
Small, one-bar town centre pub,
acquired by Ridleys in 1997.
Mock antique interior, with fairly
comfortable seating. The car-
toons in the pictures on the wall
have a legal theme.
Piped music. Parking difficult.

11-2.30 (3 Sat); 6-11 (12-3;
7-10.30 Sun)

Marsham Arms **23**
107 Waterhouse Lane (A1016)
Tel: (01245) 350345
Greene King IPA; **Tetley** Bitter;
Wadworths 6X **H**
◖ ◖ ⊞ ⊨ ⟡ ❀
Friendly, local community road-
house / local meeting place.

10-11.30 (12-10.30 Sun)

Miami Hotel **24**
Princes Road (Wood Street
Roundabout, A414/B1007)
Tel: (01245) 264848
Free-house - No Real Ale.

11-11 (closed Sun Lunch; 7-10.30
Sun)

Nags Head **25**
22 Baddow Road (nr A138)
Tel: (01245) 355016
Greene King IPA; **Ind Coope**
Burton Ale; **Tetley** Bitter **H**
◖ ◖ ❀
Small, comfortable town centre
pub. Limited parking. In street
full of culinary delights!

11-3; 6 (5.30 Sat)-11 (12-3; 7-
10.30 Sun)

New Barn **26**
Kings Road (nr B1008)
Tel: (01245) 352913
Ridleys IPA **H**
◖ ▯ ◖ ▯ ⊞ ❀
Established estate local, mind
the mirror!

11-11 (12-10.30 Sun)

O'Connors   **27**
7 Hall Street (off Moulsham
Street, nr A138)
Tel: (01245) 600037
Greene King IPA; **S&N** Courage
Directors, Theakstons BB **H**
◖◗ ◖◗ 🍺
Tastefully decorated externally,
with white walls offset by black
panels with gold lettering. The
old interior remains basic, with a
few embellishments. Formerly
the "Prince of Orange".
Stop Press - Acquired by
'Youngs', so the beer range is
likely to change.

11-11 (12-3; 7-10.30 Sun)

Oddfellows Arms   **28**
195 Springfield Road (B1137)
Tel: (01245) 490514
Greene King IPA, Abbot Ale;
Shepherd Neame Masterbrew **H**
◖◗ ◖ ◗ **R** ⊨ ❀
Popular, one-roomed town pub,
with emphasis on food. Regular
clientele. Limited parking.

11-2.30 (3 Sat); 6 (7 Sat) -11 (12-
3; 7-10.30 Sun)

Orange Tree   **29**
6 Lower Anchor Street (nr B1007)
Tel: (01245) 262664
Greene King IPA, Abbot Ale;
Shepherd Neame Masterbrew
H
◖◗ ◖ ⊞ ❀ ♿
Two-bar, Gray & Sons, town
pub, with regular guest
beers - changed monthly.
Limited parking.

11-11 (12-10.30 Sun)

Original Plough   **30**
28 Duke Street (nr A138)
Tel: (01245) 250145
Greene King IPA; **Tetley**
Bitter; **Guest Beers H**
◖◗ ◖ 🍺 ⇌
Town-centre local by the station,
now a 'Festival Alehouse', that
attracts both a young clientele
and mature ale enthusiasts. Up
to six guest beers. Occasional
live music. Parking difficult.
Formerly "Harlequins".

11-3; 5.30-11 (11-11 Sat: 12-10.30
Sun)

Partners   **31**
30 Lower Anchor Street (nr
B1007)
Tel: (01245) 265181
Crouch Vale Best Bitter;
Greene King IPA; **Guest
Beers H**
◖◗ ◖ ⊨ ☙ ❀
Friendly, renovated, street-cor-
ner local, with two or more var-
ied and interesting guest beers.
Pool played. No food at week-
ends.

11-3; 6-11 (11-11 Fri/Sat: 12-10.30
Sun)

Pickled Newt   **32**
Gloucester Avenue
Tel: (01245) 257724
Bass Draught Bass, Toby Cask;
S&N Courage Best Bitter;
Whitbread Boddingtons Bitter **H**
◖◗ ❀
Recently refurbished estate pub,
with a fishing theme. Formerly
the "Eagle & Hind".

11-11 (12-4; 7-10.30 Sun)

Railway Tavern   **33**
63 Duke Street / Park Road (nr
A1099)
Tel: (01245) 356995
Greene King IPA, Abbot Ale;
Shepherd Neame Spitfire;
Guest Beers H
◖◗ ◖ ◗ 🍺 ⇌
Completely renovated 'Grays'
pub, now with only one bar. The
walls are partly pine-panelled
and partly painted, with photos
and pictures.
Seating at rear now laid out as a
partial mock-up of a railway carriage. Parking difficult.

11-11 (12-10.30 Sun)

Rat & Parrot   **34**
84 Duke Street (nr A1099)
Tel: (01245) 256752
S&N Courage Best Bitter,
Theakstons BB, XB;
Wadworths 6X **H**
◖◗ ◖ ⇌
Large town centre pub, convert-
ed to 'Rat & Parrot' concept!.
Breakfasts available at the bar.
Parking difficult. Beware 'tight
sparklers'. Formerly the "Golden
Fleece".

11-3; 6-11 (12-3; 7-10.30 Sun)

Red Beret   **35**
Melbourne Avenue
Tel: (01245) 355412
S&N Courage Directors,
Websters Yorkshire Bitter **H**
◖◗ ◗ ⊞ ❀
Basic, two-bar estate pub.

10.30-11 (12-10.30 Sun)

Red Lion   **36**
147 New London Road (B1007)
Tel: (01245) 354092
Ridleys IPA, ESX, Witchfinder
Porter **H**
◖◗ ◗ (if requested) ◖ ⊞ 🍺
Popular workingmen's local,
with cosy, quieter saloon bar
and busy public bar. Limited
parking.

11-11 (12-3; 7-10.30 Sun)

Red Lion   **37**
249 Springfield Road (B1137)
Tel: (01245) 264255
S&N Courage Directors, John
Smiths Bitter **H**
◖◗ ◖ ◗ ⊞ 🍺
Two-bar pub, with pool in the
public bar, and satellite TV.
Garish neon signs in the saloon
bar add a certain "Je ne sais
quoi". Occasional Guest Beers.
Parking difficult.

11 (12 Sat) -11 (7-10.30 only Sun)

Rendezvous   **38**
25 Duke Street (nr A1099)
Tel: (01245) 353138
Ind Coope Ansells Mild;
Marstons Pedigree; **Tetley**
Bitter; **Wadworths** 6X **H**
◖◗ ◗ 🍺 ⇌
Trendy, one-bar pub next to
Dukes disco. Formerly "La
Ducquesa".

11-11 (12-10.30 Sun)

Rising Sun   **39**
232 New London Road (B1007)
Tel: (01245) 352782
Bass Toby Cask; **Greene King**
IPA **H**
◖◗ ◗ ◖ ⊞ ⊨ ❀
Comfortable town local to have
a quiet beer in. Limited parking.

11-11 (12-10.30 Sun)

Riverside Inn   **40**
Victoria Road (A1099)
Tel: (01245) 266881
Greene King IPA; **S&N** Courage
Directors, John Smiths Bitter **H**
◖◗ ◗ **R** ⊨ ❀ ♿
Converted 14th century riverside
mill - well worth visiting.
Formerly the "Springfield Mill".
Stop Press - Acquired by
'Youngs', so the beer range is
likely to change.

11-11 (12-10.30 Sun)

Rose & Crown   **41**
170 Rainsford Road (A1060)
Tel: (01245) 352496
Bass Toby Cask; **Fullers** London
Pride **H**
◖◗ ◖ ❀
Modernised with 1920's decor,
large garden. Suitable for fami-
lies. Beware 'tight sparklers'.

11-11 (12-10.30 Sun)

Royal Steamer   **42**
1-2 Townfield Street (nr A138)
Tel: (01245) 258800
Adnams Bitter; **Ind Coope**
Benskins BB; **Marstons**
Pedigree; **Tetley** Bitter **H**
◖◗ ◖ ◗ ⊞ ⊨ ❀ ⇌
Unspoilt back-street local.
Beware 'tight sparklers'. Parking
limited.

12-3; 5.30-11 (closed Sun)

Saracen's Head Hotel   **43**
3 High Street (nr A138)
Tel: (01245) 262368
Greene King IPA; **Hardy** Country
Bitter **H**
◖◗ ◗ **R** ⊞ 🛏 ⊨ ☙ ❀
♿ ⇌
Two smart bars, one concentrat-
ing on food. Beer variable.
Limited parking.

10-11 (12-10.30 Sun)

Ship   **44**
18 Broomfield Road (nr A138)
Tel: (01245) 265961
Ridleys IPA, ESX, Spectacular,
Rumpus **H**
◖◗ ◗ ◖ 🍺 ⇌
Popular one-bar pub, with a nau-
tical theme. Small public car
park to rear.

31

11-2.30; 6-11 (12-2.30; 7-10.30 Sun)

South Lodge Hotel **45**
196 New London Road (B1007) / Writtle Road
Tel: (01245) 264564
Adnams Bitter H
① D ① R ⌂ ⌷ ⌷ ⌷ ⌷ ⌷
Lounge bar of hotel open to public. Pool table in annexe.

11-11 (12-10.30 Sun)

Star & Garter **46**
159 Moulsham Street (nr B1007)
Tel: (01245) 600009
Butcombe Bitter; **Tolly** Original; **Guest beers** H
① ① ⌷
One-bar town pub with darts & pool. New changing guest beer policy. Limited parking.

11-11 (12-10.30 Sun)

Three Stars **47**
Trent Road/Cherwell Drive (nr A1060)
Tel: (01245) 355434
S&N Websters Yorkshire Bitter; **Guest Beers** H
⌷ ⌷
Guest beers - usually Morlands Old Speckled Hen and Wadworths 6X.

Tucker's Smokehouse **48**
Kings Head Walk, the Meadows
Tel: (01245) 350130
Free-house (Luminair Leisure) - No Real Ale. Formerly the "Chicago Rock Cafe".

11-2.30; 5-11 (11-11 Fri/Sat: 7-10.30 only Sun)

Two Brewers **49**
80-84 Springfield Road (A1099)
Tel: (01245) 263798
S&N Courage Directors, Trumans IPA; John Smiths Bitter H
⌷ ⌷ ⌷
Very pleasant town pub, built in 1620 as three cottages. Good decor and friendly service. Food reasonable and of a high quality. Large collection of plates and pictures.
Attracts office workers at lunchtime and a younger clientele in the evening.

11-11 (12-3.30; 7-10.30 Sun)

United Brethren **50**
New Writtle Street (nr B1007)
Tel: (01245) 265165
Greene King IPA, Abbot Ale; **Shepherd Neame** Masterbrew; **Guest beers** H
⌷ ⌷ ⌷
Friendly, Gray & Sons, town pub, handy for football and cricket grounds. Guest beers change monthly. No food Sundays.

11-11 (12-10.30 Sun)

Wheatsheaf **51**
28 New Street (nr A1099)
Tel: (01245) 354342
Ind Coope Burton Ale; **Tetley** Bitter H
① D ⌷
Careless talk costs years! - near the police station. Incorporates a "Mr Q" pool hall. Limited parking.

11-3; 5.30 (7 Sat)-11 (12-10.30 Sun)

White Horse **52**
25 Townfield Street / Glebe Road (nr A138)
Tel: (01245) 269556
Guest Beers H
⌷ ⌷ ⌷
Back-street free-house with a wide range of around ten constantly-changing guest beers - mostly from small independent breweries. Background 'Blues' music often played.
Bar billiards and large-screen TV for sporting events - such as Rugby. Essex 'Pub-of-the-Year' 1992. Formerly "Mulberry's", "BJ's" and "Mr Jones".

11-3; 6-11 (12-3; 7-10.30 Sun)

Wig & Mirkin **53**
50 Moulsham Street (nr A138)
Tel: (01245) 259452
Greene King IPA; **Tetley** Imperial; **Whitbread** Flowers Original H
① D ① ① ⌷
Large, one-bar pub, with live music Sunday evenings. Limited parking. Formerly the "Kings Arms".

12-3; 5 (6 Sat)-11 (closed Sun)

Wine Cellar **54**
4 Duke Street (nr A1099)
Tel: (01245) 350353
Free-house - No Real Ale.

11.30-3; 6-11 (11.30-11 Fri/Sat: 12-10.30 Sun)

Woolpack **55**
23 Mildmay Road (nr A138)
Tel: (01245) 259295
Ridleys IPA, ESX H
⌷ ⌷ ⌷ ⌷
Cheerful and comfortable back-street local. A good community pub with regular quiz on Wednesday evenings. Live music Saturday. Separate games room.

11-11 (12-10.30 Sun)

Yates's Wine Lodge **56**
1-5 Empire Walk, The Meadows II (nr A1199)
Tel: (01245) 252066
S&N Courage Directors; **Whitbread** Boddingtons Bitter H
① D ① ① ⌷ ⌷
New Yates's with 'Disneyesque' exterior, and fashionably, comfortable interior. Large downstairs bar and upstairs bar and balcony (not always open). Regular live music (can be loud). Limited beer range, and beware 'sparklers' used on the 'Directors'. Food available only until 6.30 (5 Saturday).

Chignall Smealy   C3

12 (11 Fri/Sat)-3; 6-11 (12-3 Sun)

Pig & Whistle
Chignal Road
OS: TL678112
Tel: (01245) 440245
Adnams Bitter, Broadside; **Greene King** IPA H; **Marstons** Pedigree; **Wadworths** 6X G
⌷ ① ① (not Sun) ⌷
Guest beers - good value food. Games room with crib and shove ha'penny, amongst others.

Chignall St James   C3

12 (11.30 Sat)-2.30 (3.30 Sat); 6-11 (12-3; 7-10.30 Sun)

Three Elms
Mashbury Road
OS: TL676097
Tel: (01245) 440496
Batemans XB; **Morlands** Old Speckled Hen; **Thwaites** Bitter; **Whitbread** Boddingtons Bitter H
① D ① ⌷
Comfortable, one-bar, 'beamed' country pub, with splendid old fireplace. Occasional live music. Beer range varies.

Chigwell   A4

A haunt of Dickens, who once described it as "the greatest place in the world". The area around St Marys Church and the Olde Kings Head retains some of the features he would have found attractive.

William Penn - the founder of Pennsylvania - was educated in the 17th Century Chigwell Grammar School.

12-11 (10.30 Sun)

Bald Hind
Hainault Road (A123/B173)
Tel: (0181) 500 2040
Ind Coope Burton Ale; **Marstons** Pedigree; **Tetley** Bitter; **Guest beers** H
① D ① ① ⌷ ⌷ ⌷
Outwardly impressive, ivy-covered pub. Recently-refurbished into a food-oriented outlet. Guest beers from the 'Tapsters Choice' range.
Rotating guest beers.

11-11 (12-10.30 Sun)

King William IV
High Road (A113)
Tel: (0181) 500 4122
Bass Hancocks HB; **Guest Beer** H
① D ① ① ⌷ ⌷
Large, games-oriented pub with loud music, darts, bar billiards and a distinct eating area. Built alongside the original 'Bill Ivy'.

5-11 (11-11 Sat: 12-10.30 Sun)

Sloanes
122 Manor Road (B173)
Tel: (0181) 500 3037
Bass - No Real Ale. Formerly
"No Great Shakes/NGS"

11-11 (12-10.30 Sun)

Ye Olde Kings Head
High Road (A113)
Tel: (0181) 500 2021
S&N Courage Best, Directors,
John Smiths Bitter,
Theakstons XB **H**
◑ D ◑ R ⊕ ⊑ ⋟ ✷
Very large and friendly, period
weather-boarded coaching inn,
with a conservatory, Dickens's
"Maypole" in his 1840s classic
'Barnaby Rudge'. Very popular
for food in the separate restau-
rant / carvery.

Chigwell Row   A4

*On the fringe of Hainault Forest
Country Park.*

11-11 (12-10.30 Sun)

Maypole
171 Lambourne Road (A1112)
Tel: (0181) 500 2050
Ind Coope Ansells BB; **Tetley**
Bitter; **Guest Beer H**
◑ D ◑ ◑ 🍺 ⅋
Large, airy and comfortable one-
bar pub by the church and traffic
lights. Very food-oriented. Guest
beer from the 'Tapsters Choice'
range. Close to Hainault Forest.

11-11 (12-10.30 Sun)

Retreat
Retreat Way (nr A1112)
Tel: (0181) 500 2716
Whitbread Flowers Original,
Fuggles Imperial; **Guest
Beer** (occasional) **H**
◑ D ◑ R ⊑ ✷ ⅋
One-bar 'Brewers Fayre'
pub/restaurant, with children's
play area.

11-11 (12-10.30 Sun)

Two Brewers
57 Lambourne Road (nr A1112)
Tel: (0181) 501 1313
Whitbread Boddingtons Bitter,
Flowers Original; **Guest Beer H**
◑ D ◑ ◑ R ✷ ⅋
Friendly, one-bar pub/restaurant,
usually has two guest beers
from the 'Whitbread' list.
Restaurant open evenings only.
Handy for Hainault Forest.

Childerditch Common   B4

12-11 (10.30 Sun)

Greyhound
Magpie Lane, Little Warley
OS: TQ605905
Tel: (01277) 212960
Adnams Bitter; **Ind Coope**
Burton Ale; **Tetley** Bitter **H**
◑ D ◑ ◑ ✷
Comfortable, friendly and spa-
cious, refurbished pub, with a
'U'-shaped bar, on Childerditch
Common. The huge garden has
(rather expensive) barbecues,
and there are ramped entrances
to the bar at front and rear.
Close to Thorndon Park.

Chipping Ongar   B3

*Surprisingly unspoilt small town
- the birthplace of David
Livingstone. The town's railway
link to Epping closed in 1994,
and two separate organisations
are still trying to get approval to
restore services over it.*

*The Budworth Hall in the centre
of town, hosts the Ongar Beer
Festival each May. Nearby at
Greensted is one of the few
wooden Saxon churches in
Britain.*

11-3; 6-11 (12-3; 7-10.30 Sun)

Cock Tavern
218 High Street (A128)
Tel: (01277) 362615
Greene King IPA **H**
◑
A 'Grays' local, whose long-serving landlord retired in 1997. Now
somewhat overshadowed by the
new library next door.

11-3; 5-11 (11-11 Sat: 12-10.30
Sun)

Kings Inn
117 High Street (A128)
Tel: (01277) 362009
S&N Courage Directors; **Tolly**
Original **H**
◑ ◑ R ⊑ ✷
Lively, town-centre pub with
mixed clientele, live music and
quizzes. Formerly the "Kings
Head".

Ongar Bell
High Street (A128)
Tel:
Free-house - Pub closed for
years, but still looks as if it might
reopen.

11-3; 5.30-11 (11-11 Sat: 12-10.30
Sun)

Royal Oak
99 High Street (A128)
Tel: (01277) 363893
S&N Courage Best Bitter;
Whitbread Flowers IPA **H**
◑ ◑ 🍺 ⅋
Small basic local. Beware
'Blanket Pressure' (CO2)
believed to be used!

12-11 (10.30 Sun)

Two Brewers
Greensted Road (By A128)
Tel: (01277) 362445
Ind Coope Benskins BB, Burton
Ale; **S&N** Courage Directors;
Tetley Bitter **H**
◑ D ◑ R ⊕ ✷
Trade gradually building-up
following the arrival of new
landlord in October 1994.

Chrishall   A1

*Quiet, picturesque village close
to the Cambridgeshire border.*

12-3; 6-11 (12-11 Sat: 12-10.30
Sun)

Red Cow
High Street (1M off B1039)
OS: TL446393
Tel: (01763) 838815
Greene King IPA / Abbot Ale;
Tetley Bitter; **Guest beer H**
◑ D ◑ ◑
Picturesque 15th century
thatched pub adjacent to 11th
century tithe barn. Despite its
age and cottagy appearance out-
side, the inside is very much
twentieth century, with satellite
TV.
Rotating strong guest beer.
Beware, 'Scrumpy Jack' keg
cider on handpump.

Church Langley (Harlow)   A3

*(See Harlow map for location of
pubs)*

11-11 (12-10.30 Sun)

Potters Arms   CL1
Church Langley Way (nr A414)
Tel: (01279) 629712
Marstons Pedigree; **Wadworths**
6X; **Whitbread** Boddingtons
Bitter, Flowers IPA,
Original, **Guest Beer H**
◑ D ◑ ◑ R ✷ ⅋
New 'Brewers Fayre' pub/restau-
rant, situated by a new Tesco,
on a new housing estate. Guest
beers from the 'Whitbread'
range.

Clacton-on-Sea   F3

*Popular holiday resort with
sandy beach, amusement park,
pier and dogtrack.*

11.30-2.30; 6-11 (12-10.30 Sun)

Black Bull
St Osyth Road, Rush Green
Tel: (01255) 427363
Greene King IPA, Abbot Ale **H**
◑ ◑ ⊕ 🍺
Small, comfortable, 'estate'-type
local with reproduction-fur-
nished interior.

11-11 (12-3; 7-10.30 Sun)

Carlton Hotel
67 Rosemary Road (nr A133)
Tel: (01255) 424571
Pubmaster - No Real Ale.

Chaplin's Bistro
165 Old Road (nr A133)
Free-house - Bar closed.
Formerly "Croc's" & "Circles
Wine Bar".

11-11 (12-10.30 Sun)

Coach & Horses
197 Old Road
Tel: (01255) 422116
Pubmaster - No Real Ale.

11-11 (12-10.30 Sun)

Cockney Pride
Pier Entrance, Pier Gap (By the
pier entrance)
Tel: (01255) 421115
Free-house - No Real Ale.

10-11 (12-3; 7-10.30 Sun)

Crab & Pumpkin
21/23 Jackson Road
Tel: (01255) 475415
Adnams Broadside; **Greene
King** Abbot Ale; **Guest Beers H**
🚪 ≈
Lively town centre pub, which
provides a real choice of cask-
conditioned ales. Formerly
"Darcy's Free-house" and the
"Medina". Limited parking.

Geisha Hotel
Orwell Road / Marine Parade
East
Free-house - Now a licensed
restaurant only.

11-11 (12-10.30 Sun)

Groucho's
121 Pier Avenue
Tel: (01255) 473656
S&N Courage Directors,
Theakstons BB, Websters
Yorkshire Bitter **H**
🍺🍺🍷🆁🛏🍴⊫🚬≈
Re-opened bar and restaurant in
main thoroughfare. Friendly
atmosphere, smart decor.
Formerly the "Warwick Arms".

Grand Hotel
Marine Parade
Tel: (01255) 222020
Free-house - No Real Ale.

Imperial Hotel
22 Rosemary Road
Tel: (01255) 422778
Free-house - Hotel closed.

11-11 (12-10.30 Sun)

Martello Inn
Marine Parade West (Martello
Bay)
Tel: (01255) 425739
Fullers London Pride;
Wadworths 6X; **Whitbread**
Boddingtons Bitter, Flowers
Original **H**
🍺🍷🍴🆁🚬🌸🍴♿
A typical 'Brewers Fayre', with
an interesting photographic his-
tory of Clacton characters.
Believed to be the only pub in
Clacton that caters for children.
Rather cramped toilets.

11-11 (12-10.30 Sun)

Moon & Starfish
1 Marine Parade East (nr A133)
Tel: (01255) 222998
S&N Courage Directors,
Theakstons BB; **Guest Beers H**
Guest Cider H
🍺🍷🍴♿✂🚬≈
JD Wetherspoon pub built into
the West end of the Royal Hotel.
It is divided up into three
tastefully-refurbished areas and
includes a large no-smoking
section.
Clacton's prayer for a Real Ale
seafront pub has been answered
at last! McGill postcards on display. Real Cider as well. Beer
served rather too cold.

12-3; 7-11 (closed Sun)

Nookes & Crannies
(Wine bar)
1 Carnarvon Road / Rosemary
Road (nr A133)
Tel: (01255) 426572
Free-house - No Real Ale.

11-2.30; 7-11 (12-3; 7-10.30 Sun)

Old Lifeboat House
39 Marine Parade East /
Carnarvon Road
Tel: (01255) 421260
Free-house - No Real Ale.

11-11 (12-10.30 Sun)

Plaza Hotel (Silks Bar)
5 Marine Parade East / Orwell
Road
Tel: (01255) 476021
Free-house - No Real Ale.

11-11 (12-10.30 Sun)

Queens Arms
189 Old Road (nr A133)
Tel: (01255) 421681
Inntrepreneur - No Real Ale.

11-12 (12-7 (10.30 Summer) Sun)

Rocking Horse Bar
(Royal Hotel)
Marine Parade East (nr A133)
Tel: (01255) 421215
Free-house - No Real Ale.

1-11 (12-10.30 Sun)

Sams Bar
20 Rosemary Road (nr A133)
Tel: (01255) 427116
Free-house - Pub closed.

11-11 (12-10.30 Sun)

Sandles Inn & Escape Bar
26 Rosemary Road
Tel: (01255) 421928
Tolly Cobbold Bitter **H**
🍺🍷🍴🆁🛏⊫🌸≈
Refurbished hotel bar, previous-
ly the music pub of Clacton.
Formerly the "Osborne Hotel" &
"Lord Nelson". Limited parking.

Station
Station Road (nr A133)
Inntrepreneur - Pub closed and
demolished.

11-11 (12-5; 7-10.30 Sun)

Tom Peppers
2 Marine Parade West (nr A133)
Tel: (01255) 423199
Greene King Abbot Ale **H**
⊫🚬≈
Large split-level seafront pub,
opposite the pier. Regular live
music. The refurbishment is
reminiscent of an earlier era,
with 'fake artefacts' theme on
the walls. Parking difficult.
A night-club above, 'Tubby
Isaacs' below. Formerly
"Bailey's/Franx"

Clavering   A2

*Pretty village with numerous
thatched cottages, two wind-
mills and a ford.*

12-2 (later if busy); 7-11 (10.30
Sun)

Cricketers
Wicken Road (B1038)
OS: TL482327
Tel: (01799) 550442
Whitbread Flowers IPA,
Original, seasonal beers **H**
🍺🍷🍴🆁🛏♿
Smart, 16th century and food-
oriented - now more of a large
restaurant than a pub. Egon
Ronay, Michelin and AA recom-
mended. No food Mondays. En-
suite bedrooms.

11-2.30; 5.30-11 (12-3; 7-10.30
Sun)

Fox & Hounds
High Street (B1038)
Tel: (01799) 550321
Greene King IPA, Abbot Ale,
seasonal beers; **Guest Beers H**
🍺🍷🍴🆁🍺♿
Comfortable village local.

Clayhall   A4

12-11 (10.30 Sun)

Cocked Hat
Woodford Avenue (by A1400)
Tel: (0181) 551 3848
Bass Draught Bass **H**
🍺🍷🍴🆁♿
Main road pub, converted into a
'Harvester'.

11-11 (12-10.30 Sun)

Unicorn
225 Clayhall Avenue (1/2 mile off
A1400)
Tel: (0181) 550 5811
Whitbread Boddingtons Bitter **H**
🍺🍷🍴🚪
Large, food-oriented pub, with
reasonably-priced steaks, in a
predominantly residential area.
Regular karaoke, disco and pool
evenings.

"The Woolpack Inn", Coggeshall

Cock Clarks   D4

11-11 (12-10.30 Sun)

Fox & Hounds
Birchwood Road
OS: TL814029
Tel: (01621) 828266
Ridleys IPA, ESX H
🍺 🍴 ◖◗ 🍳 🌸
Village local, beer variable.

Coggeshall   D2

Magnificent small town now bypassed. Full of beautiful buildings. Sadly shopkeepers have given way to antique dealers. Paycocke's House (NT) and the church are gems.

11-3; 7-11 (12-3; 7-10.30 Sun)

Alexandra
16 Colne Road (B1024)
Tel: (01376) 563109
Greene King IPA; **Ridleys** IPA H
🍺 🍴
A real locals pub.

11-11 (12-10.30 Sun)

Chapel Inn
4 Market Hill (B1024)
Tel: (01376) 561655
Greene King IPA; **Youngs**
Special; **Guest Beer** H
🍺 🍴 ◖◗ (Tue-Sat) R 🍳 🌸 🥄 ♿
Friendly former hotel, with live music most weekends. Guest beers change fortnightly.

11-11 (12-10.30 Sun)

Cricketers Inn
7 West Street (B1024)
Tel: (01376) 561533
Fullers London Pride;
Greene King IPA H
🍺 🍴 ◖◗ 🍳 🛏 ♿
Open fires.

11-11 (12-10.30 Sun)

East Anglian Roadhouse
11 Surrex / Colchester Road
(A120, 1 mile East of town)
Tel: (01376) 563612
Morlands Old Speckled Hen;
Ruddles Best Bitter; **S&N**
Courage Directors, Theakstons
BB H
🍺 🍴 ◖◗ R 🥄 🌸 ♿
Large open-plan family pub with emphasis on food. Formerly the "American Pilot", the "Surrex Inn" and the "Queens Head".

10-11 (12-10.30 Sun)

Fleece
27 West Street (nr B1024)
Tel: (01376) 561412
Greene King IPA, Abbot Ale H
🍺 🍴 ◖◗ 🌸
Lively inn dating from 1503, next door to Paycocke's House (NT), a fine example of pargetting craftsmanship.

Porto-Bello Inn
25 Bridge Street (B1024)
Free-house - Pub closed. Site of former Gardners Brewery at rear.

11-11 (12-10.30 Sun)

White Hart Hotel
Market End / East Street (B1024)
Tel: (01376) 561654
Adnams Bitter H
🍺 🍴 ◖◗ R 🛋 🛏 🥄
Busy multi-beamed hotel.

12-3; 6-11 (12-3; 7-10.30 Sun)

Woolpack
91 Church Street (B1024)
Tel: (01376) 561235
Tetley Bitter; **Guest Beer** H
🍺 🍴 ◖◗ R 🍳 🌸 ♿
A pair of 15th century cottages, one a former wool merchants residence. Delightfully picturesque, genuinely unspoilt. Reputedly haunted.

Yorkshire Grey
2 Robinsbridge Road
Free-house - Pub closed.

Coggeshall Hamlet   D2

11-3; 6-11 (12-3; 7-10.30 Sun)

George & Dragon
Coggeshall Road (B1024)
OS: TL856209
Tel: (01376) 561732
Greene King IPA H
🍺 🍴 ◖◗ R 🍳 🌸
Spacious pub, with site for five caravans at the rear. Pool room. Formerly the "Halfway".

35

Colchester   E2

The oldest recorded town in Britain, full of ancient and interesting buildings including the Norman castle with its museum.

The wall was built around AD 65 by the Romans, after their defeat by Boadicea. Massive Army garrisons dominate the south side of the town.

The University of Essex is situated to the South East. The Hythe area is famous for Colchester 'natives' (oysters). The local CAMRA Beer Festival is held in the Arts Centre in Church Street in mid/late May each year.

10.30-3; 6-11 (10.30-11 Sat: 12-10.30 Sun)

Abbey Arms   1
1 St John's Green (nr Southway, A134)
Tel: (01206) 579884
Tolly Cobbold Original; **S&N** Courage Directors, Websters Yorkshire Bitter; **Whitbread** Boddingtons Bitter **H**
◐ ◑ ❀ ⇌
One large split-level bar, pool table and TV. Limited parking.

Closed Lunch; 6-11 (12 Tue/Thu/Sat, 2 Fri) (7-10.30 Sun)

Adnan's   2
14 Magdalen Street (A134)
Tel: (01206) 575737
Free-house - No Real Ale.
Formerly the "Prince of Wales".

11-3; 6-11 (11-11 Sat: 12-10.30 Sun)

Albert (Beefeater)   3
Cowdray Avenue (A133)
Tel: (01206) 561914
Whitbread Best Bitter, Boddingtons Bitter, Flowers IPA, Flowers Original; **Guest Beers H**
◐ ▯ ◐ ▮ R ❀ ⇌
A 'foody' pub.

11-3 (4 Sat); 7-11 (12-4; 7-10.30 Sun)

Ancient Briton   4
7 Iceni Way, Shrub End Estate
Tel: (01206) 540986
S&N John Smiths Bitter **H**
⊟ ❀
Large two-bar estate pub, serving local community, and dating from 1956. Two pool tables in the public bar.

12-3; 5-11 (12-11 Sat: 12-4; 7-10.30 Sun)

Artilleryman   5
54-56 Artillery Street (nr A134)
Tel: (01206) 578026
Greene King IPA, Abbot Ale **H**
◐ ▯ ⊟ ❀
Quiet, back-street pub with large saloon and smaller basic public bar. Limited parking.

11-11 (12-10.30 Sun)

Balkerne Gate   6
Ipswich Road (A1232, nr A120)
Tel: (01206) 852932
Morlands Old Speckled Hen; **Wadworths** 6X; **Whitbread** Boddingtons Bitter, Flowers Original **H**
◐ ▯ ◐ ▮ R ⇔ ❀ ♿
Brand new, 100 year-old looking, pub/restaurant/motel. A typical 'Brewers Fayre' with a sprinkling of curios adorning the walls and alcoves. Children's Certificate.

12-3; 6-11 (12-3; 7-10.30 Sun)

Beehive   7
113 Bromley Road (nr A137)
Tel: (01206) 863667
Ind Coope Burton Ale; **Tetley** Bitter **H**
◐ ▯ ◐
Quiet, country local, with one long bar. Quaint exterior. Mirrors used to good effect inside.

12-2.30; 5.30-11 (12-11 Fri: 11.30-11 Sat: 12-10.30 Sun)

Beer House   8
126 Magdalen Street (A134)
Tel: (01206) 792642
Ridleys IPA, ESX, Rumpus, Spectacular **H**
◐ ▯ ◐ ❀ ⇌
Former free-house, acquired by Ridleys in spring 1998. Sadly the extensive range of guest beers has been removed. Live music Sunday lunchtimes and occasional evenings. Pool table and darts board. Sky Sports. No children in bar, OK in patio garden at rear. Formerly the "Bakers Arms".

12-3 (4 Sun); 7-11 (10.30 Sun)

Bell   9
Fingringhoe Road / Old Heath Road
Tel: (01206) 795703
Greene King IPA **H**
⊟ ❀
Locals two-bar boozer, with large comfy lounge. Pool and darts played in the public bar.

12-3; 7-11 (11-11 Sat: 12-10.30 Sun)

Blue Boar Hotel   10
3-7 Kendall Road
Tel: (01206) 792235
Pubmaster - No Real Ale.

11 (10.30 Sat)-4 (5 Fri/Sat); 7-11 (12-5; 7-10.30 Sun)

Brewers Arms   11
31 Osborne Street (nr A134)
Tel: (01206) 570080
S&N John Smiths Bitter **H**
◐ ▯ ◐ ⇌
Ancient town pub, with pool table and dart board. Parking difficult.

11-3; 5.30-11 (11-11 Sat: 12-3; 7-10.30 Sun)

Bricklayers   12
27 Bergholt Road (B1508) / Mile End Road (A134)
Tel: (01206) 852008
Adnams Bitter, Broadside, seasonal beers; **Guest Beers H**
◐ ▯ ◐ ▮ ⊟ ❀ ⇌
Large, two-bar pub near 'North' station. Excellent range of four guest beers available. Pool, darts and quiz teams. Occasional quiz nights.

12-3; 7-11 (12-11 Fri/Sat: 12-10.30 Sun)

Britannia   13
42 Meyrick Crescent / Berechurch Road
Tel: (01206) 574391
Greene King IPA **H**
◐ ▯ ◐ ▮ ⊟ ⊫ ❀
Large, corner pub with two bars and an off-sales in between. A locals, rather than squaddies, pub.

11-2.30 (3 Fri/Sat); 7-11 (12-3; 7-10.30 Sun)

British Grenadier   14
67 Military Road
Tel: (01206) 791647
Adnams Bitter, seasonal beers (occasional), Old (Winter) **H/G**
◐ ⊟ ❀
Great traditional boozer with darts, dominoes, cards and pool. Popular, with good atmosphere in public bar. At the rear of Hyderabad barracks. Limited parking.

Buck's Horns   15
46 Greenstead Road
Pubmaster - Pub closed and demolished in 1994.

11.30-2.30; 7-11 (12-3; 7-10.30 Sun)

Bugle Horn   16
30 Barrack Street
Tel: (01206) 795843
Tolly Cobbold Bitter; **Whitbread** Flowers IPA **H**
◐ ⊟ ❀ ⇌
Friendly one-bar pub, with pool table and dart board.

11-11 (12 some Thu-Sat) (12-10.30 Sun)

Bull   17
4 Crouch Street
Tel: (01206) 572892
S&N Courage Directors, Websters Yorkshire Bitter **H**
◐ ◐ ❀ ⇌
The oldest pub in Colchester, dating from the early 15th century, and reputedly haunted. Used by soldiers in the evenings. Pool table, games machines and loud music on the CD jukebox. Karaoke Monday nights. Scalextric night on alternate Sundays.

COLCHESTER
Town Centre

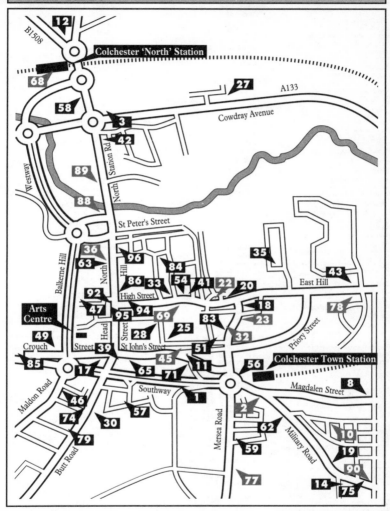

B1508

12

Colchester 'North' Station

68

58

27   A133

3   Cowdray Avenue

42

89

88

Westway

North Station Rd

St Peter's Street

36   35

63   96   84

86   33   54   41   22   20   East Hill   43

92   High Street   78

47   95   94   69   18   Priory Street

Arts Centre   83   23

49   28   25   32

Crouch   39   51

Head Street   St John's Street   45   11   56   Colchester Town Station

85   17   65   71   Magdalen Street   8

Balkerne Hill   North Hill

Maldon Road   46   Southway   1

74   57   Mersea Road   2   62   Military Road   10

79   30   59   19

Butt Road   77   90

14   75

11-11 (12-10.30 Sun)

Cafe Brahms   **18**
7 Queen Street
Tel: (01206) 763183
Ridleys IPA **H**
⓭ Ⅾ ◖◗ ⇌
Attractive, small 'beamed' bar
with competitively priced beer
and a good range of meals
(including vegetarian).
Part of a sixteenth century building, that was previously a shop -
converted in 1990. Formerly the
"Brahms & Liszt".

11-11 (12-10.30 Sun)

Cambridge Arms   **19**
94 Military Road (nr A134)
Tel: (01206) 577866
Greene King IPA; **Tetley**
Bitter **H**
⓭ Ⅾ ◖◗ & ⇌
Large, single-bar pub, with a
delightful exterior. Much-altered
to accommodate live music at
weekends - a trend which seems
essential in this area to enable a
pub to survive. Sunday roasts.
Pool table. Parking difficult.

11-11 (12-10.30 Sun)

Castle   **20**
92 High Street (A1232)
Tel: (01206) 563988
S&N Theakstons BB **H**
⓭ Ⅾ ◖◗ ⛾ 🖛 & ⇌
Aptly-named, single-bar pub, in
the shadow of the Norman
castle. Popular with the young
crowd in the evenings at
weekends. Limited parking.

Centurion 21
Hawthorne Avenue, Greenstead
Benskins - Pub closed in 1996,
and converted to a community
centre.

Champagne Charlies 22
105 High Street (A1232)
Tel: (01206) 369875
Free-house - No Real Ale
(despite the notice in the
window).

Chicago Rock Cafe 23
35/37 Queen Street
Tel: (01206) 578857
Free-house - No Real Ale.

Churchill Arms 24
18/20 Barrack Street (A134)
Tel: (01206) 790322
Free-house - Pub closed.
Formerly the "Duke of York".

11-3.40; 5-11 (11-11 Fri/Sat:
12-10.30 Sun)

Clarence 25
Trinity Street / Eld Lane
Tel: (01206) 574550
Tetley Bitter; **Guest Beer H**
◖◗ ◖▶ ⓡ ❀ ⇌
Large, 'L'-shaped bar with pool
table at one end. Restaurant at
the rear. Full meals only in the
evenings. Busy lunchtimes.
Music quite loud in the bar.
Peanut and jellybaby machines!
Parking difficult.

12-3; 5.30-11 (12-10.30 Sun)

Clarendon Arms 26
6 Harwich Road (A137)
Tel: (01206) 860359
Greene King IPA, Abbot Ale **H**
◖◗ ◖ ⓓ ➤
Basic, two-level, oak-beamed
local with excellent value food.
Parking difficult.

11-2.30 (weekdays only); 5-7
(Thu/Fri only)

Cowdray Arms 27
Block H, Cowdray Centre, Mason
Road (nr A133)
Tel: (01206) 578095
Greene King IPA; **Guest Beers H**
◖◗ ◖
Smart, comfortable, single-bar
pub, dating from 1984, and
mainly catering for workers on
the industrial estate / business
park - hence the unusual
opening hours.

11-11 (12-3; 7-10.30 Sun)

Cups 28
2-3 Trinity Street
Tel: (01206) 766506
Greene King IPA, Abbot Ale,
seasonal beers **E**
◖◗ ◖ ⇌
Busy town centre pub, dating
from 1977. Frequented by young
'Rock' and 'Indie' clientele. Loud
CD jukebox. Ornamental hand-
pumps. Parking difficult.

11-2.30; 5.30-11 (11-11 Sat: 12-
10.30 Sun)

Dog & Pheasant 29
24 Nayland Road, Mile End
(A134)
Tel: (01206) 852427
Greene King IPA, Abbot Ale,
seasonal beers **H**
◖◗ ◖▶ ⓡ ⓓ ❀ ⓖ
Extensively refurbished with a
pleasant public bar and large
"King's Fayre" restaurant area.
Large beer garden with children's play area and bouncy castle. Darts and bar billiards
played. Large car park.

11-2.30; 5.30-11 (12-3; 7-10.30
Sun)

Dragoon 30
82 Butt Road (B1026)
Tel: (01206) 573464
Adnams Bitter, Broadside,
seasonal beers; **Guest Beers H**
◖◗ ❀ ⇌
Old, timbered pub near Le
Cateau Barracks. Saturday
breakfast specials and Sunday
roast lunches. Pool and darts
played. Parking limited.

12-3; 5.30-11 (11-11 Sat: 12-10.30
Sun)

Drury Arms 31
1 Layer Road (B1026)
Tel: (01206) 575757
Tetley Bitter; **Whitbread**
Flowers IPA **H**
◖◗ ◖▶ ⓡ ⓓ ❀ ⓖ
Near the football ground, and
dominated by a massive satellite
TV projector. Pool and crib
played. Children's certificate
applied for.

11-11 (12-10.30 Sun)

Fashion Cafe Bar 32
2 St Botolphs Street
Tel: (01206) 562157
Free-house - No Real Ale.
Formerly "Palms Wine Bar".

11-11 (12-10.30 Sun)

Faunus & Firkin 33
128 High Street (A1232) / East
Stockwell Street
Tel: (01206) 564367
Firkin Ale Caesar, Faunus
Ale, Old Horny, Dogbolter **H**
◖◗ ◖ ◖┗ ⇌
Typical, non-brewing, 'Firkin'
pub with 'Firkin Breweryana' on
every wall. Upstairs balcony is
non-smoking at lunchtimes.
Games nights and other activi-
ties.
Four pint jug for the price of
three on Wednesday evenings.
Beware Addlestones Cider on
handpump with CO2. Formerly
the "Lamb" and the "Bay &
Say".

11-3; 7-11 (11-11 Sat: 12-10.30
Sun)

Flying Fox 34
Harwich Road (A137)
Tel: (01206) 864341
Greene King IPA **H**
◖◗ ◖ ⓓ ┗ ⓥ ❀ ⓖ
Large town pub, with mock-
Edwardian exterior. Darts, pool
and dominoes played.

11-11 (12-10.30 Sun)

Foresters Arms 35
1-2 Castle Road (nr A1232)
Tel: (01206) 542646
Morlands Old Speckled Hen;
Whitbread Boddingtons Bitter,
Flowers IPA; **Guest Beer H**
◖◗ ◖▶ ❀ ⓖ ⇌
Unspoilt pub, near town centre,
with occasional live music.
Regular guest beers. Darts, bar
billiards and crib played.

11-11 (5.30-11 Sat: closed Sun)

Forty Five Cafe Bar 36
45 North Hill
Tel: (01206) 766166
Free-house - No Real Ale. This
bar has definitely had an identity
crisis over the last few years -
formerly "Zac's", "Ivory's",
"Frog & Bears", "Bikini" and the
"Waikiki Beach Bar"!

Forum Wine Bar 37
400 The Crescent, Severalls Park
(nr A120/A1232)
Tel: (01206) 844155
Free-house - Pub closed.

11-2.30; 4.30-11 (11-11 Fri/Sat:
12-10.30 Sun)

Foundry Arms 38
83 Artillery Street (nr A134)
Tel: (01206) 790183
Greene King IPA **H**
◖◗ ◖ ⓓ ❀ ⓖ
Friendly town pub with pool and
darts. Evening snacks are early
evening only.

11-3; 6-11 (12-10.30 Sun)

Fox & Fiddler 39
1 St John's Street / Headgate (nr
A134)
Tel: (01206) 560545
Tolly Cobbold 'House' Beer;
Guest Beers H
◖▶ ⇌
Comfortable town centre pub,
with darts, pool and chess.
Formerly the "Boadicea"

11-3; 5-11 (11-11 Fri/Sat:12-3; 7-
10.30 Sun)

Friar 40
St Christopher Road / St
Dominic Road
Tel: (01206) 843402
S&N Theakstons XB, Websters
Yorkshire Bitter **H**
🍺
Typical estate pub, with 'L'-
shaped bar, and quiet, older
clientele. Occasional 50s & 60s
music night . Pool table.

11-2.30; 5.30-11 (12-10.30 Sun)

George Hotel 41
116 High Street (A1124)
Tel: (01206) 578494
Adnams Bitter **H**
◖◗ ◖▶ ⓡ ⊨ ┗ ⓥ ❀ ⓖ
⇌
Excellent, quality 15th century
hotel. In good weather there are
tables and chairs on the pavement at the front.

Globe Hotel 42

71 North Station Road
Tel: (01206) 573881
Greene King IPA; **Ind Coope**
Ansells Mild; **Nethergate**
Bitter; **Guest Beers H**

◑ ▯ ◗ ▯ 🍺 ⛵ ✦ ♿ ⇌

Lively pub with pool, darts,
dominoes, crib, karaoke, disco
nights, cabaret and barbecues.
Regular guest beers.
Unpretentious menu. 12 ensuite
bedrooms.

11-2.30; 6-11 (11-11 Sat: 12-10.30
Sun)

Goat & Boot 43

70 East Hill (A1232)
Tel: (01206) 867466
Greene King IPA, Abbot Ale **H**

◑ ◗ ▯ ✦

Large horseshoe bar separates
the public bar and the comfortable lounge, with its huge open
fire. Pool table and dart board in
the Snugs. Meet 'Bernie' the
(sometimes) swearing parrot.

12-3; 6-11 (12-3; 7-10.30 Sun)

Grapes 44

87 Mersea Road (B1025)
Tel: (01206) 44035
Marstons Pedigree; **S&N**
Trumans IPA **H**

◑ ▯ ◗ ▯ ⬛ 🍴 ♿

Spacious local with strong darts
and pool following. A sporting
pub for all ages. Very reasonably
priced food.

11.30-11 (closed Sun)

Greenlands Continental Vodka Bar 45

33 Osborne Street (nr A134)
Tel: (01206) 766664
Free-house - No Real Ale.
Another bar that has suffered
numerous changes of name.
Formerly "Jackpots",
"Colchester Bar", "Cromwells",
"Cavaliers", "Mossy's" and the
"Vintage Bistro"!

12-2.30; 7-11 (12-6.30 Sun only,
may close earlier)

Grosvenor Hotel 46

62 Maldon Road (B1022) /
Alexandra Road
Tel: (01206) 572975
S&N Websters Yorkshire
Bitter **H**

◗ ▯ 🍺

Hotel, with popular locals bar.

11.30-11 (12-3; 7-10.30 Sun)

Hole in the Wall 47

Balkerne Passage (nr A134)
Tel: (01206) 760331
Ind Coope Friary Meux BB,
Burton Ale; **Tetley** Bitter;
Guest Beers H

◑ ◗ ▯ ✦

Built 1493 on gate of old Roman
wall. Breakfasts from 9am
Monday to Friday. Pool table.
Quiz nights on Sundays. Parking
difficult.

11-2.30; 6-11 (11-11 Sat: 12-10.30
Sun)

Huntsman's Tavern 48

177 Shrub End Road (B1022)
Tel: (01206) 576397
S&N John Smiths Bitter,
Theakstons BB, Websters
Yorkshire Bitter **H**

◑ ▯ ◗ ▯ 🍺 ⬛ ⇌ 🍴

Pub/Restaurant. Formerly the
"Berechurch Arms".

11-11 (12-10.30 Sun)

Kings Arms Hotel (Hogshead) 49

61-63 Crouch Street (nr A134)
Tel: (01206) 572886
Fullers London Pride;
Wadworths 6X; **Whitbread**
Abroad Cooper, Boddingtons
Bitter, Castle Eden Ale,
Flowers IPA, Original **H**;
Guest Beers G
Guest Cider G

◑ ▯ ✦ ♿ ✦

Now a 'Hogshead' traditional ale
pub, with several guest beers.
Sunday roasts and Thai dishes.
Bank Holiday beer festivals.
Chess, cards played, and quizzes
on Sundays.

11-2.30 (3 Fri); 5.30-11 (11-11 Sat:
12-10.30 Sun)

Leather Bottle 50

Shrub End Road (B1022) /
Straight Road
Tel: (01206) 766018
Adnams Bitter; **Ind Coope**
Ansells Mild, Bitter; **Tetley**
Bitter; **Guest Beers H**

◑ ◗ ▯ ✦

Very attractive pub with large
real fire in middle of lounge bar.
Nice garden, with children's
facilities and barbecues in
Summer. Pool played.
Regular guest beers from the
"Tapster's Choice" range.

10.30-3; 6.30-11 (Closed Sun)

Little Crown 51

12 Short Wyre Street
Tel: (01206) 575469
Tetley Bitter; **Whitbread**
Flowers IPA; **Guest Beer H**

◑ ▯ ◗ ▯ ⇌

Small, pleasant, town centre
pub, with karaoke and theme
nights. Parking difficult.

11-2.30; 6-11 (12-4; 7-10.30 Sun)

Lord Nelson 52

134 Hythe Hill (A134)
Tel: (01206) 798820
S&N John Smiths Bitter **H**
Cosy, friendly, one-bar, street-
corner local, noted for its games
- darts and pool. England's number one dart player has been on
the ochie here!

Maltsters Arms 53

Haven Road, Hythe Quay (nr
A134)
Tel: (01206) 860323
Ex Trumans - Pub closed.

10.30-11 (12-10.30 Sun)

Market Tavern 54

117 High Street (A1124)
Tel: (01206) 570674
S&N John Smiths Bitter,
Websters Yorkshire Bitter **H**

♿ ⇌

One-roomed pub, with
Scalextric nights, Sunday discos,
karaoke, live music (Autumn and
Winter) and Sky TV. Parking difficult.

11-11 (12-3; 7-10.30 Sun)

Mill Hotel (Colchester Bar) 55

East Street (A1232)
Tel: (01206) 865022
Free-house - No Real Ale.

11-11 (closed Sun)

Molly Malones 56

St Botolphs Circus (A134)
Tel: (01206) 571763
Greene King IPA **H**

▯ 🍴 ⬛ ✦ ♿ ⇌

Refurbished in the 'Irish' style.
Music downstairs and discos
upstairs too. Closed Sunday
lunch. Formerly the "Dickens
Hotel" & the "Carousel".

11-3; 5-11 (11-11 Thu-Sat: 12-
10.30 Sun)

New Inn 57

36/38 Chapel Street South (nr
A134)
Tel: (01206) 575277
Whitbread Flowers IPA; **Guest
Beers H**

◑ ◗ ▯ ⬛ ✦ ⇌

Friendly, two-bar locals boozer,
with pool, darts and cards in the
public bar. A winner of the
'Colchester in Bloom' award for
its hanging flower baskets and
terrace. Two guest beers and
good value food.

11-2.30 6-11 (12-3; 7-10.30 Sun)

Norfolk 58

132 North Station Road (nr
A134)
Tel: (01206) 45257
Greene King IPA, Abbot Ale,
seasonal beers **H**

◑ ▯ ◗ ▯ ✦ ⇌

Popular town pub, with darts,
pool, discos and quiz nights.

4-11 (only Mon-Thu) (11-11
Fri/Sat: 12-10.30 Sun)

Odd One Out 59

28 Mersea Road (B1025)
Tel: (01206) 578140
Archers Best Bitter; **Ridleys**
IPA; **Guest Beers H**
Guest Ciders G

◑ ◗ ▯ ⬛ ✦ ✂ ⇌

An oasis, with an excellent, well-
kept, beer range with five guest
beers including mild. Good
value ale - the best in town?
Unfortunately not open Monday
to Thursday lunchtimes. Parking
difficult.

12-2.30 (3 Sat); 6-11 (12-10.30 Sun)

Olde King Coel 60
160 Ipswich Road (A1232)
Tel: (01206) 867130
Ind Coope Ansells Bitter, Benskins BB; **Whitbread** Flowers IPA **H**
◖◗●**R**♨🏠⛱👨‍👩‍👧♿
Large family-style pub, now a comfortable 'Hungry Horse' pub/restaurant. Formerly the "Olde King Cole", the "Clockmakers" & "Hoofers".

11-11 (12-10.30 Sun)

Old Siege House 61
75 East Street (A1232)
Tel: (01206) 867121
Whitbread Best Bitter **G**, Boddingtons Bitter, Flowers Original; **Guest beers H**
◖◗●**R**⛱♿
A 'Beefeater' pub/restaurant on the site of the Civil War battle. Kiddies clown 1 to 3pm on Sundays.

Closed lunchtimes; 7-11 (1am Fri/Sat, 10.30 Sun)

Oliver Twist 62
25 Military Road / Golden Noble Hill (nr A134)
Tel: (01206) 562453
Greene King IPA, Abbot Ale **H**
◖♨🏠♿🚆
Live music venue - from 'Folk' through to 'Metal'

COLCHESTER
Blackheath, Lexden & Maypole Green

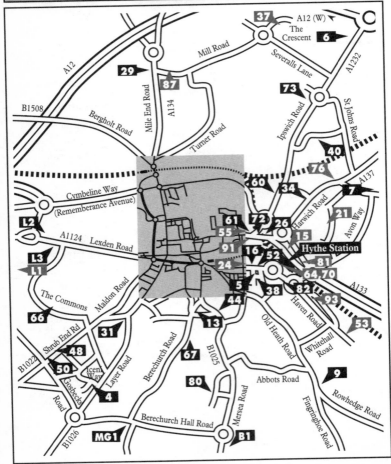

11.45-2.30; 5.30-11 (closed Sun lunch; 7-11 Sun eve)

Peveril Hotel 63
51 North Hill
Tel: (01206) 574001
Adnams Bitter; **Greene King** IPA; **Guest Beer** (sometimes) H
🝙🝙🝙🝙🝙🝙
Small, plush, town centre hotel bar with friendly atmosphere, and excellent 'Mine Host'.

Piccolo's 64
Spurgeon Street, The Hythe (nr A134)
Free-house - Pub closed. Formerly the "Piccolo Padre Wine Bar".

11-11 (12-10.30 Sun)

Playhouse 65
4 St Johns Street (nr A134)
Tel: (01206) 571003
Marstons Pedigree; **S&N** Courage Directors, Theakstons BB; **Guest Beers** H
🝙🝙🝙🝙🝙🝙🝙
Newish Wetherspoon in former cinema, with occasional beer festivals.

11-2.30; 5.30-11 (11-11 Fri/Sat: 12-10.30 Sun)

Prettygate 66
The Commons (nr B1022)
Tel: (01206) 573060
Ruddles Best Bitter; **S&N** Theakstons BB, Websters Yorkshire Bitter H
🝙🝙🝙
Modern estate pub with facilities for disabled, and a comfortable saloon.

11-11 (12-10.30 Sun)

Queens 67
Berechurch Road
Tel: (01206) 573350
Fullers London Pride H
Refurbished one-bar free-house - a recent Real Ale convert. Possible guest beers. TV.

11-8.30 (12-8 Sun)

Quick Snack

(Upside Bar) 68
Platform 4, Colchester (North) Station (nr A134)
Tel: (01206) 573440
Free - No Real Ale. Formerly the "Station Buffet".

12-3; 6-30-11 (12-3; 7-10.30 Sun)

Red Lion Hotel 69
43-44 High Street (A1124)
Tel: (01206) 577986
S&N John Smiths Bitter H
🝙🝙🝙🝙🝙🝙🝙
Excellent quality hotel with pianist on Saturdays and 'Murder-Mystery' evenings.

Rising Sun 70
3 Hythe Station Road / Hawkins Road (nr A134)
Greene King - Pub closed and boarded-up.

11-11 (12-10.30 Sun)

Robin Hood 71
45 Osborne Street / Whitwell Road (nr A134)
Tel: (01206) 576854
Wadworths 6X; **Whitbread** Flowers IPA H
🝙
Refurbished pub. Ask for the 'sparkler' to be removed when ordering your beer.

11-2.30; 6.30-11 (11-11 Sat: 12-3.30; 7.30-10.30 Sun)

Rose & Crown Hotel 72
51 East Street (A137)
Tel: (01206) 866677
Adnams Broadside; **Tetley** Bitter; **Tolly Cobbold** IPA H
🝙🝙🝙🝙🝙🝙🝙🝙🝙
Comfortable, rambling, half-timbered 17th century hotel bar. International evenings every two months. Probably the oldest inn in Colchester.

11-11 (12-10.30 Sun)

Rovers Tye Tavern 73
Highwoods Approach, Ipswich Road (A1232)
Tel: (01206) 845345
S&N John Smiths Bitter, Theakstons XB, Websters Yorkshire Bitter H
🝙🝙🝙🝙🝙🝙🝙🝙
Large, attractive, immaculately-kept pub, in farmhouse style. 'Duck or grouse'. Good traditional English food.

11-11 (12-10.30 Sun)

Royal 74
65 Butt Road (B1026)
Tel: (01206) 577990
Greene King IPA, Abbot Ale H
Friendly, basic public bar. Pictures in the lounge.

5 (7 Mon/Tue)-11 (12-3; 7-11 Sat: 12-3; 7-10.30 Sun)

Royal Mortar 75
120 Military Road
Tel: (01206) 790214
Greene King IPA, Abbot Ale H
🝙🝙🝙🝙🝙
Completely refurbished and structurally altered 'New Town' pub.

Royal Oak 76
354 Harwich Road, Parsons Heath (A137)
Free-house - Pub closed in 1996, and converted to a restaurant.

Royal Standard 77
34 Mersea Road (B1025)
Free-house - Pub closed in the early 1990s.

11-11 (12-3; 7-10.30 Sun)

Rumpoles 78
35 East Hill (A1232)
Tel: (01206) 862785
Free-house - No Real Ale. Formerly "Hill Street Blues" & "Maximillians".

11-11 (12-10.30 Sun)

Salisbury Hotel 79
122 Butt Road (B1026)
Tel: (01206) 572338
Greene King IPA; **Tetley** Bitter H
🝙🝙🝙🝙🝙🝙🝙🝙
Spacious, privately-run hotel, with reasonably-priced accommodation.

Silver Oyster 80
Queen Elizabeth Way / Prince Philip Way, Monkwick
Tel: (01206) 577320
Recently acquired by Ridleys - A range of Ridleys Real Ales is likely!

Six Bells 81
289 Greenstead Road (nr A133)
Inntrepreneur - Pub closed and demolished in 1994. A new Tesco has now been built on the site.

11-11 (11-3; 7.30-11 Sat: 12-3; 7-10.30 Sun)

Spinnaker 82
21 Hythe Quay, The Hythe
Tel: (01206) 793176
S&N John Smiths Bitter; **Guest Beer** H
🝙🝙🝙🝙🝙
Small free-house on the waterside. Overlooks boats moored on Hythe quay. Formerly the "Anchor".

11-11 (12-10.30 Sun)

Spoofers Cafe Bar 83
4 St Botolphs Street
Tel: (01206) 766644
Whitbread - No Real Ale. Formerly "Churchill's" & "Muswells".

10.30-11 (10.30-4; 6.30-11 Sat: 12-4; 7-10.30 Sun)

Stockwell Arms 84
18 West Stockwell Street (nr A1124)
Tel: (01206) 575560
Greene King IPA; **Marstons** Pedigree; **Nethergate** Bitter; **S&N** Courage Best Bitter, Directors, Theakstons BB; **Wells** Bombardier H
🝙🝙🝙🝙🝙🝙
Part of the old, acclaimed, Dutch quarter. Music night every fortnight. Sunday roasts (booking advisable).

11-2.30; 5.30-11 (11-11 Sat: 12-3; 7-10.30 Sun)

Tap & Spile 85
123 Crouch Street / Hospital Lane (nr A1124)
Tel: (01206) 573572
Adnams Bitter; **Marstons** Pedigree; **Nethergate** Bitter; **S&N** Theakstons BB H
🝙🝙🝙
Shove ha'penny, bar skittles, darts, crib. Quiz night Monday. Live music (duos). Open fires. Several Guest beers. Four pint carry-outs. Parking difficult. Formerly the "Hospital Arms".

"The Tap & Spile", Colchester

11-11 (12-3; 7-10.30 Sun)

Times Cafe Bar   **86**
2 North Hill
Tel: (01206) 41111
Greene King IPA, Abbot **H**
⟨ D ⟨ ▶ R ⊫
Cosy free-house/restaurant, with
an emphasis on food. DJ
Thursdays, theme nights Friday.
Parking difficult. Formerly the
"Wig & Pen" and "William
Scraggs".

Travellers Friend   *87*
5 Mill Road, Mile End (nr A134)
Inntrepreneur - Pub closed in
1995, and demolished.

11-11 (6.30-11 only Sat: closed Sun)

Trotters   *88*
22 Middleborough (nr A134)
Tel: (01206) 766111
Free-house - No Real Ale, since
the handpump was removed.
Except for "Adnams Tally Ho"
straight from the cask - in Winter
only. Returned to its original
name after a period as "Deals"
and "Carrick's".

11-11 (12-3; 7-10.30 Sun)

Victoria Inn   *89*
10 North Station Road
Tel: (01206) 514510
Free-house - No Real Ale.

Vitos   *90*
138 Military Road / Wimpole
Road
Free-house - Pub closed follow-
ing a fire, now converted to flats.
Formerly the "Recreation Hotel".

6.30-11 (12-3; 6.30-11 Sat: 12-3;
7-10.30 Sun)

Waffles Wine Bar   *91*
24 East Street (A1232)
Tel: (01206) 870967
Free-house - No Real Ale.

11-11 (12-10.30 Sun)

Waggon & Horses   **92**
66 North Hill (nr A1124)
Tel: (01206) 574351
Tetley Bitter **H**
⟨ D ⟨ ⌨ ⅙
'Mr Qs' theme pub with pool
tables and quiz machine. Parking
difficult.

Waterside Inn   *93*
King Edward Quay, Hythe Quay
(nr A134)
Pubmaster - Pub closed and
demolished. Formerly the "New
Dock".

11.30-11 (7-10.30 only Sun)

Wig & Pen   **94**
156 High Street (A1124)
Tel: (01206) 769995
Bass Draught Bass; **Everards**
Tiger; **Morlands** Independents
IPA, Old Speckled Hen; **S&N**
Theakstons BB; **Tetley** Bitter;
Guest Beer H
⟨ D ⟨ ▶ H
New Morlands 'Wig & Pen'
theme conversion of the former
Cullingfords store, 'feels' rather
like a London pub with lots of
wood-panelling. Eating area at
the rear. Parking difficult.

11-11 (12-10.30 Sun)

Yates's Wine Lodge   **95**
1-3 Head Street
Tel: (01206) 710471
S&N Courage Directors **H**
⟨ ⟨ ⅙
New town-centre pub, with a
grand, pseudo-Victorian flavour.
Popular with business folk at
lunchtimes and the younger set
in the evenings.
Full menu, plus daily specials.
Parking Difficult.

11-11 (12-10.30 Sun)

Ye Olde Marquis   **96**
25 North Hill
Tel: (01206) 577630
S&N Courage Best Bitter,
Directors **H**
⟨ D ⟨ ▶ R ⊞ ※ ⅙
16th century, timbered inn with
pool and quiz nights. Patio garden, car park at rear. Live music
(duos) and karaoke, also loud
jukebox. Formerly the "Marquis
of Granby".

Cold Norton   D4

11.30-3; 6-11 (12-4; 7-10.30 Sun)

Norton Barge
54 Latchingdon Road
Tel: (01621) 829569
Greene King IPA; **Wells**
Bombardier; **Guest Beers H**
⟨ ▶ R ⊫ ⇲ ※
Family-run and family-oriented
pub with fresh fish (home-
cooked) on the menu. Formerly
the "Barnside Tavern".

Collier Row   A4

11-11 (12-10.30 Sun)

Bell & Gate
248/250 Collier Row Lane (B174)
Tel: (01708) 765080
S&N Courage Best Bitter **H**
⟨ D ⟨ ⊞ ※
Large and busy main road pub
with pool table.

Charcoal Burner
Turpin Avenue, Havering Park
Grand Met - Pub closed and
demolished.

11-11 (12-10.30 Sun)
Colley Rowe Inn
54/56 Collier Row Road (B174, nr B175)
Tel:
Greene King IPA; **S&N** Courage Directors, Theakstons BB;
Guest Beers H
❶ⅅ❶❶ & ⅍ 🗗
New 'Wetherspoon', opened June 1998, in a former travel agents and chemist sundries shop - despite local opposition. Larger than it appears from the front. Ask for the 'Sparklers' to be removed from Southern beers.

11-11 (12-10.30 Sun)
Marlborough
163 Mawney Road (nr A12)
Tel: (01708) 769287
Ind Coope 'House' Bitter;
Tetley Bitter **H**
❶ⅅ❶❶⊕🛏🚐
Two-bar pub with pool and darts. Picnic tables in the car park.

11-11 (12-10.30 Sun)
Mid City Lanes
Collier Row Road / Whalebone Lane North (by A1112)
Tel: (0181) 924 4000
Ruddles Best **H**
❶ⅅ❶❶ R ⊕ &
More than just the usual bowling alley. The downstairs 'Bowl Bar' has now been replaced by the 'Mid City Bar', which reopened in Summer 1998 as part of a major re-development. Formerly "Rollerbowl".

12-3; 6-11 (11-11 Sat: 12-4; 7-10.30 Sun)
Pickled Newt
Gobions Avenue, Chase Cross (nr B175)
Tel: (01708) 749995
Greene King Martha Greene's, Abbot Ale; **S&N** Courage Best Bitter **H**
❶❶⊕ 🌸
Bingo on Tuesdays, quiz night Sunday. Formerly the "Aspen Tree".

11-11 (12-10.30 Sun)
Pinewoods
St Johns Road / Clockhouse Lane
Tel: (01708) 762965 (Restaurant 749201)
Greene King IPA, Abbot Ale;
S&N Courage Best Bitter **H**
❶ⅅ❶❶ R ⊕ 🐾 🌸
Recently-altered pub on the edge of Havering Park, expanding rapidly to cater for families.

11-11 (12-10.30 Sun)
White Hart
Collier Row Road / White Hart Lane (B174)
Tel: (01708) 746757
Ind Coope 'House' Bitter;
Tetley Bitter **H**
❶❶⊕🚐🐾🌸
Regular discos and live music. Formerly the "Double Top"

Colne Engaine D2

11-3; 7-11 (12-10.30 Sun)
Five Bells
7 Mill Lane
OS: TL851303
Tel: (01787) 224166
Greene King IPA **H**
❶ⅅ❶❶ R ⊕ 🛏 🌸
Restored village free-house, occasional live music and children's entertainment.

Cooksmill Green (Highwood) B3

11.30-3; 6-11 (closed Mon: 12-3; 7-10.30 Sun)
Fox & Goose
Wyse's Road / Ongar Road (by A414)
OS: TL639052
Tel: (01245) 248245
Greene King IPA, Abbot Ale;
Wadworths 6X **H**
❶❶❶⊕🌸
Large roadside pub which retains its character. It serves well kept beer and is renowned for its food. Interesting sign.

Coopersale A3

Almost part of Epping.

11-11 (12-10.30 Sun)
Garnon Bushes
13 Coopersale Common (nr B181)
OS: TL477030
Tel: (01992) 573096
Fullers London Pride;
Guest Beers H
❶ⅅ❶❶ R 🌸
Popular local near Epping forest, comprising two terraced cottages. Renowned for its food.

11-3; 6-11 (12-3; 7-10.30 Sun)
Theydon Oak
Stonnards Hill / Coopersale Street
Tel: (01992) 572618
Bass Draught Bass; **Greene King** IPA; **Wadworths** 6X **H**
❶ⅅ❶❶ 🌸 &
Attractive, comfortable and busy weather-boarded pub with beams, brasses, a real fire and two gardens. Serves good food.

Copford D2

Kings
London Road (B1408)
Free-house - Converted to a night-club. Formerly the "Windmill"

Copford Green D2

12-3 (4 Sat); 6 (6.30 Sat)-11 (12-3; 7-10.30 Sun)
Alma
School Road (1 mile South of B1408)
OS: TL928227
Tel: (01206) 210607
Greene King IPA, Rayments Special Bitter, Abbot Ale, seasonal beers; **Guest Beers H**
❶ⅅ❶❶ 🌸 &
Friendly, country local, with darts, shove-halfpenny and dominoes. The meeting place for various car and motor cycle clubs.

Cornish Hall End C1

11.30-2.30; 6.30-11 (12-4; 7-10.30 Sun)
Horse & Groom
Cornish Hall End (B1057)
Tel: (01799) 586306
Greene King - No Real Ale.

Corringham C5

12-11 (10.30 Sun)
Bull
Church Road (nr A1014)
Tel: (01375) 672223
Bass Worthington BB;
Guest Beer H
❶ⅅ❶❶ 🌸
Regularly-changing guest beers. Parking can be difficult at busy times.

11-11 (12-10.30 Sun)
Whispers
St John's Way
Tel: (01375) 671101
Bass - No Real Ale.

Coxtie Green B4

11-3; 6-11 (12-4; 7-11 Sun: 12-3; 7-10.30 Sun)
White Horse
173 Coxtie Green Road (1 Mile West of A128)
OS: TQ564959
Tel: (01277) 372410
Guest Beers H
❶ⅅ❶❶⊕🌸
Cosy, friendly & traditional country local with huge garden, and children's play area. Beer festival held in a tent here each July.
Four to six constantly-changing guest beers. Good value food, but no food Sunday Lunchtimes. Close to South Weald Park.

Cranham B5

The last resting place of General Oglethorpe - founder of the State of Georgia.

11-11 (10.30 Sun)

Golden Crane
117 Avon Road (nr A127)
Tel: (01708) 222388
Bass Draught Bass; **Fullers** London Pride; **Guest Beer** (occasional) **H**
⊕ ⊄ ⊄ ⊕ ⊕ ⊱ ⊱ ⊛
Friendly, family pub dating from 1958.

11-11 (12-10.30 Sun)

Jobbers Rest
St Mary's Lane (B187)
Tel: (01708) 223251
S&N Courage Best Bitter, Directors **H**
⊕ ⊄ ⊄ ⊱ ⊛
Relaunched as a rather expensive 'Steak and Ale House', after a much-needed refurbishment. Extensive children's facilities in garden.

12-11 (12-4.30; 7-10.30 Sun)

Plough
83 Front Lane/Ingrebourne Gardens (nr B187)
Tel: (01708) 220408
Bass Stones Bitter; **Greene King** IPA **H**
⊕ ⊄ ⊄ ⊱ ⊛
Well-furnished, but rather bland, family pub. Pool played. Entertainment last Saturday of the month.

11.30-11 (12-10.30 Sun)

Thatched House
348 St Mary's Lane (B187)
Tel: (01708) 228080
Bass Draught Bass; **Fullers** London Pride; **Guest Beers H**
⊕ ⊄ ⊄ **R** ⊛
Considerably-extended, popular, family pub on edge of countryside, now dominated by its food trade.

Crays Hill C4

11-11 (12-10.30 Sun)

Belvedere
Hardings Elm Road (nr A127)
Tel: (01268) 522828
Whitbread Boddingtons Bitter, Flowers IPA; **Guest Beers H**
⊕ ⊄ ⊄ **R** ⊱ ⊛ ⊱
Recently built in an open setting. Large comfortable bar with live entertainment most nights. Large barbecue weekends and bank holidays. English and Malaysian food and carvery. Guest beers from the Whitbread range.

11-11 (12-10.30 Sun)

Shepherd & Dog
Crays Hill (A129)
OS: TQ726924
Tel: (01268) 521967
Ind Coope Friary Meux BB, Burton Ale; **Tetley** Bitter; **Guest Beers H**
⊕ ⊄ ⊄ ⊕ ⊕ ⊱
Old pub, tastefully refurbished, with conservatory restaurant, and greatly-enlarged lounge bar, but retaining its original public bar, complete with bare wooden floor (dogs allowed).
Over 55s discount Tuesdays and Thursdays. The 'shepherd & dog' statue which once adorned the front, has been preserved in the lounge bar. Quiz nights Wednesdays.

Creekmouth (Barking) A5

(See Barking map for location of pub)

11-11 (12-10.30 Sun)

Crooked Billet C1
113 River Road (1½ miles south of A13)
Tel: (0181) 594 2623
Bass Draught Bass;
Guest Beers H
⊕ ⊄ ⊄ **R** ⊛ ⊛
Pleasant, traditional local in industrial area, with small, smart saloon and lively 'Creek' bar. Bar billiards played. Piano singalongs at weekends.
Guest beers from independent breweries every two weeks. Worth a visit. Beware keg cider on handpump.

Cressing C2

The ancient Temple Barns are opened annually.

11.30-11 (12-10.30 Sun)

Fowlers Farm
Galley's Corner, Braintree Road (B1018, by A120)
OS: TL779219
Tel: (01376) 555041
Bass Draught Bass, Hancocks HB **H**
⊕ ⊄ ⊄ ⊕ ⊱
Basic restaurant-cum-pub with bare walls and wood floor, located at the south-eastern corner of Braintree, and converted from a derelict early 15th century farmhouse.
The beers are unfortunately served too cold, ask for the 'sparkler' to be removed from the 'swan-neck' before ordering your drinks.

12-2.30; 7-11 (12-3; 7-10.30 Sun)

Inn For A Penny
Jeffreys Road, Tye Green (nr B1018)
Tel: (01376) 326356
Guest Beers H
⊛ ⊋
Modern estate pub, with a constantly-changing guest beers. Formerly the "Pullman".

11.30-3; 7-11 (12-3; 7-10.30 Sun)

Three Ashes
Lanham Green Road/Ashes Road (nr B1018)
Tel: (01376) 583143
Greene King IPA, Abbot Ale **H**
⊕ ⊄ ⊄ **R** ⊕ ⊛
Village pub, retaining its public bar - with cheaper prices. Good home-cooked, fresh food. The landlord is a Real Ale enthusiast.

11-3; 7-11 (12-3; 7-10.30 Sun)

Willows
The Street (nr B1018)
Tel: (01376) 583399
Adnams Bitter, Broadside **H**
⊕ ⊄ ⊄ **R**
400 year old, country pub with a relaxing atmosphere and an emphasis on food. Quiet, easy-listening music, on Thursday evenings. No food Sundays or Saturday evening.

Dagenham A5

Parts of the original village centre still survive alongside Britain's largest housing estate and Ford's motor factory.

11-11 (12-4; 7-10.30 Sun)

Admiral Vernon
141 Broad Street (nr A1240)
Tel: (0181) 592 0431
S&N Courage Best Bitter; Websters Green Label **H**
⊕ ⊕ ⊖
Large, two-bar pub, with almost circular bar and extensive wood panelling. 'Courage Best' not always available.

11-11 (12-10.30 Sun)

Anglers Retreat
New Road (A13)
Tel: (0181) 592 0279
Free-house - No Real Ale.

11-11 (12-10.30 Sun)

Beacon
201 Oxlow Lane (between A1112 & A1240)
Tel: (0181) 595 8014
Ind Coope 'House' Bitter **H**
⊕ ⊄ ⊄ ⊕ ⊱ ⊛
Lively pub in residential area. Saloon opens at weekends only and is available for hire. Children's play area planned for the garden.

11-11 (12-10.30 Sun)

Bull
Rainham Road South / Ballards Road (A1112/B178)
Tel: (0181) 592 0047
S&N Courage Best Bitter, Directors **H**
⊕ ⊄ ⊄ **R** ⊛ ⊖
Games bar with pool.

11-11 (12-10.30 Sun)

Cherry Tree
Wood Lane (A124)
Tel: (0181) 592 1859
S&N - No Real Ale.

Chiquito Restaurant & Bar
Dagenham Leisure Centre,
Ripple Road (A13)
Tel: (0181) 593 7682
Free-house - No Real Ale.

11-11 (12-10.30 Sun)

Church Elm
Heathway/Church Elm Lane
(A1240)
Tel: (0181) 592 4194
Allied - No Real Ale (Handpump
disused).

11-11 (11-3; 5.30-11 Sat: 12-3;
7-10.30 Sun)

Cross Keys
Crown Street (nr B178)
Tel: (0181) 592 0883
Free-house - No Real Ale.

11-3; 5 (6 Sat)-11 (12-3; 7-10.30
Sun)

Eastbrook Hotel
Rainham Road
South/Dagenham Road (A1112)
Tel: (0181) 592 1873
Bass Draught Bass; **Fullers**
London Pride; **Ruddles** County;
S&N Courage Best Bitter **H**
◧ ◖ 🆁 🆀 🛏 ⇤ 🍴
Large, expensive free-house
with superb wood-panelling.

11-3; 5 (7 Sat)-11 (12-3; 7-10.30
Sun)

Farmhouse Tavern
Dagenham Road (½ mile off
A1112)
Tel: (0181) 592 0301
Free-house (Davies) - No Real
Ale.

11-11 (12-10.30 Sun)

Hinds Head
2a Burnside Road (nr A118)
Tel: (0181) 590 2465
Whitbread - No Real Ale.

12-11 (2am Thu-Sat: 12-10.30
Sun)

Jake & Elwoods
24-26 New Road (A13)
Tel: (0181) 593 5510
Free-house - No Real Ale.

11-11 (12-10.30 Sun)

Lord Denman
270-272 Heathway (A1240)
Tel: (0181) 984 8590
Fullers London Pride; **S&N**
Courage Directors, Theakstons
BB; **Guest Beers H**
◧ ◨ ◖ ◗ & 🍴 ✂ ⊖
New split-level 'Wetherspoon' in
former DHSS office. Surprisingly
nice with no games.

11-11 (12-10.30 Sun)

Matapan
945 Green Lane (A1083)
Tel: (0181) 592 2145
J & T Davies - No Real Ale.

Me An' O'Brien's
26-28 Goresbrook Road
Tel: (0181) 984 9026
Free-house - No Real Ale.
Formerly "Blitz".

Merry Fiddlers
Wood Lane, Becontree Heath
(A124)
Taylor Walker - Pub demolished,
a petrol station has now been
built on the site.

New Inn Hotel
40 New Road (A13)
Tel: (0181) 592 0098
Free-house - Bar closed. Hotel
remains open.

11-11 (12-10.30 Sun)

Pipers
Amesbury Road / Gale Street
Tel: (0181) 592 5224
Ruddles Best Bitter **H**
◧ ⇤ 🐝 ⊖
Two large bars, with a wealth of
wood-panelling. Real Ale not
always available. Parking
Difficult.

12-3; 7-11 (10.30 Sun)

Railway
Shafter Road / Rainham Road
South (A1112)
Tel: (0181) 592 0593
Tetley Bitter; **Guest Beer H**
◧ ◖ ◧ ⇤ 🍴 ⊖
Large pub with fairly plush 'L'
shaped saloon and contrasting
public bar. Discos on Fridays.
Sky sports avidly watched in the
Saloon.

11-11 (12-10.30 Sun)

Robin Hood
807 Longbridge Road (A124)
Tel: (0181) 590 2361
Whitbread - No Real Ale
(Handpumps disused).

11-11 (12-10.30 Sun)

Roundhouse
Porters Avenue / Lodge Avenue
(B1423)
Tel: (0181) 592 1605
S&N Courage Directors, John
Smiths Bitter, Theakstons BB **H**
◧ ◖ ◧
Circular pub with games room
and leaded lights. A serious
lager-drinkers pub! No food
Sundays.

11-11 (12-10.30 Sun)

Royal Oak
715 Green Lane (A1083)
Tel: (0181) 590 1194
Inntrepreneur - No Real Ale.

12-11 (10.30 Sun)

Ship & Anchor
Wood Lane, Becontree Heath
(A124)
Tel: (0181) 595 6412
Ind Coope 'House' Bitter;
Youngs Bitter **H**
◧ ◗ ◖ ◧
Two bars around a large horse-
shoe-shaped serving area. A
homely feel only spoilt by a very
noisy fruit machine. Basic menu
with burgers and 'shakes', etc.

Spoofers Cafe-Bar
Dagenham Leisure Centre,
Ripple Road (A13)
Tel: (0181) 595 2729
Regent Inns - No Real Ale.

Spooners
20-22 Goresbrook Road (Nr
A13/A1240)
Free-house - Pub closed.

11-11 (12-10.30 Sun)

Three Travellers
Wood Lane, Becontree Heath
(A124)
Tel: (0181) 592 2441
Tetley Bitter; **Youngs** Bitter;
Guest Beer H
◖ ◗ ◧ 🐝 &
Fairly large pub facing main
road, with an area outside cor-
doned-off for lunchtime trade.
Children's play area in garden.
Guest beers from the 'Tapsters
Choice' range.

Danbury   C3

*Unspoilt village on high ground,
Danbury Palace is a country
park.*

12-3; 5-11 (12-11 Sat: 12-10.30
Sun)

Anchor
Wash Road, Runsell Green (nr
A414)
Tel: (01245) 222457
Ridleys IPA, seasonal beers **H**
◖ ◗ 🆁 ◧ ⇤ 🐝
Very attractive and popular pub
with live music Sundays and bar
billiards. New conservatory
restaurant featuring 'large'
meals.

Bakers Arms
Eves Corner, Main Road (A414)
Tel: (01245) 223180
Gray & Sons - No Real Ale.

11.30-3; 5.30-11 (12-3; 7-10.30
Sun)

Bell
128 Main Road (A414)
Tel: (01245) 222028
Ind Coope ABC Bitter, Friary
Meux BB; **Whitbread** Castle
Eden Ale **H**
◖ ◗ ◖ ◗ 🐝
Friendly, comfortable one-bar
pub. Good food, with daily spe-
cials.

11-3; 6-11 (12-10.30 Sun)

Cricketers Arms
Penny Royal Road, Danbury
Common (nr A414)
OS: TL779047
Tel: (01245) 222022
Ind Coope Friary Meux BB,
Burton Ale; **Guest Beer H**
Addlestones Cider H
◖ ◗ ◖ ◗ 🆁 ◧ ⇤ 🐝
Traditional, country local,
overlooking the common, with
changing guest beer.

45

11-11 (12-10.30 Sun)

Griffin Tavern
64 Main Road (A414)
Tel: (01245) 412905
S&N Theakstons BB, XB; **Guest Beer H**
◑ ◐ ◐ **R** ⊫ ❀
Old, 'beamed' pub, tastefully refurbished. Good views from garden.

Debden (nr Saffron Walden)   B1

12-3; 6-11 (12-3; 7-10.30 Sun)

Plough
High Street
OS: TL558333
Tel: (01799) 541899
Greene King IPA, Abbot Ale, seasonal beers **H**
◑ ◐ ◐ ❀
A warm welcome is assured in this 17th century village local. Landlord is a keen Real Ale enthusiast. Good value food, but no food Mondays. Excellent garden for children.

12-3; 6-11 (12-3; 7-10.30 Sun)

White Hart
High Street
OS: TL556334
Tel: (01799) 541109
Greene King IPA, Abbot Ale **H**
◑ ◐ ◗ 🚃
Recently refurbished village local with a warm welcome. No food Sunday & Monday evenings.

Debden (Loughton)   A4

Large post-war estate.

(See Loughton map for location of pubs)

12-11 (12-3; 7-10.30 Sun)

Clydesdale   D1
41 Westall Road (A1168)
OS: TQ441969
Tel: (0181) 502 5881
Greene King Abbot Ale (Winter); **S&N** Courage Best Bitter, Directors; **Wadworths** 6X (Winter) **H**
◑ ◐ ⊞ ⊫ ⌚ ❀ ⅏
Large, comfortable and spacious, catering mainly for the younger set. Two dart and pool teams, golf society. Sea fishing trips. Friendly manager.

11-11 (12-3; 7-10.30 Sun)

Cottage Loaf   D2
Jessell Drive
OS: TQ444974
Tel: (0181) 508 6103
S&N Websters Yorkshire Bitter **H**
◑ ⊫ ❀ ⅏
Friendly estate local, becoming more of a family pub. Guest beers expected. Formerly "Cobs".

11-11 (12-10.30 Sun)

Gunmakers Arms   D3
133 Chester Road (nr A1168)
OS: TQ438975
Tel: (0181) 508 4355
Bass Draught Bass, Worthington BB **H**
◑ ◐ ◗ ⊞ ❀
Friendly estate pub with live music on Saturdays.

11-11 (12-10.30 Sun)

Sir Winston Churchill   D4
The Broadway (A1168)
Tel: (0181) 508 7160
S&N Theakstons BB **H**
◑ ◐ ⊞ ❀ ⊖
Large modern pub named after the former MP for Woodford. Mainly a lager drinkers pub. Pool played.

Dedham   E2

Delightful village in Constable country, with huge 16th century church and many half-timbered, plastered and brick houses along the high street.

11-4; 6-11 (11-11 Sat: 12-10.30 Sun)

Anchor Inn
The Heath
OS: TM061317
Tel: (01206) 323131
Greene King IPA **G**
◑ ◐ ◐ **R** ❀ ⅏
Pleasant free-house situated on the outskirts of the village. No food Sunday evenings.

11-11 (12-10.30 Sun)

Lamb Inn
131 Birchwood Road, Lamb Corner (off B1029)
OS: TM045316
Tel: (01206) 322216
Greene King IPA **H**
◑ ◐ ◐ **R** ⊫ ⌚ ❀ ⅏
Fine rural pub with excellent basic bar, comfortable lounge and restaurant. Bookings advisable for restaurant.

10-11 (12-10.30 Sun)

Marlborough Head
Hotel
Mill Lane (B1029)
Tel: (01206) 323250
Bass Worthington BB; **Ind Coope** Burton Ale **H**
◑ ◐ ◐ **R** 🛏 ⌚ ❀ ⅏
Popular 500 year old former master-weaver's house with separate 'family' room. Traditional English and vegetarian cooking.

12-3; 6-11 (12-3; 7-10.30 Sun)

Rose & Crown
Crown Street (off B1029)
Tel: (01206) 322197
Guest Beers H
◑ ◐ ◐ **R** ⊞ ⊫ ❀ ⅏
Friendly family local with unique seating arrangement and new restaurant. Beer range constantly changing.

46

11-2.30; 6-11 (12-3; 7-10.30 Sun)
Sun Hotel
High Street (B1029)
Tel: (01206) 323351
Adnams Bitter; **S&N** John
Smiths Bitter; **Guest Beers H**

Built in 16th century. Quiet bar,
though popular in summer.
Good food, extensive menu and
beer. Large garden. One of the
guest rooms has a four poster
bed.

Delvin End (Sible Hedingham   C1

7-11 (12-11 Sat: 12-10.30 Sun)
Bottle Hall
Toppesfield Road, Delvin End
OS: TL756353
Tel: (01787) 462405
Mauldons White Adder;
Woodfordes Wherry; **Guest
Beers H**

Cosy, restored, rural pub -
remote, but well worth finding.
Closed weekday lunchtimes.

Dengie   E4

12-11 (10.30 Sun)
White Horse
Tillingham Road (B1021)
Tel: (01621) 779288
Ridleys IPA **H**

Isolated pub in small hamlet,
with long-standing reputation
for live music on Saturday
nights. Six sports and social
teams.

Dobbs Weir   A3

*Small gathering of houses in Lea
Valley Park.*

11-11 (12-10.30 Sun)
Fish & Eels
Three Quarter Mile Road (nr
A1170)
OS: TL386082
Tel: (01992) 440029
Ind Coope Benskins BB,
Burton Ale; **Tetley** Bitter;
Guest Beer H

Popular, family-oriented pub by
the River Lea, with separate
restaurant.

Doddinghurst   B4

Dormitory village for Brentwood.

11-3; 6-11 (11-11 Sat: 12-10.30
Sun)
Moat
Church Lane
OS: TQ588990
Tel: (01277) 821650
Nethergate Porters Suffolk
Bitter; **Whitbread** Boddingtons
Bitter, Castle Eden Ale **H**

(Fri/Sat Eves & Sun
Lun)
Much-improved village pub with
real fires. A better pub atmosphere, since the two bars were
restored. The restaurant doubles
as a family room / meeting
room.

Dovercourt   F2

*'Hi-De-Hi' filmed at the holiday
camp.*

Bird In Hand
567 Main Road
Pubmaster - Pub closed and
demolished for new housing.

11.30-3; 6-11 (12-3; 7-10.30 Sun)
Cliff Hotel
Marine Parade (B1414)
Tel: (01255) 503345
Greene King Abbot Ale; **S&N**
Youngers IPA **H**

Mid-Victorian hotel on seafront
with a choice of two bars - modern or traditional - overlooking
the sea. Les Routiers listed.

12-2.30; 7-11 (12 Music Nights)
(12-3; 7-10.30 Sun)
Devonshire Arms
1 Ramsey Road (B1032) / Oakley
Road (B1414)
Tel: (01255) 506525
Tolly Cobbold Mild; **Whitbread**
Flowers IPA **H**

Classic, 1930s semi-circular pub,
with emphasis on live music and
discos. The former public bar
has been converted to a function
room. Late license.

11-11 (12-10.30 Sun)
Hotel Continental
28-29 Marine Parade (B1414) /
Lee Road
Tel: (01255) 551298
Guest Beer H

Hotel bar on the front.

10.30-11 (12-10.30 Sun)
King's Arms Hotel
178 High Street (A136)
Tel: (01255) 503709
Greene King IPA; **Tolly
Cobbold** Mild **H**

Bold, Victorian interior, with a
profusion of etched windows
and panels. Limited parking.

11-3; 7-11 (11-11 Sat: 12-10.30
Sun)
Phoenix
Lower Marine Parade
Tel: (01255) 502071
Websters Yorkshire Bitter **H**

Seafront pub with live music at
weekends. Children welcome.
Night-club Fridays and
Saturdays - open until 2am.

10.30-11 (12-10.30 Sun)
Queens Hotel
119 High Street
Tel: (01255) 502634
Ruddles Best Bitter; **S&N**
Courage Directors **H**

Charming, thatched bar in the
lounge, darts and jukebox in the
public.

12-3; 6-11 (12-10.30 Sun)
Royal
387 Main Road (B1032)
Tel: (01255) 502893
Tolly Cobbold Mild; **Whitbread**
Flowers IPA **H**

Basic 1930s pub, with assorted
animals in the large garden.
Coach parties and meetings
easily catered for.

10.30-2.30; 6-11 (12-4; 7-10.30
(12-10.30 Summer) Sun)
Royal Oak Inn
Main Road (B1032)
Tel: (01255) 502883
Free-house - No Real Ale.

11-3; 7-11 (12-3; 7-10.30 Sun)
Tower Hotel
Main Road (B1032)
Tel: (01255) 504952
Free-house - No Real Ale.

11-3.30; 7-11 (12-10.30 Sun)
Trafalgar
616 Main Road (B1032)
Tel: (01255) 502234
Greene King IPA; **Tetley** Bitter **H**

400 year old country, coaching
inn, now enveloped by suburban development.

11-11 (12-3; 7-10.30 Sun)
Victoria Hotel
Victoria Street (off East Street)
Tel: (01255) 502980
Ridleys Spectacular; **S&N**
Courage Directors, Websters
Yorkshire Bitter **H**

Solid, Victorian hotel, opposite
the station.

11-11 (12-10.30 Sun)
White Horse
489 Main Road (B1032)
Tel: (01255) 502065
S&N Websters Yorkshire
Bitter; **Wadworths** 6X **H**

Large, family-oriented roadside
pub. Operated by Five Star
Leisure.

Downham C4

11-11 (12-10.30 Sun)

De Beauvoir Arms
2 Downham Road
Tel: (01268) 710571
Morlands Old Speckled Hen;
Ridleys IPA; **Guest Beers** H

◖◖▐▬ ❀

Old village pub, converted to one bar. Tudor Barn available for functions, large garden with play area. Evening food available in Summer.
Note all handpumped beers on 'blanket' pressure at time of survey.

Duddenhoe End A1

Remote north-west Essex hamlet.

12-3; 6.30-11 (12-3; 7-10.30 Sun)

Woodman Inn
Duddenhoe End (less than 1 mile off B1039)
OS: TL460367
Tel: (01763) 838354
Greene King IPA H

◖◗ ◖◗ ▐ ▐▬ ❀

Partly-thatched and comfortable. Caravans and camping attached. Pool table.

Duton Hill (Gt Easton) B2

12-3; 7-11 (10.30 Sun)

Rising Sun
(½ mile West of B184)
OS: TL603269
Tel: (01371) 870204
Ridleys IPA H

◖◗ ❀

Friendly, village local with large garden. No food Tuesdays.

12-2.30 (Not Wed); 6-11 (12-3; 7-10.30 Sun)

Three Horseshoes
(nr B184)
OS: TL606268
Tel: (01371) 870681
Ridleys IPA H

◖◗ ◖◗ ▐▬ ❀ ♿

Enjoyable village local.

Earls Colne D2

Large village noted for agricultural machinery.

12-2; 6-11 (12-2; 7-10.30 Sun)

Bird In Hand
Coggeshall Road (B1024) / America Road
Tel: (01787) 222557
Ridleys IPA; seasonal beer H/G

◖◗ ◖◗ ▐ ▬

Unspoilt, 19th century local by old American airbase, which had a flat roof built during WW2 as the pub was at the end of a runway. A 'normal' roof was added when the base closed.

11-11 (12-10.30 Sun)

Castle
77 High Street (A1124, was A604)
Tel: (01787) 222694
Greene King IPA, Rayments Special, Seasonal Ales, Abbot Ale H

◖◗ ◖◗ ▐ ▐▬ ▬ ▬ ❀ ♿

Friendly local built 1320, 16th century mural in dining room.

11-3.30; 6-11 (12-3; 7-10.30 Sun)

Coachman Inn
34 Upper Holt Street (A1124, was A604) / Tey Road
Tel: (01787) 222330
Greene King IPA, Abbot Ale H

◖◗ ◖◗ ▐ ▐▬ ▬ ▬

15th century coaching inn near the priory. Full of beams. Emphasis on meals, including Sunday roasts. Conservatory.

7-11

Drapers Mill
53 High Street (A1124, was A604)
Tel: (01787) 223666
Free-house - No Real Ale. Closed Lunchtimes. Formerly "Judges".

11-11 (12-10.30 Sun)

Drum Inn
21 High Street (A1124, was A604)
Tel: (01787) 222368
Fullers London Pride; **Greene King** IPA, Abbot Ale; **Guest Beers** (occasional) H

◖◗ ◖◗ ▐ ▬

Modernised & popular pub. Six bedrooms. No food Sundays or Monday evenings.

12-3; 6-11 (11-11 Sat:12-10.30 Sun)

Earl Trout/Riverside Inn
42 Lower Holt Street (A1124, was A604)
Tel: (01787) 222281
Greene King IPA; **Wadworths** Henry's IPA H

◖◗ ◖◗ ▐ ▐▬ ▬ ▬ ❀ ♿

Free-house on the banks of the River Colne, live music Thursdays. Large garden ideal for children.

11.30-3; 6.30-11 (12-3; 7-10.30 Sun)

Lion
11 High Street (A1124, was A604)
Tel: (01787) 224120
Whitbread Boddingtons Bitter, Flowers IPA H

◖◗ ◖◗ ▐ ▐▬ ▬ ▬ ❀ ♿

No meals Mondays. Disco music.

East Donyland E2

12-3 (Sat/Sun only); 8 (7.30 Fri/Sun, 7 Sat, not Mon)-11 (10.30 Sun)

Walnut Tree
Fingringhoe Road (1 mile East of B1025)
OS: TM021216
Tel: (01206) 728149
Crouch Vale Woodham IPA; **Fullers** London Pride; **Guest Beers** H

◖◗ ◖◗ ❀

Friendly, basic pub, with a good choice of guest beers from Independent Breweries. Cheeses from around the world on Friday nights. Great burgers, with a choice of more than 10 toppings!.
Pool table and Vinyl 'Rock' jukebox. In the garden is an aviary, chickens and 'Nutty' the one-horned goat!

East Hanningfield C4

11-3; 6-11 (12-10.30 Sun)

Three Horseshoes
The Tye
Tel: (01245) 400204
Morlands Old Speckled Hen; **Ruddles** Best Bitter; John Smiths Bitter, Websters Yorkshire Bitter H

◖◗ ◖◗ ▬ ❀

Pleasantly-situated in village conservation area.

11-11 (12-10.30 Sun)

Windmill Tavern
The Tye, Main Road
OS: TL771012
Tel: (01245) 400315
Crouch Vale Best Bitter; **Marstons** Pedigree; **Whitbread** Boddingtons Bitter; **Guest Beers** H

◖◗ ◖◗ ▐ ▐▬ ▬ ❀

Comfortable and popular free-house, opposite the village green, with regularly changing guest beers. Traditional, home-made British food, discounts for the over 55s, on Wednesday and Thursday lunchtimes.
Restaurant open Thursday to Saturday evenings and Sunday lunchtime. No food Monday evenings.

48

"The House Without a Name", Easthorpe

East Horndon   B4

The former Deer park of Thorndon Hall, owned by the Petre family since the times of Henry VIII, now forms the North and South sections of Thorndon Country Park.

11-11 (12-10.30 Sun)

Halfway House
Southend Arterial Road (by A127 Eastbound, at A128 interchange)
Tel: (01277) 811235
Ruddles Best Bitter; **S&N** Courage Directors; **Tetley** Bitter; **Guest Beer H**
⓪ Ɗ ◖ ▮ Ꭱ ⌸ ▙ ⌵ ֍
Refurbished, split-level roadhouse with conservatory and children's bar. Emphasis on food. Marquee available for meetings and functions. Various car clubs meet here, including Escorts and Humbers.

East Mersea   E3

12-3; 6-11 (12-3; 7-10.30 Sun) All day in summer.

Dog & Pheasant
East Mersea Road
OS: TM055146
Tel: (01206) 383206
Greene King IPA; **Guest Beer** (Summer) **H**
⓪ Ɗ ◖ ▮ ⌸ ▙ ⌵ ֍
Large, fairly remote, well-kept garden.

East Tilbury Village   C5

11-11 (12-10.30 Sun)

Ship
Princess Margaret Road
OS: TQ686771
Tel: (01375) 843041
Ind Coope Ansells Mild; **Ridleys** IPA; **S&N** Courage Directors **H**
⓪ Ɗ ◖ ▮ ⌸ ֍
The traditional and interesting saloon includes a collection of poes! The noisier and usually busier public bar sits opposite the pub garden. Older children welcome in the saloon.

Easthorpe   D2

Near Marks Tey point to point racecourse. Easthorpe village is attractive. Domesday church.

11-3; 6-11 (11-11 Sat: 12-10.30 Sun)

House Without a Name
Easthorpe Road (1½ miles off A12)
Tel: (01206) 213070
Greene King IPA; **Guest Beers H**
⓪ Ɗ ◖ ▮ Ꭱ ▙ ֍
Large, 16th century village pub, popular with the local community. Three guest beers.

Eastwood   D5

11-11 (12-10.30 Sun)

Bell House
321 Rayleigh Road (A1015)
Tel: (01702) 524271
Bass Hancocks HB, Draught Bass; **Ruddles** County **H**
⓪ Ɗ ◖ ▮ Ꭱ ֍
Old rectory converted to a pub, with a Harvester restaurant upstairs.

11-11 (12-10.30 Sun)

Brookside Tavern
357 Rayleigh Road (A1015)
Tel: (01702) 525195
Greene King IPA; **Morlands** Old Speckled Hen; **Whitbread** Boddingtons Bitter **H**
⓪ Ɗ ֍ ⌶
Compact, locals pub with darts and football teams. Summer barbecues, and live music on Thursday evenings. Occasional 'Cask Collection' beers.

11-11 (12-10.30 Sun)

Loyal Toast
Western Approaches (near Southend Airport)
Tel: (01702) 529822
S&N John Smiths Bitter **H**
⓪ Ɗ ◖ ▮ ⌶
Quiet, friendly estate local, dating back to the 'other' royal wedding in 1981. Good atmosphere and food. Handy for the 'Safeways' supermarket.

11-11 (12-10.30 Sun)

Oakwood
Rayleigh Road (A1015)
Tel: (01702) 525857
Bass Worthington BB **H**
⓪ Ɗ ◖ ▮
Extensive pool emporium at rear, plus separate lounge bar. Real Ale not always available.

11-11 (12-10.30 Sun)

Silver Jubilee Inn
629 Rayleigh Road (A1015)
Tel: (01702) 522357
Marstons Pedigree; **Morlands**
Old Speckled Hen; **Wadworths**
6X; **Whitbread** Boddingtons
Bitter, Flowers Original **H**
⟨D ⟨D **R** ♋ 👤 &
Family-oriented 'Beefeater',
much-changed since its opening
in 1977 as a free-house. Large
beer garden with kiddies'
amusements (swings, slides
etc.), ideal for families.
Tuesday night quizzes. All beers
on 'sparklers' - ask for them to
be removed when ordering.

11-11 (12-10.30 Sun)

Woodcutters Arms
307 Eastwood Road North (nr
A127)
Tel: (01702) 420643
Inntrepreneur - No Real Ale.
Formerly the "Eastwood
Lodge".

Edney Common
(Highwood)   B3

12-11 (10.30 Sun)

Green Man
Edney Common, Highwood
Road (nr A414)
OS: TL649044
Tel: (01245) 248076
Greene King IPA; **Morlands**
Old Speckled Hen; **Guest
Beers H**
⟨D ⟨D ⟐ ⊞ ⊫ ✿
Old building in 16 acre grounds,
with duck pond. Ever-changing
range of guest beers. Pool table
in the public bar area. Juke box.

Eight Ash
Green   D2

12-2; 5-11 (12-11 Sat: 12-3; 7-
10.30 Sun)

Brick & Tile
Halstead Road (A1124, was
A604)
Tel: (01206) 540468
Ind Coope Friary Meux BB;
Tetley Imperial; **St Austell**
Dartmoor BB **H**
✿
Popular, one-bar pub with pool,
darts and Sky TV. Three pigs in
the garden! Barbecues in
summer (pig roasts). Karaoke.

11-11 (12-10.30 Sun)

Traders Bar (Forte
Posthouse)
Abbots Lane, Halstead Road
(Near A1124, was A604)
Tel: (01206) 767740
S&N Courage Best, Directors **H**
⟨D ⟨D **R** ⊨ ✿ &
Built in 1993, with comfortable
log-cabin effect bar.

Elm Park
(Hornchurch)   B5

11-11 (12-10.30 Sun)

New Elm Park
Broadway Parade, Elm Park
Avenue
Tel: (01708) 444015
Youngs Bitter **H**
⊞ ✿ ✿
Two-bar pub with spacious
saloon and small public bar.
Real Ale not always available.
New fish and chip shop in pub.

Elmdon   A1

11-3; 7-11 (11-11 Sat: 12-10.30
Sun)

Kings Head
Heydon Lane
OS: TL461396
Tel: (01763) 838358
Adnams Bitter; **Greene King**
IPA; **S&N** John Smiths Bitter;
Whitbread Flowers Original **H**
⟨D ⟨D **R** ⊨ ⊨ ✿
Comfortable village pub in fine
setting.

Elmstead
Market   E2

11-11 (12-10.30 Sun)

Bowling Green
Clacton Road (A133)
Tel: (01206) 822598
Free-house - No Real Ale.

11-11 (12-10.30 Sun)

Kings Arms
Clacton Road (A133)
Tel: (01206) 822579
Greene King IPA; **Ridleys** IPA **H**
⟨D ⟨D **R** ⊫ ✿
Large beer garden with chil-
dren's facilities. The interior
decor gives the pub a 1930s
'feel'.

Elsenham   B2

Home of an up-market jam
factory and also once of Alsa the
Viking.

11-2.30; 6-11 (12-3; 7-10.30 Sun)

Crown
High Street (B1051)
Tel: (01279) 812827
Shepherd Neame Spitfire;
Guest Beers H
⟨D ⟨D ⊞ ✿
Deservedly popular, timbered
village pub, with fine pargetted
exterior, an inglenook fireplace
and a good atmosphere. Usually
two varying guest beers. Good
reputation for food.

Epping   A4

A market town which has had
much of its character removed
in the interests of 'progress'.

11-11 (12-10.30 Sun)

Black Lion
293 High Street
Tel: (01992) 578670
Ind Coope 'House' Bitter;
Tetley Bitter **H**
⟨D ⟨ **R** ⊞
16th century coaching inn with
two bars. Limited parking.

11-11 (12-10.30 Sun)

Duke of Wellington
36 High Street (B1393)
Tel: (01992) 572388
Ind Coope ABC Bitter;
Whitbread Boddingtons Bitter,
Castle Eden Ale, Flowers IPA;
Tetley Bitter **H**
⟨D ⟨D **R** ✿ & ⊖
Large garden. Pub features
beers from the Whitbread 'Cask
Collection'.

11 (10 Mon)-3; 7-11 (11-11
Fri/Sat: 12-6 only Sun)

Entertainer
Cuttis Lane, High Street (by
B1393)
Tel: (01992) 560444
S&N Courage Directors; **Tetley**
Bitter **H**
⟨D ⟨D **R** ⊨ ⊖
New bar that opened in
November 1994, next to the old
"Illusions" / "La Taverna" night-
club. Live music
Mon/Wed/Fri/Sat evenings. Pool,
chess, monopoly and crib
played.

12-11 (12 Fri/Sat, 10.30 Sun)

Forest & Firkin
208 High Street (B1393)
Tel: (01992) 573671
Firkin Turpins Tipple, Forest
Ale, Dogbolter **H**
⟨D ⟨D ✿ & ⊖
Long-fronted, busy town centre
local that is over 400 years old.
Converted to a non-brewing
'Firkin' in December 1996, with
large screen TV and live music
every Friday and Saturday.
Formerly the "George &
Dragon".

10-3; 5.30-11 (12-3; 7-10.30 Sun)

Forest Gate Inn
111 Bell Common / Theydon
Road (nr B1393)
OS: TL451011
Tel: (01992) 572312
Adnams Bitter **H**, Broadside;
Greene King Abbot Ale **G**;
Ridleys IPA **H**; **Guest Beers G**
Guest Cider G
⟨D ⟨ ✿
A boozer for the discerning
drinker, dating from the 17th
century, on the edge of Epping
Forest and close to M25 motor-
way.

"The Forest Gate Inn", Epping

11-11 (12-10.30 Sun)
Globe
18 Lindsey Street
Tel: (01992) 573220
Bass Draught Bass, Hancocks
HB; **Ind Coope** Friary Meux BB;
Tetley Bitter **H**
◖ ◗ ◖ ◗ ✿
A "Globe" public house has
existed here since medieval
times, when Epping had 22
pubs! The present house was
built in the 1920s, and recently
refurbished. A locals pub.
Beware 'tight sparklers'!

11-11 (12-10.30 Sun)
Half Moon
26 High Street (B1393)
Tel: (01992) 577063
Marstons Pedigree **H**
◖ ◗ ◖ ◗ ⊞ 🛏 ⊖
Refurbished, popular 300-year-
old pub. Home-made food available all day. Parking difficult.

11-11 (12-10.30 Sun)
Thatched House
High Street (B1393)
Tel: (01992) 578353
Morlands Old Speckled Hen;
S&N John Smiths Bitter;
Wadworths 6X **H**
◖ ◗ ◖ ◗ **R** 🛏 ⊢ ✿
Free-house Hotel / Restaurant,
smart dress required.

11-11 (12-10.30 Sun)
Traders (Forte Post House)
High Road (B1393)
Tel: (01992) 573137
S&N John Smiths Bitter **H**
◖ ◗ ◖ ◗ **R** 🛏 ⊢ ✿ ♿
Large hotel on edge of Epping
Forest. Formerly the "Bell Inn".

Epping Forest   A4

12-11 (10.30 Sun)
Old Orleans
High Road / Woodredon Hill
(A121/B1393 roundabout)
Tel: (01992) 812618
S&N - No Real Ale. Rebuilt
alongside the original "Wake
Arms", and formerly the "City
Limits".

Epping Green   A3
*Attractive village, providing base
for local walks.*

11-3; 5-11 (12-10.30 Sun)
Cock & Magpie
Epping Upland (B181)
Tel: (01992) 561649
Greene King IPA; **S&N** Trumans
IPA **H**
◖ ◗ ◖ ◗ **R** ⊞ 🛏
Food-oriented, posey and cater-
ing mainly for the younger set.

11-3; 5-11 (12-10.30 Sun)
Travellers Friend
(B181)
Tel: (01992) 572462
Bass Draught Bass; **McMullens**
Original AK, Country, Gladstone
H
◖ ◗ ◖ ◗ **R** ✿ ♿
Restored and rejuvenated by
McMullens, it must be the bric-a-
brac pub of Essex. Over 21s and
smart dress only.

Feering   D2
*Attractive village divided by the
main railway line.*

11-3; 6-11 (12-3; 7-10.30 Sun)
Bell Inn
The Street (½ mile off B1024)
OS: TL872203
Tel: (01376) 570375
Greene King IPA, Abbot Ale **H**
◖ ◗ ◖ ◗ **R** ✿
Tastefully refurbished and
extended 14th century rural
Grays Inn. Restaurant closed
Sun and Mon evenings.

11-3; 5.30-11 (11-11 Sat: 12-3;
7-10.30 Sun)
Old Anchor
132 Feering Hill (B1024)
Tel: (01376) 570634
Greene King IPA **H**
◖ ◗ ◖ ◗ **R** ⊞ 🛏 ⊢ ✿ ♿
Pleasant old pub. Popular with
younger drinkers and families.

11-3; 6-11 (12-3; 6-10.30 Sun)
Sun Inn
3 Feering Hill (B1024)
Tel: (01376) 570442
Guest Beers H
Addlestones Cider H
◖ ◗ ◖ ◗ **R** ⊢ ✿ ⇌
Plush and friendly, heavily-
beamed pub with log fires, a
large attractive garden and
patio. Good value home-made
food. Petanque Wednesday
evenings.
Varying selection of five or more
guest beers, and regular beer
festivals at the Spring and
August Bank holidays. Phone for
camping details.

Felsted C2

Sleepy village with public school.

12-11 (closes 2.30-6 Mon-Thu in Winter: 12-10.30 Sun)

Chequers
Braintree Road (B1417)
Tel: (01371) 820226
Ridleys IPA **H**
🌑🇩🌑🅁🔒📮⛟🐾⛽♿
Friendly, Victorian, village local near Felsted school. Long-serving landlady. Summer barbecues.

11-3; 7-11 (11-11 Sat: 12-10.30 Sun)

Swan Hotel
Chelmsford Road / Station Road (B1417)
Tel: (01371) 820245
Ridleys IPA, ESX **H**
🌑🇩🌑🔒📮🐾⛽♿
Large, comfortable hotel in centre of village.

Yew Tree
Chelmsford Road, Causeway End (B1417)
OS: TL682196
Ridleys - Pub closed.

Fiddlers Hamlet (Epping) A4

11-2.30; 5.30 (6 Sat)-11 (12-3; 7-10.30 Sun)

Merry Fiddlers
4 Fiddlers Hamlet (1 mile off B1393)
OS: TL473010
Tel: (01992) 572142
Adnams Bitter; **Morlands** Old Speckled Hen; **Tetley** Bitter **H**
🌑🇩🌑🅁⛟🐾
17th century pub, with area of bar reserved for diners and children. Large garden with play area. Beer range may vary.

Finchingfield C2

Delightful, 'chocolate-box' village with pond, green, windmill, almshouses and hump-back bridge. Overrun with tourists in the summer season.

Finch Inn
Church Hill (B1053)
Free-house - Pub closed. Formerly the "Green Man".

11-11 (12-10.30 Sun)

Fox
The Green (B1053/B1057)
Tel: (01371) 810151
Batemans XB G; **S&N** Courage Directors, John Smiths Bitter, Websters Yorkshire Bitter **H**
🌑🇩🌑🅁
Popular pub in picturesque setting, facing the duck pond. Very busy in the Summer season.

11.30-3; 5.30-11 (11.30-11 Fri/Sat: 12-10.30 Sun)

Red Lion
6 Church Hill (B1053)
Tel: (01371) 810400
Ridleys IPA, Rumpus, seasonal beer **H**
🌑🇩🌑🅁⛟🐾
500 year old traditional pub opposite the guildhall and the church. Pool and bar billiards played. Friendly atmosphere.

12-2.30; 6 (5 Fri)-11 (12-4; 7-11 Sat: 12-3; 7-10.30 Sun)

Three Tuns
Wethersfield Road (B1053)
Tel: (01371) 810165
Greene King IPA, Abbot Ale **H**
🐾🍺
A basic, quiet pub for the locals, in a village that can be swamped by tourists. A piano and good community atmosphere. Dogs allowed. Looks fairly uninspiring from outside, but is clean and friendly inside.

Fingringhoe E3

11-3; 6-11 (12-3; 7-10.30 Sun)

Whalebone Inn
Tel: (01206) 729307
Guest Beers H
🌑🇩🌑🐾🐾
Very friendly rural pub in picturesque surroundings. Extensive menu.

Fobbing C5

Associated with 14th century peasants revolt.

(See Basildon map for the location of the pubs).

11-11 (12-10.30 Sun)

Haywain F1
High Road (nr B1420 / A13)
Tel: (01268) 554500
Fullers London Pride; **Wadworths** 6X **H**
🌑🇩🌑🅁⛟🐾🐾⛽♿
A standard 'Beefeater', built in 1996, with bare bricks and beams, and 'Travel Inn' attached. Disappointingly small selection of Real Ales - seems to be more interested in 'Nitrokeg'!

"The Sun", Feering

12-3; 5.30-11 (12-11 Fri/Sat: 12-4;
7.30-10.30 Sun Winter: 12-10.30
Sun Summer)

White Lion **F2**
Lion Hill (nr B1420)
Tel: (01375) 673281
Greene King IPA; **Marstons**
Pedigree; **Morlands** Old
Speckled Hen **H**
⏸ ◀ ⏸ ⊕ ❀ ⛻
300 year old, timber-framed,
two-bar pub with rambling out-
buildings - a true village pub,
near the top of Lion Hill. Not far
from Basildon - but far enough!

Ford End C3

*A village that has sadly lost both
of its pubs since the last edition
of this guide.*

Spread Eagle
Church Lane (A130)
Free-house - Pub closed and
converted to residential use.

Swan
Main Road (A130)
Ridleys - Pub closed in 1991.

Fordham D2

11-11 (12-3; 7-10.30 Sun)

Three Horseshoes
72 Church Road
OS: TL928282
Tel: (01206) 240195
Greene King IPA; **S&N** Websters
Yorkshire Bitter **H**
⏸ D ◀ ⏸ R ⊕ ❀
Comfortable village local, with
exposed beams and a large real
fire. Popular with the locals.

11-3 (Not Tue); 5-11 (12-3; 7-
10.30 Sun)

Vulcan Inn
10 Moat Road
Tel: (01206) 240446
Greene King IPA; **Guest Beer** **H**
⏸ D ◀ ⏸ ⛻ ❀ ♿
Popular village local with a good
following - something for every-
one.
Stop press - reported to be
closed early Summer 1998.

Fordham Heath D2

12-3; 6-11 (12-3; 6.30-10.30 Sun)

Cricketers
Spring Lane (nr A1124, was
A604)
Tel: (01206) 240666
Greene King IPA, Abbot Ale **H**
⏸ D ◀ ⏸ R ❀ ♿
Large, open-plan Greene King
eating house, where children are
welcome. Formerly the "Star".

Fordstreet (Aldham) D2

12-3; 5-11 (12-3; 7-10.30 Sun)

Coopers Arms
Ford Street (A1124, was A604)
Tel: (01206) 241177
Greene King IPA, **Woodfordes**
Wherry; **Guest Beers** **H**
⏸ D ◀ ⏸ ❀
Friendly and comfortable pub in
a nice village setting. Good col-
lection of porcelain spirit bottles.
The landlord runs a fishing club
and golf society.

12-2.30; 6-11 (12-3; 7-10.30 Sun)

Old Queen's Head
Ford Street (A1124, was A604)
Tel: (01206) 241584
Greene King IPA; **Ruddles** Best
Bitter or **S&N** Courage
Directors **H**
⏸ D ◀ ⏸ R ⊕ ❀
Large and popular village inn,
that has been extensively refur-
bished. Large garden. Narrow
car park entrance.

Fordstreet (Fordham) D2

12-2.30; 6.30-11 (12-3; 7-10.30
Sun)

Shoulder of Mutton
Halstead Road (A1124, was
A604)
Tel: (01206) 795997
Whitbread Flowers IPA,
Flowers Original **H**
⏸ D ◀ ⏸ ⊕ ❀
Attractive, weather-boarded, 500
year old, riverside pub on route
of the Essex Way. Low ceilings
and beams everywhere.
Allegedly haunted, this pub cap-
tures a piece of olde England.

Foster Street A3

*A good walking and cycling area
close to Harlow.*

11-2.30 (3 Sat); 5.30-11 (12-3; 7-
10.30 Sun)

Horns & Horseshoes
Foster Street, Harlow Common
OS: TL486088
Tel: (01279) 422667
Morlands Old Speckled Hen;
S&N Courage Best Bitter,
Directors, Trumans IPA **H**
⏸ ◀ ❀
Attractive pub on Harlow border,
with an abundance of brass and
rural artefacts. Beer range may
vary. Courtesy bus service at
weekends.

Foulness Island (Churchend) E4

*'Closed' Ministry of Defence
Island in the Thames estuary.
Access is restricted to residents,
their friends and relatives, and
other authorised persons.*

11-2.30; 7-11 (12-2.45; 7-10.30
Sun)

George & Dragon
Churchend
OS: TR024937
Tel: (01702) 219460
Greene King IPA **H**
⏸ D ◀ ⏸ R ⊕ ⌂ ⊢ ⛻ ❀
The pub retains its rustic charm,
unchanged by the march of time,
due to its forced isolation, and is
set-back from the 'main' road,
by 'St Mary the Virgin' church.
An interesting museum of the
island has been established in
an adjacent building, showing
maps and photographs of the
local flora and fauna, and the
late, lamented, Kings Head pub,
which has been partly
demolished.
To visit the pub, it is necessary
to contact the licensee first to
make arrangements. Please note
that there are restrictions on
what may be brought onto the
island. Real Ale NOT always
available.

Fox Street (Ardleigh) E2

11.30-2.30; 5.30-11 (12-3; 7-10.30
Sun)

Welshwood Inn
Fox Street (A137)
Tel: (01206) 864011
Adnams Extra; **Greene King** IPA;
Shepherd Neame Spitfire;
Whitbread Boddingtons Bitter;
Guest Beer **H**
⏸ D ◀ ⏸ R ⊢ ❀
Large pub with cosy decor.

Frating E2

11-3; 6-11 (11-11 Sat: 12-10.30
Sun)

Kings Arms
Clacton Road (A133/B1029)
OS: TM090233
Tel: (01206) 250277
Greene King IPA, Abbot Ale **H**
⏸ D ◀ ⏸ R ⊢ ⛻ ❀
Daniels Brewery-etched win-
dows in front. Bright, mellow,
plush and food-oriented with a
relaxed atmosphere.

Tooto's
Clacton Road
Free-house / Night-club
- Closed and demolished to
make way for new housing
estate. Formerly the "Tartan
House".

Frinton-on-Sea F3

*Not a town for the lads' night
out. A sleepy seaside resort, the
haunt of gentlefolk.*

*No pubs within 'the Gates', but
'JD Wetherspoons' were
attempting to change this by
converting the former 'Blowers'
store.*

11-2.30; 6.30-11 (12-10.30 Sun)

Essex Skipper
Rochford Way (nr B1034)
OS: TM239211
Tel: (01255) 673574
Greene King IPA, Abbot Ale **H**
◖ (Not Mon) ◖ (Sun only)
🍴 ❀ ⇌
Robust, modern building, near
Triangle shopping centre.
Unusually its public bar has beer
a 'tad' cheaper than the lounge!
Sunday lunches are bookable.
Recently converted to a 'Hungry
Horse'.

Fryerning B4

11.30-3; 6-11 (12-3; 6-10.30 Sun)

Woolpack
Mill Green Road, Blackmore
Road
OS: TL640002
Tel: (01277) 352189
Adnams Bitter, Broadside;
Guest Beer H
◖ ◗ ◖ ◗ **R** ❀
Food-oriented free-house, with
fortnightly-changing guest
beers. Formerly the
"Huntsman".

Fuller Street (Fairstead) C3

Collection of cottages on 'Essex Way' footpath.

11.30-3.30; 6-11 (11 (11.30
Winter)-11 Sat: 12-4; 7-10.30
Sun)

Square & Compasses
Fuller Street (1½ miles East of
A131)
OS: TL748161
Tel: (01245) 361477
Ridleys IPA **G**
◖ ◗ ◖ ◗ ❀
Small, cosy, country pub with
three rooms. Interesting choice
of home-prepared food. Unusual
pitch-penny stool in old public
bar area.

Fyfield B3

Pretty village in Roding Valley.

11-2.30 (3 Sat); 6-11 (12-3; 7-
10.30 Sun)

Black Bull
Dunmow Road (B184)
Tel: (01277) 899225
S&N Courage Directors,
Trumans IPA; **Wadworths** 6X **H**
◖ ◗ ◖ ◗ ❀
Built between 1370 and 1420,
this food-oriented pub offers a
fish menu on Thu and Fri.

11-3; 6-11 (11-11 Sat: 12-3; 7-
10.30 Sun)

Queens Head
Queen Street (off B184)
Tel: (01277) 899231
Adnams Bitter; **Mansfield**
Bitter; **Smiles** Best Bitter;
Guest Beers H
◖ ◗ ◖ ◗ ❀ ♿
Welcoming, 500-year old, fami-
ly-run village local, with spa-
cious alcoves in the long bar.
Three constantly-changing guest
beers make this a local CAMRA
favourite. Essex 'Huffers'. Fish
night on Thursdays. No food
Saturday evenings.

Galleywood C3

Site of former race course that encircles the church.

11-11 (12-10.30 Sun)

Eagle
Stock Road (B1007)
OS: TL705027
Tel: (01245) 356175
Ridleys IPA, Rumpus **H**
◖ ◖ ❀
Popular, modernised, comfort-
able, single-bar pub, with a
seafood stall in the car park.

11.30-3; 6-11 (11-11 Sat: 12-3; 7-
10.30 Sun)

Horse & Groom
Horse & Groom Lane,
Galleywood Common (nr B1007,
approach via Goat Hall Lane)
OS: TL701030
Tel: (01245) 261653
Greene King XX Mild, IPA,
Abbot Ale; **Guest Beers H**
◖ ◗ ◖ ◗ 🍴 ☙ ❀
On the edge of the common, a
well-worth finding, two-bar
Grays pub. No meals on
Sundays.

11.30-11 (12-10.30 Sun)

Running Mare
Stock Road (B1007)
OS: TL703034
Tel: (01245) 261663
Tetley Bitter; Youngs
Special; **Guest Beers H**
◖ ◗ ◖ ◗ ❀ ♿
Sunday night discos and
occasional fun days, with banger
racing and bungee jumping.

11-11 (12-10.30 Sun)

Seabright's Barn
Galleywood Road (nr B1009)
OS: TL718038
Tel: (01245) 478033
Ind Coope Greenalls Original;
Tetley Bitter **H**
◖ ◗ ◖ ◗ ☙ ❀ ♿
Converted, historic barn with
emphasis on food and families.
Comfortable and popular - a
Greenalls "Miller's Kitchen".

11-3; 6-11 (11-11 Fri/Sat: 12-10.30
Sun)

White Bear
Watchouse Road / Well Lane (nr
B1007)
OS: TL708032
Tel: (01245) 353034
Greene King IPA; **Guest Beers H**
◖ ◗ ◖ ◗ ❀
Popular village pub, with plans
for a new restaurant.

Gants Hill A4

11-11 (12-10.30 Sun)

Beehive
Beehive Lane (B192, nr A12)
Tel: (0181) 550 3361
Fullers London Pride **H**
◖ ◗ ◖ ◗ **R** ┣ ❀ ♿ ⊖
Large 'Harvester' restaurant with
separate bar and varied menu.
Detached 'Travelodge', popular
with businessmen. Beers may
vary. Formerly "Sullivans".

11-11 (12-2 or 3; 7-10.30 Sun)

Hypa Hypa
19 Sevenways Parade,
Woodford Avenue (A1400/A12)
Tel: (0181) 252 6200
Free-house - No Real Ale.
Formerly "Champs Bar".

12-11 (7-11 Sat: 12-6 Sun)

Hobnobs
545 Cranbrook Road (A123)
Tel: (0181) 554 6454
Free-house - No Real Ale.
Formerly "AJ's", "Winners Bar"
and "Harts".

11-11 (12-10.30 Sun)

King George V
645 Cranbrook Road (A123, Nr
A12)
Tel: (0181) 550 5642
S&N Courage Best Bitter **H**
◖ ◗ ◖ 🍴 ♿ ⊖
Friendly, comfortable and
pleasant roadside pub, catering
for mainly local trade.
11-11 (12-10.30 Sun)

Ye Olde Valentine
27-37 Perth Road (Gants Hill
Roundabout, by A12)
Tel: (0181) 554 6005
S&N - No Real Ale. Formerly the
"Valentine".

Gestingthorpe D1

12-3; 6 (7 Sun)-11 (10.30 Sun)

Pheasant
Audley End
OS: TL813376
Tel: (01787) 461196
Adnams Bitter; **Bass** Draught
Bass; **Greene King** IPA;
Guest beers H
◖ ◗ ◖ ◗ **R** 🍴 ┣ ❀
Multi-roomed, traditional village
local. Good food, booking advis-
able weekends, no food Sunday
evenings. Regular guest beers
include mild.

Gidea Park B4

Early 20th century development with attractive parks.

11-2.30; 5-11 (11-11 Sat: 12-3; 7-10.30 Sun)
Archers
194 Main Road (A118)
Tel: (01708) 427770
Greene King IPA, Abbot Ale **H**
Loud pub catering for young-sters, with separate pool room and meeting room upstairs. Not really for the discerning drinker. Not food Sunday evenings. Previously a Charrington 'Tapas' bar.

11-11 (12-10.30 Sun)
Drill
Brentwood Road, Heath Park
Tel: (01708) 477478
Ind Coope 'House' Bitter; **Tetley** Bitter; **Youngs** Bitter **H**
Large pub by roundabout, con-verted to a 'Mr Qs', with strong pool and games theme. Quiz nights and barbecues. Parking difficult.

11-11 (12-10.30 Sun)
New Inn
Squirrels Heath Lane (nr A118)
Tel: (01708) 458750
Ind Coope 'House' Bitter; **Tetley** Bitter **H**
Friendly, fairly unspoilt, locals pub, with centrally located bar. Still retaining many original features, including stained-glass windows. Quizzes and darts.

12-2 (3 Sun); 6-11 (10.30 Sun)
Plough
Colchester Road, Gallows Corner (A12/A127)
Tel: (01708) 342043
Free-house - No Real Ale.

Ship Inn
93 Main Road (A118)
Tel: (01708) 741571
S&N Courage Directors, Theakstons BB, XB, Websters Yorkshire Bitter **H**
Pleasant pub, nearly 500 years old, with low-ceilinged bars, tim-ber beams and a comfy atmos-phere. Full of character, and possibly was a brewery in the eighteenth century. Limited parking.

11-11 (12-10.30 Sun)
Squirrels
420 Brentwood Road / Squirrels Heath Lane
Tel: (01708) 441801
S&N John Smiths Bitter **H**
Noisy, one-bar youngsters' pub, with plenty of games machines. Live DJs Thursday to Sunday. Formerly "Cardinals".

11-11 (12-10.30 Sun)
Unicorn
91 Main Road (A118)
Tel: (01708) 740131
Marstons Pedigree; **Tetley** Bitter **H**
Food-oriented pub.

Goldhanger D3

11-2.30; 6.30-11 (12-3; 7-10.30 Sun)
Chequers
The Square (nr B1026)
Tel: (01621) 788203
Ind Coope Ansells Bitter, Friary Meux BB, Burton Ale **H**
15th century labyrinth, with four bars. Popular and characterful - children welcome.

11-3; 6-11 (12-10.30 Sun)
Cricketers
33 Church Street (B1026)
Tel: (01621) 788250
Greene King IPA; **Nethergate** IPA **H**
Country free-house, where games such as 'Devil amongst the tailors' and Shove Ha'penny are played.

Good Easter B3

Pleasant village with fine church

Fountain
Main Road (A1060)
OS: TL618110
Ridleys - Pub closed, a sadly-missed Victorian country pub - now a private house.

11-2.30; 6-11 (12-3; 7-10.30 Sun)
Star
The Endway (off A1060)
Tel: (01245) 231337
Ridleys IPA **H**
Village pub, on the 'Essex Way' long distance footpath.

Goodmayes A5

11-11 (12-10.30 Sun)
Bridge House
62/64 Goodmayes Road (B177) / Ashgrove Road
Tel: (0181) 590 4600
Greene King IPA, Abbot Ale **H**
A former restaurant that opened as a pub in 1995. Friendly atmosphere. Various functions including regular DJs. Additional drinking area planned.

11-11 (12-10.30 Sun)
Lord Napier
521 Green Lane (A1083)
Tel: (0181) 597 5953
Tetley Bitter **H**
Situated around a curved bar, with large saloon - mind the steps! and public bar. Live music and regular DJs. Snacks available until early evening. Bar billiards in saloon.

11-11 (12-10.30 Sun)
White Hart
629 Green Lane (A1083)
Tel:
Bass - No Real Ale.

Gosfield C2

Gosfield Hall Lake is used for Aqua Sports.

11-3; 6.30-11 (12-3; 7-10.30 Sun)
Green Man
The Street (A1017)
Tel: (01787) 472746
Greene King IPA, Abbot Ale **H**
Quiet, 'restaurantified' pub, with parts dating back to the 15th century. Attractive garden. Beer cheaper in the public bar. Regularly wins awards for food. No food Sunday evenings.

11-3; 6-11 (11-11 Sat: 12-4; 7-10.30 Sun)
King's Head
The Street (A1017)
Tel: (01787) 474016
Whitbread Flowers IPA, **Guest Beer** (Whitbread) **H**
Comfortable, large 15th century pub with conservatory restau-rant that seats 60. Friday nights are food feasts and speciality event nights. No food Monday evenings.
Can be very busy at weekends. Pool team and two football teams.

Grays B5

Rejuvenated industrial riverside town. The fine 'art-deco' State Theatre, although no longer used as a cinema, still houses the Compton cinema organ, and concerts are held.

The Grays Athletic Football Club (in Bridge Road) has a good range of varying guest beers. Admission is available to card-carrying CAMRA members or on production of a copy of CAMRA's 'Good Beer Guide'.

"The Wharf", Grays

11-3; 5.30-11 (11-11 Fri/Sat: 12-4;
7-10.30 Sun)

Bricklayers Arms
48 Bridge Road (nr A126)
Tel: (01375) 372265
Bass Draught Bass; **Fullers**
London Pride **H**
◐ Ɗ ◐ ◖ ⊞ ┗ ✿
Friendly, traditional, street-corner local with two bars and
conservatory. Regular Saturday
night entertainment. Occasional
quiz nights.

11-11 (12-3; 7-10.30 Sun)

Courtyard Inn
Clarence Road
Tel: (01375) 391491
Free-house - No Real Ale.

11-11 (12-10.30 Sun)

JD's
36 Orsett Road (A126)
Tel: (01375) 383887
S&N Courage Directors Bitter **H**
◐ ◖ ┗ ⇌
Free-house. Formerly "Chester's
Wine Bar". Parking difficult.

11-11 (12-10.30 Sun)

Pullman Tavern
61 High Street
Tel: (01375) 375730
Bass - No Real Ale. Formerly the
"Railway".

10.30-11 (12-10.30 Sun)

Rising Sun
High Street
Tel:
Bass - No Real Ale, handpumps
disused.

10.30-3 (4 Sat); 5.30-11 (11-11 Fri,
12-10.30 Sun)

Theobald Arms
Kings Walk (nr A126)
Tel: (01375) 372253
S&N Courage Best Bitter;
Guest Beers H
◐ Ɗ ◐ ◖ ⊞ ✿ ⇌
Fine traditional local, with two
guest beers, often from the
Courage and Crouch Vale port-
folios. Unusual, revolving pool
table in the public bar.

11-3 (4 Sat); 6 (7 Sat)-11 (12-3; 7-
10.30 Sun)

Wharf
Wharf Road (nr A126)
Tel: (01375) 372418
Hardys Best Bitter; **Ind Coope**
Burton Ale; **Tetley** Bitter;
Guest Beers H
◐ ◖ ⊞ ✿
Refurbished, listed, old riverside
pub below river wall, in new
housing development.
Regularly-changing guest beers.

11-3; 6-11 (12-3; 7-10.30 Sun)

White Hart
Kings Walk (nr A126)
Tel: (01375) 373319
Tetley Bitter **H**
◐ ◖ ⊞ ⇦ ┗ ✿ ⇌
Local in rundown part of town,
close to major new house-build-
ing project.

Great Baddow C3

*The former Baddow Brewery is
now a furniture showroom.*

*(See Chelmsford map for loca-
tion of pubs)*

10.30-3; 6-11 (10.30-11 Fri/Sat:
12-10.30 Sun)

Beehive **GB1**
Baddow Road (B1009)
Tel: (01245) 353022
Ridleys Mild, IPA, ESX **H**
◐ Ɗ ◖ ┗ ✿
The two bars became one
during refurbishment. Live
music, once a month,
background music from the
radio. Barbecues.

11-11 (12-10.30 Sun)

Blue Lion **GB2**
Tabors Hill (nr A414)
Tel: (01245) 471657
Adnams Bitter; **Guest Beers H**
◐ ◖ ⊞ ⇓ ✿
Friendly pub with varied clien-
tele. Guest beer from the
'Tapsters Choice' range. Bands
on one Saturday a month, 'Jam'
night on Thursdays.

11.30-11 (12-10.30 Sun)

Carpenters Arms **GB3**
Baddow Road (B1009)
OS: TL720056
Tel: (01245) 491188
Guest Beer H
◐ ⊟
Young persons pub, with pool,
darts and large-screen, satellite
TV.

11-11 (12-10.30 Sun)

Kings Head **GB4**
49 Maldon Road (nr A414)
OS: TL730052
Tel: (01245) 471980
Bass Worthington BB;
Greene King IPA;
Guest Beers H
◐ Ɗ ◐ ◖ ✿
Large, plush, one-bar pub with
pleasant garden, which has barn
owls. Occasional, mini beer fes-
tivals. Meals finish at 7pm on
Sundays.

56

11-3; 5-11 (11-11 Thu-Sat: 12-10.30 Sun)

Star GB5
199 Baddow Road (B1009)
Tel: (01245) 251577
Greene King IPA **H**
🍺
Gray and Sons local. Live music Thursday night. The landlord has greatly improved the beer quality. 'Real' Abbot Ale expected.

11-11 (12-10.30 Sun)

White Horse GB6
76/78 High Street (nr A414)
Tel: (01245) 471160
Bass Hancocks HB, Draught Bass; **Guest Beer H**
🍺🍺🍺 R 🍺 ⬅ 🍺
Large, 'beamed' local, retaining some character, with a genuine public bar and a comfortable lounge. Several changes of management has affected range and quality of the beers.

Great Bardfield C2

Picturesque village with windmill and craft museum.

11-3; 6-11 (11-11 Sat: 12-3; 7-10.30 Sun)

Bell
Dunmow Road (B1057)
Tel: (01371) 811097
Greene King IPA, Abbot Ale **H**
🍺🍺🍺 🍺 ❀
Cosy and friendly two-bar pub with log fire in the saloon. Evening meals and snacks Friday to Sunday only, no food Monday.

11-3; 6-11 (12-3; 7-10.30 Sun)

Vine
Vine Street (B1057)
Tel: (01371) 810355
Ridleys XXX Mild, IPA, Rumpus **H**
🍺🍺🍺 🍺 ❀
Friendly, family pub with sociable village atmosphere. Quizzes, darts, dominoes and pool. Live music monthly.

Great Bentley E2

Pretty village, with possibly the largest village green in the UK.

Dusty's Wine Bar
The Green
Free-house - Pub closed and demolished. Formerly "Squirrels".

11-11 (12-10.30 Sun)

Flag
Flag Hill, Colchester Road (B1027)
OS: TM117180
Tel: (01255) 820233
Tetley Bitter **H**
🍺🍺🍺 R ❀
Large roadside pub, south of the village, with a single 'beamed' bar, a separate restaurant and a games room.

11-3; 6-11 (12-3; 7-10.30 Sun)

Plough Inn
Plough Road
Tel: (01206) 250563
Ruddles Best Bitter; **S&N** John Smiths Bitter, Websters Yorkshire Bitter **H**
🍺🍺🍺🍺 ❀ ⬅
14th century village pub, with many exposed beams and a large dining area. Just up the road from the station.

Red Lion
The Green
Tel: (01206) 250527
Inntrepreneur - Pub closed.

Great Braxted D3

The original village of Great Braxted was relocated to an area previously known as Bung Row, on the orders of the Lord of the Manor in the 19th Century.

A four-and-a-half mile brick wall was built around the Braxted estate during the 1820s and 1830s to provide employment after the Napoleonic Wars. It is still standing.

11.30-3; 6.30-11 (12-3; 7-10.30 Sun)

Du-Cane Arms
Tiptree Road
Tel: (01621) 891697
Adnams Bitter; **Greene King** IPA; **Guest Beers H**
🍺🍺🍺 R 🍺 ❀
Village pub with excellent, nicely-decorated restaurant. The bar counter is made up of old ha'pennys. Hanging baskets and tubs of flowers adorn the outside.

Great Bromley E2

12-2.30; 6.30-11 (12-2.30; 7-10.30 Sun)

Cross Inn & Motel
Ardleigh Road, Bromley Cross (B1029)
OS: TM067274
Tel: (01206) 230282
Guest Beers H
🍺🍺🍺🍺 ❀
Eccentric, country pub, with clock collection and a genuine enthusiasm for Real Ales. Constantly-changing range of three guest beers.

11-3; 7-11 (12-3; 6.30-10.30 Sun, may vary in Summer)

Old Black Boy
Harwich Road (B1029)
Tel: (01206) 250322
Greene King IPA; **Marstons** Pedigree **H**
🍺🍺🍺 R 🍺 ⬅ ❀
Refurbished, 18th century pub.

12-3; 7-11 (10.30 Sun)

Snooty Fox
Frating Road, Balls Green
OS: TM092240
Tel: (01206) 251065
Adnams Bitter; **Ruddles** Best Bitter; **S&N** Courage Best Bitter **H**
🍺🍺🍺 R 🍺 ❀
Smart, food-based pub, with a nice selection of games. Beware keg cider on handpump. Formerly the "Whistle & Flute" and the "Tailors Arms".

Spread Eagle
Brook Street (B1029)
Benskins - Pub closed and delicensed - converted to a private house.

Great Burstead C4

11.30-11 (12-10.30 Sun)

Burstead Plough
Southend Road, South Green (A129)
Tel: (01277) 622978
Free-house (Enterprise Inns) - No Real Ale.

10-11 (12-10.30 Sun)

Duke of York
Southend Road (A129)
Tel: (01277) 651403
Greene King IPA, Rayments Special, Abbot Ale; **Guest Beer H**
🍺🍺🍺🍺 R 🍺
Attractive Gray and Sons pub/restaurant, dating from 1868, that was formerly two cottages. Emphasis on food - Les Routiers. Reputedly haunted.

12-11 (10.30 Sun)

Kings Head
Southend Road (A129)
Tel: (01277) 658785
Bass Hancocks HB, Draught Bass **H**
🍺🍺🍺🍺 R 🍺 ❀ ♿
Refurbished as a predominantly 'food' outlet, in the 'Farmhouse Kitchen' style. No smoking dining areas for those with and those without children. Once a stagecoach stop on the Brentwood to Rochford road. Beware keg cider on fake handpump.

Great Chesterford B1

Village with many fine old buildings.

12-3 (4 Sat); 6-11 (12-4; 7-10.30 Sun)

Crown & Thistle
High Street/Manor Lane
(between B1383 & B184)
Tel: (01799) 530278
Greene King IPA; **Tetley** Bitter **H**
◑ ◖ R ⊟ 📛 ⊫ 📛 ❀
Old, refurbished village pub,
with a welcoming atmosphere, a
good "6 o'clock trade", and an
inglenook fireplace, and pool
room. No food Sunday or
Monday evenings.

11-3; 6-11 (12-3; 7-10.30 Sun)

Plough
High Street (between B184 &
B1383)
Tel: (01799) 530283
Greene King IPA, Abbot Ale **G/H**
◑ ◑ ◖ R ⊫ 📛 ❀ ⅋
Refurbished, 18th century village
local, with two Inglenook
fireplaces. Petanque played.

Station Wine Bar & Nightspot
Great Chesterford Station,
London Road (nr B1383)
Free-house - Pub closed.

Ye Olde Lock Stock & Barrel
Church Street (between B1383 &
B184)
Free-house - Pub closed and
converted to residential use.
Formerly the "Elm Tree".

Great Clacton F3

(Hours vary).

Brace of Pistols
421 St Johns Road, Bockings
Elm (B1027)
Tel: (01255) 424517
S&N Courage Directors; **Guest
Beer H**
◑ D ◖ (Sun) 📛 ❀
Pleasant pub on the edge of
town.

11-11 (12-6; 7-10.30 Sun)

Plough
1 North Road (nr B1032)
Tel: (01255) 429998
Greene King IPA; **Tetley**
Bitter; **Whitbread** Flowers
Original **H**
◑ D ◑ ◖ ⅋ ❀
Interesting pub with oak beams,
made up of cottages knocked
together. Shove ha'penny,
cards, dominoes, etc. Pub bands
at weekends.

11-3; 6.30-11 (12-10.30 Sun)

Queen's Head Hotel
16 St Johns Road (B1032)
Tel: (01255) 423069
Ind Coope Benskins BB;
Whitbread Flowers IPA **H**
◑ D ◑ ◖ R ⊟ ⊫ ❀
16th century, listed hotel, one of
the original buildings in the village. Children allowed in the
bars. Strong food trade.

11-3; 6-11 (11-11 Fri/Sat; 12-10.30
Sun)

Robert Burre
183 Burrs Road, Burrsville Park
OS: TM186174
Tel: (01255) 421108
Greene King IPA, Abbot Ale;
Tetley Bitter **H**
◑ D ◑ ◖ R 📛 ❀
Converted farmhouse 1 mile
north-east of Great Clacton. Live
music Saturday evenings,
karaoke Monday evenings.
Carvery Friday to Sunday
lunchtimes, barbecues Sunday
nights.

11-11 (12-10.30 Sun)

Robin Hood
211 London Road (A133)
Tel: (01255) 421519
Bass Hancocks HB, Draught
Bass **H**
◑ D ◑ ◖ ❀ ⅋
A pub with lots of atmosphere -
despite its food-orientation.

11-3; 7-11 (11-11 Fri/Sat; 12-3; 7-
10.30 Sun)

Ship Inn
2 Valley Road (B1032)
Tel: (01255) 423324
Greene King IPA **H**
◑ D ❀
Sixties bar in an oak-beamed,
listed building, at the heart of
the village.

Great Dunmow B2

*Fine market town, with half-tim-
bered old town hall. Greatly
relieved by bypass.*

12-2.30; 6-11 (12-3; 7-10.30 Sun)

Angel & Harp
16 Church Street, Church End
(B1057)
Tel: (01371) 872438
S&N Courage Best Bitter,
Directors **H**
◑ D ◑ ◖ ❀
Emphasis on food. American
landlord supportive of CAMRA.
Sky TV.

10.30-11 (12-3; 7-10.30 Sun)

Boars Head
37 High Street (B184)
Tel: (01371) 873630
Ind Coope Benskins Best Bitter;
Marstons Pedigree **H**
◖ ◖ (Not Sun) ❀
Fine traditional pub with award-
winning garden. Fish and chip
night Wednesdays. "The little
pub with the big atmosphere".

11-11 (12-3; 7-10.30 Sun)

Chequers Inn
27 Stortford Road (nr B184)
Tel: (01371) 872456
Greene King IPA **H**
◖ ◖ ⊟ ⊫ 📛 ❀
Popular 'beamed' pub, which
has had a number of small
rooms knocked together into
one large bar.

11-11 (12-3 (or later); 7-10.30
Sun)

Cricketers
22 Beaumont Hill (B184)
Tel: (01371) 873359
Ridleys IPA, Rumpus **H**
◑ ◖ R ❀
Excellent, popular pub at the
northern edge of town, near the
sports centre. Old-fashioned
ovens in saloon bar walls. Good
value food, including Sunday
Lunches and 'huffers'.
Garden and patio. Various live
music Fridays and Saturdays
alternate weekends.

11-3; 5-11 (11-11 Sat; 12-3; 7-
10.30 Sun)

Dunmow Inn
15 High Street (B184)
Tel: (01371) 872163
Bass Draught Bass,
Worthington BB **H**
◑ D ◑ ◖ ❀
Large single bar in town centre.
Good range of home-cooked
food. Beer variable. Formerly the
"White Hart".

11.30-2.30; 6-11 (12-3; 7-10.30
Sun)

Kicking Dickey
Ongar Road (B184)
OS: TL632211
Tel: (01371) 872071
Greene King IPA, Abbot Ale;
Nethergate Bitter; **Guest
Beer H**
◑ D ◑ ◖ R ⊫ ❀
Clean and friendly. No food
Sunday evenings. 'Dickey' is the
old Essex word for donkey.

5.30-11 (closed lunchtimes Mon
to Sat) 12-10.30 Sun)

Kings Head
30 North Street (B184)
Tel: (01371) 872052
Whitbread Boddingtons Bitter;
Guest Beer H
⅋ ᵭ
Basic local with pool and some
very rare guest beers.

11-2.30; 6-11 (12-3; 7-10.30 Sun)

Queen Victoria
79 Stortford Road (nr A120)
Tel: (01371) 873330
Adnams Bitter; **S&N** Courage
Directors **H**
◑ D ◑ ◖ (Not Sun) R ⊟ ❀
Picturesque thatched pub dating
from 1553, with low beams!
Guest beer in Summer.
Specialises in flambees (table
cooking).

11-11 (12-10.30 Sun)

Saracen's Head Hotel
High Street (B184)
Tel: (01371) 873901
Fax: (01371) 875743
Adnams Bitter; **S&N** Courage
Directors **H**
⬤ D ⬤ ⬤ **R** ⬤ ⬤ ⬤ ⬤
16th century 'Forte Hotel' with a
small bar. Very comfortable,
plush, drinking area. Quite
expensive food - but of very
good quality.

Great Easton   B2

*Quiet, compact village with
small green and ford.*

11-3; 6-11 (12-3; 7-10.30 Sun)

Swan
The Endway (nr B184)
OS: TL606255
Tel: (01371) 870359
Greene King IPA **H**
⬤ D ⬤ ⬤ ⬤ ⬤ ⬤
Lively pub, a weekend retreat for
London commuters, which
retaining two contrasting bars.
Has a reputation for food. The
'Cygnet Room' is available for
functions.

Great
Hallingbury   B2

*Attractive village, surprisingly
quiet in view of proximity to
motorway and airport.*

11-3; 6-11 (12-4; 7-10.30 Sun)

Hop Poles
Bedlars Green (nr A120 & M11
Jcn 8)
OS: TL524203
Tel: (01279) 757042
Guest Beer H
⬤ D ⬤ ⬤ ⬤ ⬤
Small, friendly and busy, family
country pub close to Hatfield
Forest. Fresh fish night on
Tuesdays. Guest beer is usually
from the Carlsberg-Tetley range.

Great Holland   F3

11-3 (or later); 7-11 (or earlier)
(12-4; 7-10.30 Sun)

Lions Den
Little Clacton Road / Clacton
Road (B1032)
Tel: (01255) 675137
Greene King IPA; **Mauldons**
'House' Bitter; **Guest Beers H**
⬤ D ⬤ ⬤ **R** ⬤ ⬤
Homely, roadside halt, between
Clacton and Frinton, offering
good value food.

11-3; 7-11 (12-3; 7-10.30 Sun)

Ship
Rectory Road (nr B1032)
Tel: (01255) 674809
Greene King IPA; **Tetley** Bitter **H**
⬤ ⬤ ⬤
Once a smugglers' inn - a carved
ship's figurehead overlooks the
bar.

Great
Horkesley   E2

11-2.30 (4 Sat); 5 (6 Sat)-11 (12-
2.30; 7-10.30 Sun)

Half Butt Inn
Nayland Road (A134)
Tel: (01206) 271202
Adnams Bitter; **Ruddles** Best
Bitter **S&N** Websters Yorkshire
Bitter **H**
⬤ ⬤ ⬤
Basic but popular, village local,
featuring a 'L' shaped bar.
Good value basic range of food.
Pool, darts and crib played.

11.30-3; 5 (5.30 Sat)-11 (12-3; 7-
10.30 Sun)

Rose & Crown
Nayland Road (A134)
Tel: (01206) 271251
Greene King IPA, Abbot Ale **H**
⬤ D ⬤ ⬤ **R** ⬤
Comfortable, smart, 'beamed'
roadside pub with large car park.
Very popular 'eating house',
with extensive menu.

11-11 (12-10.30 Sun)

Yew Tree
The Causeway / Nayland Road
(A134)
Tel: (01206) 271747
S&N Courage Directors; John
Smiths Bitter, Websters
Yorkshire Bitter **H**
⬤ D ⬤ **R** ⬤
Partly-thatched with fine garden,
nice patio with fountain and chil-
dren's play area. Carvery at rear,
though bar meals are also avail-
able. Very popular 'eating
house' with carvery.

Great Leighs   C3

*Permanent site of Essex Show.
Willows for cricket bats grown
here.*

11.30-3; 6-11 (12-3; 7-10.30 Sun)

Dog & Gun
Boreham Road
OS: TL739142
Tel: (01245) 360211
Greene King IPA, Rayments
Special **G**
⬤ D ⬤ ⬤ **R** ⬤ ⬤
Large, isolated pub, two miles
south of the village, with empha-
sis on freshly-prepared food.
Formerly a row of cottages.

11-3; 6-11 (11-11 Sat: 12-3; 7-
10.30 Sun)

Dog & Partridge
Main Road (A131)
Tel: (01245) 361331
Ridleys IPA, ESX **H**
⬤ D ⬤ ⬤ **R** ⬤ ⬤ ⬤
Friendly, roadside pub, near the
Essex Showground and the
Essex Way. Conservatory
restaurant and large garden.

11-3; 6-11 (11-11 Sat: 12-3; 7-
10.30 Sun)

St Anne's Castle
Main Road (A131)
Tel: (01245) 361253
Greene King IPA **H**
⬤ D ⬤
Ancient pub, one of many
claimants to be Britain's oldest,
with obligatory ghost! Now
rather food-biased.

Great Notley
Garden Village C2

*New 'garden village', off the
A131, just south of Braintree,
with unusual, ramped, block-
paved, mini-roundabouts that
most vehicles have to drive
over.*

*The site for a pub/restaurant has
been identified in the village
centre, near the community centre, between Notley Green
Village and Oaklands Manor
Hamlet. Watch out for it.*

Great Oakley   F2

11-11 (12-10.30 Sun)

Maybush Inn
Farm Road (B1414)
Tel: (01255) 886183
Tetley Bitter; **Guest Beers H**
⬤ ⬤
Authentic village local, without
food.

Great Saling   C2

12-3.30; 5.30-11 (12-11 Sat: 12-
10.30 Sun)

White Hart
The Street (2 miles north of
A120)
OS: TL701254
Tel: (01371) 850341
Ridleys IPA, Rumpus **H**
⬤ D ⬤ ⬤ **R** ⬤ ⬤ ⬤
Superb, 16th century, beamed,
Tudor pub, with a timbered
gallery in the saloon bar.
Remains of the world's largest
smooth-leaved elm (destroyed
by Dutch elm disease in 1974)
are opposite.
Food speciality is the Essex
'Huffer' - a large roll with choice
of fillings, of which the pub
claims to be the 'birthplace'. Bar
menu changes daily. New 46
seat restaurant in former bake-
house.
Can become very crowded on
Summer weekends, and has featured in the 'Lovejoy' TV series.

Great
Sampford   B1

Attractive village.

Black Bull
B1051/B1053
OS: TL643353
Free-house - Pub closed.

12-3; 5.30-11 (12-10.30 Sun)

Red Lion Inn
Finchingfield Road (B1053)
Tel: (01799) 586325
Ridleys IPA; Rumpus **H**
◐ ▯ ◑ ▮ 🅡 ⇰ ▙ ❀
Unspoilt, friendly and pleasant
one-bar pub, with good verbal
banter amongst locals. No food
Sundays.

Great Tey   D2

11-3, 6.30-11 (12-4; 7-10.30 Sun)

Chequers
The Street (1½ miles north of
A120)
Tel: (01206) 210814
Greene King XX Mild, IPA,
Abbot Ale, seasonal beers **H**
◐ ▯ ◑ ▮ 🅱 ❀
16th century, village local, with a
low-beamed ceiling. Petanque
played. Views of the village
church from the garden. No
food Monday evenings.

Great Totham   D3

11-3; 6-11 (11-11 Fri/Sat: 12-4; 7-
10.30 Sun)

Compasses
12 Colchester Road (B1022)
OS: TL868131
Tel: (01621) 891238
Greene King IPA; **Ind Coope**
Friary Meux BB **H**
◐ ▯ ◑ ▮ 🅡 🅱 ❀
Traditional 16th century pub,
with two contrasting bars. The
public bar is home to darts,
dominoes and football teams.
Fresh fish Thursdays - booking
advisable.

Great Totham
(South)   D3

11-11 (12-10.30 Sun)

Bull
2 Maldon Road (B1022)
Tel: (01621) 893385
Bass M&B Brew XI; **Ind Coope**
Burton Ale; **Whitbread**
Boddingtons Bitter **H**
◐ ▯ ◑ ▮ 🅡 🅱 ❀ ♿
Pleasant village pub, good for
village cricket matches in
Summer. Curries available.
Beware keg cider on handpump.

Crown
Broad Street Green Road
(B1022)
OS: TL860097
Free-house - Pub closed and
demolished in Summer 1998, for
new housing.

11-3; 5-11 (12-3; 7-10.30 Sun)

Prince of Wales
Prince of Wales Road (nr B1022)
Tel: (01621) 891162
Ind Coope Friary Meux BB;
Tetley Bitter; **Whitbread**
Flowers IPA; **Guest Beer H**
◐ ▯ ◑ ▮ 🅡 ❀ ♿
Caters for the local trade, with
numerous special events and
charity functions, this refur-
bished, single-bar pub has an
unusual island servery.
Renowned for its Sunday lunches.

Great
Wakering   D5

The gateway to Foulness Island.

11-11 (12-10.30 Sun)

Anchor
23 High Street (B1017)
Tel: (01702) 219265
Fullers London Pride; **Ridleys**
IPA; **Guest Beers H**
Real Cider G
◐ ▯ ◑ ▮ 🅱 🖼 ❀ ♿
Friendly, family-run pub, with
great atmosphere. Collection of
walking sticks above the bar. No
evening meals Mondays. Pool
and darts played.

11-11 (12-10.30 Sun)

Exhibition Inn
241 High Street (B1017)
Tel: (01702) 219220
Morlands Old Speckled Hen;
S&N John Smiths Bitter,
Websters Yorkshire Bitter **H**
◐ ▯ ◑ ▮ 🅱 ❀
Two-bar pub, used by old and
young drinkers alike. Food
recommended.

11-11 (12-10.30 Sun)

Red Lion
High Street (B1017)
Tel: (01702) 219296
Greene King IPA, Abbot Ale;
Guest Beers H
◐ ▯ ◑ ▮ 🅱 ❀
Popular, friendly pub with pool
table. Imaginative menu - spe-
cialising in fish.

10-12 (12-10.30 Sun)

White Hart
High Street (B1017)
Tel: (01702) 219222
Marstons Pedigree; **Ridleys**
IPA; **S&N** John Smiths Bitter **H**
◐ ▯ ◑ ▮ 🅡 ▙ ❀ ▯
Small and friendly with one-bar -
the 'bric-a-brac pub' of
Wakering.

Great Waltham C3

*Attractive village, huddled
around the church, much qui-
etened by the bypass. Old
Guildhall. Real bakery still uses
coal-fired oven.*

11.30-3; 6.30-11 (12-3; 7-10.30
Sun)

Beehive
Barrack Lane / Main Road (nr
A130)
Tel: (01245) 360356
Ridleys IPA, ESX, Spectacular
(Summer),
Witchfinder Porter (Winter) **H**
◐ ▯ ◑ ▮ 🅱 🖼
1950s replacement for the
original pub, which was demolished for road widening. A two-
bar pub, with basic public bar,
and a lounge that is popular
with diners.

12-3 (Sat only); 6.30-11 (12-3; 7-
10.30 Sun)

**Great Waltham Free
House**
Chelmsford Road, Minnow End
(nr A130)
Tel: (01245) 360359
Whitbread Boddingtons Bitter;
Guest Beers H
▙ 🖼
Refurbished, 17th century free-
house, at the fringe of the vil-
lage.

Six Bells
The Street (nr A130)
Tel: (01245) 361515
Free-house - Pub closed.

12-3; 6.30-11 (closed Sun)

Windmill
Chelmsford Road, Minnow End
(nr A130)
Tel: (01245) 360292
Adnams Bitter **H**
◐ ▯ ◑ ▮ 🅡 ▙
Predominantly an up-market
restaurant, of high repute.
Drinkers are welcome in the
genteel lounge bar, which offers
bar snacks and drinks.

Great Warley   B4

*Small unspoilt village, the attrac-
tive church has a tunnel-vaulted
nave. Warley gardens are
opened to the public once a
year.*

11-11 (12-10.30 Sun)

Headley
Headley Common / Warley Gap
(nr B186)
Tel: (01277) 216104
S&N Courage Directors,
Theakstons BB **H**
◐ ▯ ◑ ▮ 🅡 🖼
Modern, much-altered pub with
duck pond. Pool and video
games played in the games
room.

11-2.30; 5.30 (7 Sat)-11 (12-3; 7-10.30 Sun)

Horse & Groom
Warley Road/Mascalls Lane (B186)
Tel: (01277) 220280
Greene King IPA; **Ind Coope** Burton Ale; **Tetley** Bitter **H**
❢ ❢ �〜

Traditional, wood-panelled local with large island bar. Two dartboards, and a collection of poes and jugs. No food at weekends.

11-11 (12-10.30 Sun)

Inn
Brentwood Park, Holdens Wood, Warley Gap
Tel: (01277) 211994
Greene King IPA, Abbot Ale **H**
❢ D ❢ ❢ 🕳 🚗 ❋

Newish pub in sports centre complex. Quiz night on Tuesdays, darts played.

12-3; 6-12 (12-12.30 Sat: 12-3; 7-10.30 Sun)

New World Hotel
Great Warley Street (B186)
Tel: (01277) 226418
Free-house - No Real Ale.

11-11 (12-10.30 Sun)

Thatchers Arms Tavern
Great Warley Street (B186)
Tel: (01277) 233535
Ruddles Best Bitter, County; **S&N** Theakstons BB **H**
❢ ❢ ❢ 🚗

15th century, food-oriented pub, on the busy route to Brentwood. The pub supports the Essex Wildlife Trust, and is situated next to Warley Gardens.

Great Yeldham C1

The dead stump of Yeldham Oak is preserved by the main road.

11-2; 7-11 (12-3; 7-10.30 Sun)

Three Bottles
Leather Lane (nr A1017, was A604)
OS: TL761384
Tel: (01787) 237122
Greene King - No Real Ale.

11-11 (12-10.30 Sun)

Waggon & Horses
High Street (A1017, was A604)
Tel: (01787) 237936
Greene King IPA, Abbot Ale; **Guest Beers H**
❢ D ❢ R 🍴 🕳 🍽 ❋

Friendly village pub, restored at great expense, and with strong local support. The landlord is keen on Real Ales. A wide range of good value food available. Note that the meeting / children's room is only available when the restaurant is not in use.

10-3; 6-11 (12-3; 7-10.30 Sun)

White Hart Hotel
Poole Street (A1017, was A604)
OS: TL762377
Tel: (01787) 237250
Adnams Bitter; **Guest Beers H**
❢ D ❢ ❢ R 🕳 ❋

Genuine, olde-worlde, 16th century, tudor inn, set in picturesque gardens.

Greenstead Green D2

Small village that has lost both its pubs since the last guide.

Hare & Hounds
Grange Hill Road
(1½ miles off A1124, was A604)
OS: TL822278
Free-house - Pub sadly closed and converted to a private house - despite appearances!

Plough
(1½ miles off A1124, was A604)
OS: TL821278
Free-house - Pub closed.

Hadleigh D5

The ruined castle once painted by Turner is a pleasant spot on the cliffs overlooking Canvey Island and the Thames Estuary.

11-11 (12-10.30 Sun)

Castle
High Street (A13)
Tel: (01702) 558452
Bass Hancocks HB, Draught Bass, **Greene King** IPA; **Guest Beer H**
❢ D ❢ ❢ R 🍽 ❋

Large, single-bar 'beamed' pub, on the westbound one-way system, near the castle. Sky TV. Conservatory built in 1991, as a non-smoking extended eating area - which also doubles as a family room.

12-11 (12-3; 7-10.30 Sun)

Crown
London Road/High Street (A13)
Tel: (01702) 556927
Ind Coope 'House' Bitter; **Tetley** Bitter; **Guest Beer H**
❢ D ❢ ❢ ❋

Pleasant, refurbished pub, on island in the middle of the one-way system. Occasional jazz nights, bingo nights and special nights, e.g. Irish and Mexican.

12-11 (10.30 Sun)

Hadley's
32 Benfleet Road (B1014)
Tel: (01702) 558671
S&N Courage Directors; **Guest Beers H**
❢ D ❢ ❢ ❋

Free-house created from the conversion of two shops. Pool, Sky TV and quiz nights.

12-3; 6.30-11(12 Tue/Wed, 1 Thu-Sat) (12-3; 7-10.30 Sun)

Spencers Wine Bar
20 High Street (A13)
Tel: (01702) 558166
Free-house - No Real Ale.

12-11 (12-3; 7-10.30 Sun)

Waggon & Horses
139 London Road (A13)
Tel: (01702) 555374
Morlands Old Speckled Hen; **Whitbread** Boddingtons Bitter, Flowers Original; **Guest Beers H**
❢ D ❢ ❢ R ❋

Refurbished Beefeater with split-level bar, large three-level restaurant and conservatory, where children are permitted.

Hadstock B1

The most northerly Essex village with a beautiful church and a wealth of thatch.

11.30-2.30; 6-11 (12-3; 7-10.30 Sun)

Kings Head
Linton Road (B1052)
Tel: (01223) 893473
Ind Coope Friary Meux BB; **Guest Beers H**
Guest Cider (occasional) **G**
❢ D ❢ ❢ 🍴 ❋

Welcoming, 16th century village local, whose landlord will not part with his original Tolly Cobbold sign! No food Mondays, evening meals Fridays only. Bar billiards played.

Hainault A4

11-11 (12-3; 7-10.30 Sun)

Alfred's Head
Manford Way
Tel: (0181) 500 0544
Bass - No Real Ale.

11-11 (12-10.30 Sun)

Badger
88 Manford Way (nr B173)
Tel: (0181) 501 0223
Phoenix - No Real Ale.

11-11 (12-10.30 Sun)

Forester
107 Burrow Road
OS: TQ463926
Tel: (0181) 500 3473
Greene King IPA; **S&N** Courage Directors, Websters Yorkshire Bitter **H**
❢ ❢ R 🍴 🕳 ❋

Comfortable and food-oriented.

12-3; 5-11 (12-10.30 Sun)

Oak
710 New North Road / Romford Road (by A1112)
Tel: (0181) 501 0611
Hardys Hardy Country Bitter; **Ind Coope** 'House' Bitter **H**
❢ D ❢ ❢ 🍴 ❋

Large, modernised pub opposite Hainault Forest. Formerly the "Old Hainault Oak".

Hale End   A4

Residential area - bordering Epping Forest.

11-12 (10.30 Sun)

Royal Oak
320 Hale End Road / Oak Hill (nr B160)
Tel: (0181) 527 2022
Tetley Bitter; **Youngs** Bitter; **Guest Beers H**
◗ ◖ 🍺 (Pool room) 🌻
Huge, traditional and homely with pool room and dartboards. Guest beers very popular. Occasional live music.

Halstead   D2

Attractive, characterful market town, with a very steep High Street and attractive historic buildings and features.

These include Courtaulds weaving mill and weavers cottages, and the Octagon - now a Tourism Information Centre.

11-11 (12-10.30 Sun) - may close afternoons out of season.

Bird In Hand
54 Chapel Hill (nr A131)
Tel: (01787) 475656/479250
Greene King IPA **H**
◗ D ◖ ❙ **R** 🚃
New restaurant at rear. Charity socials. Ask for the 'sparkler' to be removed when ordering.

10-11 (12-10.30 Sun)

Bull Hotel
Bridge Street (A131)
Tel: (01787) 472144
Adnams Bitter; **Greene King** IPA, Abbot Ale; **Marstons** Pedigree; **Youngs** Bitter **H**
◗ D ◖ ❙ **R** 🍺 🛏 ⊨ ► 🛏 🌻 ♿
Plush hotel with a wealth of beams, dating from the 14th century. Draught cider. Range of live music.

Carpenters Arms
Mount Pleasant (nr A131)
Pubmaster - Pub closed and boarded-up.

12-2.30; 6-11 (12-3; 7-10.30 Sun)

Dog Inn
37 Hedingham Road (A1124, was A604)
Tel: (01787) 477774
Adnams Bitter; **Nethergate** Bitter; **Guest Beer H**
◗ D ◖ ❙ 🍺 🛏 🌻
Popular and well-restored, 'beamed' 16th century pub. Regular guest beers and cider. B&B ensuite. Background music. Limited parking.

---

12 (4 Tue/Wed)-11 (12-10.30 Sun)

Essex
Trinity Street (A131)
Tel: (01787) 472440
Greene King IPA; **Wadworths** 6X **H**
🚃
Sky sports, pool and darts. Formerly the "Essex Arms".

10-11 (12-10.30 Sun)

Globe
Parsonage Street (nr A1124, was A604)
Tel: (01787) 478200
Greene King IPA; **Nethergate** IPA, Porters Suffolk Bitter; **S&N** Theakstons BB; **Whitbread** Boddingtons Bitter; **Guest Beers H**
◗ D ◖ ❙ 🌻
Friendly local with a public bar only. Darts, pool and football teams. Live music and discos. Any two of these beers available at a time. An expanding range of guest beers expected.

5-11 12-3; 6.30-11 (12-3; 7-10.30 Sun)

Griffin
Parsonage Street (nr A131)
Tel: (01787) 476569
Greene King IPA, Abbot Ale **H**
◗ ◖ 🍺 🌻
Quiet, sleepy local with no juke box.

9-5 Mon-Thu, 7-11 Fri/Sat, 12-4 Sun

Ivory's Piano Bar & Coffee House
11 Weavers Court, off High Street (nr A131)
Tel: (01787) 479444
Ridleys IPA **H**
◗ D ◖ ❙
Cafe-bar with limited opening hours, which opened in Summer 1996. Tucked away near the River Colne.

11-11 (12-10.30 Sun)

Locomotive
3 Butler Road (nr A131)
Tel: (01787) 472425
Whitbread Boddingtons Bitter, Flowers IPA, Flowers Original **H**
Addlestones Cider H
◗ D ◖ ❙ 🍺 🌻 ♿
Large garden with pet animals, barbecue and play area.

3 (2 Fri, 11 Sat)-11 (12-10.30 Sun)

Red Lion
5/7 New Street / Mount Pleasant (nr A131)
Tel: (01787) 477093
Free-house - No Real Ale.

Rose & Crown
48 Head Street (A131)
Free-house - Pub closed and delicensed. Formerly the "Gold Rush".

11-2; 7-11 (12-3; 7-10.30 Sun)

Royal Oak
58 High Street (A131)
Tel: (01787) 477705
Greene King IPA **H**
🍺 🌻 ♿
1580 grade 2 listed pub with beams and settles. Rather run down. Parking difficult.

11-11 (12-3; 7-10.30 Sun)

Three Pigeons
Mount Hill (A131)
Tel: (01787) 472336
Greene King IPA, Abbot Ale **H**
◗ D 🍺 🌻 ♿
Good local with children's certificate. Pool, darts and dominoes teams.

10-11 (12-10.30 Sun)

White Hart Inn
15 High Street (A131)
Tel: (01787) 475657
Greene King IPA; **S&N** Courage Directors, John Smiths Bitter; **Ruddles** BB **H**
◗ D ◖ ❙ **R** 🍺 🛏 ⊨ ► 🛏 🌻
Fine old hotel, built in 16th century, with open fires and home-cooked food. A young peoples pub with discos Fridays, Saturdays and Sundays. All beers on 'sparklers'. Limited parking.

White Horse
32/34 Parsonage Street (Nr A1124, was A604)
Greene King - Pub closed.

11-2; 7-11 (12-3; 7-10.30 Sun)

Woodman Inn
Colchester Road (A1124, was A604)
Tel: (01787) 476218
Tetley Bitter; **Whitbread** Flowers IPA; **Guest Beer** (occasional) **H**
◗ ◖ 🍺 🛏 ► 🛏 🌻
Large open-plan, young people's pub, with regular live music Fridays and Saturdays, barbecues, pool, darts and dominoes. Evening meals by prior arrangement.

Harlow   A3

Large post-war town, masterminded by Frederick Gibberd in 1947, now matured, with artificial ski slope, fine swimming pool and parklands.

11-3.30; 5.30-11 (11-11 Fri/Sat: 12-10.30 Sun)

Archer's Dart   1
Partridge Road, Coppice Hatch
Tel: (01279) 418883
Greene King IPA, Abbot Ale **H**
◗ ◖ 🚃 ♿
One of the better estate-style pubs.

HARLOW
Church Langley, Old Harlow & Potter Street

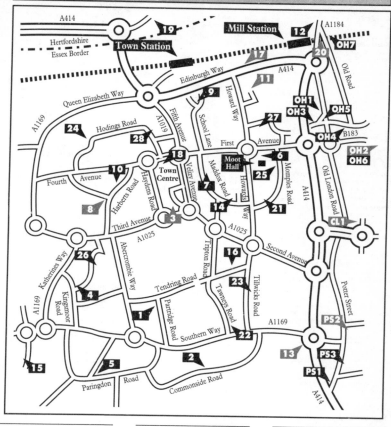

11-11 (12-10.30 Sun)

Chequers   **2**
Commonside Road, Latton Bush
(nr A1169)
OS: TL456079
Tel: (01279) 428691
Tetley Bitter **H**
◖◗ ◖◗ 🍴 🏠
Horseshoe pitching a pub pastime. Family room and restaurant planned.

Chicago Rock Cafe   **3**
Terminus Street
Tel: (01279) 425225
Free-house - No Real Ale.

11-2.30 (3 Sat); 5 (6 Sat)-11

Cock Inn   **4**
1 Three Horseshoes Lane, Great
Parndon
Tel: (01279) 423921
Bass Draught Bass; **McMullens**
Original AK, Country, Gladstone
H
◖◗ ◖🍴 ⛲
Large, timbered 16th century inn
with wood-panelling. A welcoming local with a large open fire,
darts, crib, horseshoes and football teams.
Beware the beers on 'sparklers'.

11-11 (12-10.30 Sun)

Drinker Moth   **5**
Ployters Road, Sherrards Hatch
(nr A1169)
Tel: (01279) 436997
S&N Theakstons BB **H**
◖◗ ◖◗ 🏠
Recently-refurbished, with live
music on Saturday nights.

12-11 (10.30 Sun)

Essex Skipper   **6**
The Stow (nr First Avenue)
Tel: (01279) 866506
Hardys Potters Pride;
Morlands Old Speckled Hen;
Wadworths 6X **H**
◖◗ 🍴 ❀
Re-opened after a period of closure, one of only two Harlow
pubs to hold a full music licence.
Beware beers on 'sparkler' and
Scrumpy Jack Cider on fake
handpump.

11-3; 5-11 (11-11 Fri/Sat: 12-10.30 Sun)

Garden Tiger 7
Maddox Road, Fishers Hatch
Tel: -
S&N John Smiths Bitter;
Ruddles County H
🍺
Two large bars - comfortable saloon and basic public. Live music/discos Friday and Saturday. Pool, darts and jukebox.

11-3; 5-11 (12-3; 7-10.30 Sun)

Golden Swift 8
Todd Brook, Harberts Road,
Hare Street
Tel: (01279) 424970
Allied Domecq - No Real Ale.

11-11 (12-10.30 Sun)

Greyhound 9
12 School Lane, Nettleswell
Tel: (01279) 424018
Ind Coope Burton Ale; **Tetley**
Bitter; **Guest Beer** H
🍺🍴🍺🍺🌸
A 'Big Steak' Pub, situated in the town park, that has been tastefully extended. Busy in Summer, live music some evenings.

11.30-2.30 (3.30 Fri/Sat); 5.30 (7 Sat)-11

Hare 10
100 Hare Street Springs
Tel: (01279) 424280
Bass Draught Bass; **McMullens**
Original AK, Country, Gladstone
H
🍺🍴🍺 R 🍺🌸
Large three-roomed pub with no-smoking restaurant. Popular with office workers at lunchtimes. Horseshoes in car park.

Harlow 11
7 The Oaks Industrial Estate,
Howard Way (by A414)
Formerly the **"Berni Inn"**
- Pub closed and converted to a drive-in "McDonald's".

11-11 (12-10.30 Sun)

Harlow Mill 12
Cambridge Road (A1184)
Tel: (01279) 442545
Greene King IPA; **Whitbread**
Boddingtons Bitter, Flowers
Original H
🍺🍴🍺 R A🌸🍺🚃
Above-average 'Beefeater' on banks of River Stort, with separate drinkers bar and children's play area.

12-2.30; 5.30-11 (12-3; 7-10.30 Sun)

Harlow Moat House 13
Southern Way (A414)
Tel: (01279) 422441
Bass - No Real Ale.

11-3.30; 6-11 (11-11 Fri/Sat: 12-10.30 Sun)

Heart & Club 14
Maddox Road, Long Ley (nr A1025)
Tel: (01279) 425151
Whitbread Flowers IPA H
🍺🍴🍺🍺🍴
Recently-refurbished, with occasional live music.

11-3; 5-11 (11-11 Fri/Sat: 12-10.30 Sun)

Herald 15
Broadley Road, Sumners Hatch
(nr B1133)
Tel: (01279) 437965
McMullens Original AK,
Country, Gladstone H
🍺🍴🍺🍺🌸
Large McMullen's 1980s pub, with comfortable lounge. Public bar is very games-oriented - most requiring payment.

11-11 (12-10.30 Sun)

Humming Bird 16
Waterhouse Moor, Elm Hatch
Tel: (01279) 451667
S&N Websters Yorkshire Bitter;
Whitbread Boddingtons Bitter H
🍺🌸
No comment from landlord.

Jazzbo Brown's 17
Unit 14, Queensgate Centre,
Edinburgh Way (by A414)
Free-house - Pub closed and converted to a "Bella Pasta".

11-11 (12-10.30 Sun)

Jean Harlow 18
1 The Rows, The High
Tel: (01279) 425875
S&N John Smiths Bitter H
🍺
Boisterous 'Fun' pub, aimed at the younger set!

11-11 (12-10.30 Sun)

Moorhen 19
Burnt Mill Lane (nr A414)
Tel: (01279) 427257
Greene King IPA, Abbot Ale,
seasonal ale H
🍺🍴🍺🍺 R 🌸🍺🚃
Huge pub on the Lee and Stort Navigation, recently-reopened following rebuilding as a "King's Fayre". Ground floor cafe.

Oasis Hotel 20
2 Hart Road / Cambridge Road
(by A1184)
Tel: (01279) 427208
Free-house - No Real Ale.

11-11 (12-10.30 Sun)

Phoenix 21
Tillwicks Road / Little Brays
Tel: (01279) 425688/626452
Ruddles County H
🍺🌸
Two large bars. Refurbishment expected.

11-11 (12-10.30 Sun)

Poplar Kitten 22
Tawneys Road, Bush Fair (nr A1169)
Tel: (01279) 422641
S&N John Smiths Bitter,
Websters Yorkshire Bitter H
🍺🍴🍺🍺🍺
Modern estate pub with emphasis on games, such as ten pin bowling, pool and table football.

11-3.30; 5.30-11 (11-11 Thu-Sat: 12-10.30 Sun)

Purple Emperor 23
Momples Road, Burgoyne Hatch
(nr A1025)
Tel: (01279) 418102
Bass Toby Cask; **Morlands** Old
Speckled Hen; **Wadworths** 6X H
🍺🌸
Public bar has pool, darts and pinball. Pleasant, comfortable saloon. Karaoke or live music every weekend.

11.30-3; 5.30-11 (11-11 Fri/Sat: 12-10.30 Sun)

Shark 24
Hobtoe Road / Hodings Road,
Colt Hatch
Tel: (01279) 416297
McMullens Original AK,
Country Bitter, Gladstone H
🍺🍴🍺🍺🍺🍺 &
McMullen's local.

11-11 (12-10.30 Sun)

Small Copper 25
Churchfield / Momples Road
Tel: (01279) 425777
S&N Courage Best Bitter H
🍺🍺🍺
Small community pub, a short distance from the cycle museum. Limited parking.

11-11 (12-10.30 Sun)

Three Horseshoes 26
Three Horseshoes Road, Great
Parndon (nr A1025)
Tel: (01279) 423411
Ind Coope Benskins BB, Burton
Ale; **Tetley** Bitter H
🍺🍺🌸
15th century coach-house, known locally as the 'Shoes', in the original village of Great Pardon at Cock Green.
Now part of the 'Big Steak' pub chain, with a special menu for tiny tots and senior citizens. Pinball, pool, darts and dominoes also played.

11-3; 5.30-11 (11-11 Fri/Sat: 12-10.30 Sun)

White Admiral 27
1 Ward Hatch / Mowbray Road
Tel: (01279) 424839
Bass Worthington BB H
🍺🍺🍺🍺
Deservedly popular back street local, with two bars. One of the better pubs in Harlow. Guest beers available some weekends.

11-3; 5.30-11 (11-11 Fri/Sat: 12-3;
7-10.30 Sun)

Willow Beauty 28
Hodings Road (nr A414)
Tel: (01279) 437328
Greene King IPA, Abbot Ale,
seasonal beers **H**

🍺 ◀ 🍺 ❀ ♿ ⇌

Restored pub by cricket ground
and sports centre.

Harold Hill B4

*Post-war housing estates on the
fringe of the countryside. A
desert for decent beer!*

10-11 (12-4; 7-10.30 Sun)

Alderman
Chippenham Road / Dartfields
Tel: (01708) 345359
Ruddles Best Bitter **H**

🍺 🍺 🚲

Two small bars with a pool table
in the public. Live music on
Saturday nights.

Bow & Arrow
156 Straight Road (½ mile North
of A12/A127)
Whitbread - Pub closed and
converted to a "McDonald's",
late in 1997.

11-11 (12-10.30 Sun)

Duckwood
59 Whitchurch Road
Tel: (01708) 342113
S&N John Smiths Bitter **H**

🍺 D ◀ ▶ 🍺 ❀

Reasonably-plush bar with a
view over the Harold Hill estate.
Formerly "Drakes".

11-11 (12-10.30 Sun)

Morris Dancer
Melksham Close (nr A12)
Tel: (01708) 343271
S&N John Smiths Bitter,
Theakstons BB **H**

🍺 D ◀ ▶ ❀ ♿

Friendly estate pub with an eastern flavour. Small playground in
garden.

10-11 (12-3; 7-10.30 Sun)

Pompadours
105 Hilldene Avenue / Edenhall
Road
Tel: (01708) 371677
Allied - No Real Ale.

11-11 (12-10.30 Sun)

Saxon King
198 Petersfield Avenue / St
Neots Road (nr A12)
Tel: (01708) 345077
S&N Courage Best Bitter **H**

🍺 🍺 ❀

Two bars linked by an archway,
the handpumps are in the left-
hand bar area.

11-11 (12-10.30 Sun)

William the Conqueror
88 Petersfield Avenue (nr A12)
Tel: (01708) 345000
Bass M&B Brew XI **H**

🍺 D 🍺 ❀

A true, two-bar, community
estate pub. The square public
bar is relatively untouched by
brewery refurbishments.

Harold Wood B4

11-3; 5.30-11 (11-11 Fri/Sat: 12-3;
7-10.30 Sun)

King Harold
51 Station Road (½ mile South
of A12)
Tel: (01708) 342030
Ind Coope Burton Ale; **Tetley**
Bitter; **Youngs** Bitter **H**

🍺 🍺 ❀ ⇌

Comfortable, medium-sized
saloon, and more basic (and
cheaper) public bar. No food
Sundays.

11-11 (12 Sat) (12-10.30 Sun)

Palms Piano Bar
(Hilton National Hotel)
Southend Arterial Road (A127)
Tel: (01708) 346789
Free-house - No Real Ale.

11-11 (12-10.30 Sun)

Shepherd & Dog
91 Shepherds Hill
OS: TQ556905
Tel: (01708) 342028
Marstons Pedigree; **S&N**
Courage Best Bitter,
Theakstons BB, Websters
Yorkshire Bitter **H**

🍺 D ◀ ▶ R 🍺 🍺

Friendly, family pub with softly-
lit lounge and a more boisterous
public bar with a central pool
table. No food Sunday evenings.

Harwich F2

*Busy and historic port with
many fine buildings, the tread-
mill crane and some very quaint
streets. The main port facilities
have moved upstream to
Parkeston Quay.*

11.30 (11 Sat)-3; 7-11 (11-11
Fri/Sat in Summer: 12-3; 7-10.30
Sun, 12-10.30 Sun in Summer)

Alma Inn 1
25 Kings Head Street (off quay)
Tel: (01255) 503474
Greene King IPA, Abbot Ale;
Whitbread Flowers Original **H**

🍺 D ◀ ▶ 🍺 ❀

An unusual, circular bar is the
main feature of this pub, with
various artefacts reflecting the
nautical history of Harwich.
Good value food, but no
evening meals Sundays or
Mondays.

11-11 (may close if quiet: 12-3;
7-10.30 Sun)

Anchor Hotel 2
7 Stour Road, Bathside (nr A120)
Tel: (01255) 503897
Tolly Cobbold Original **H**

🍺 🛏 🐕 🍴 ⇌

Wedge-shaped, yellow-brick
pub, built in 1900, with an old-
fashioned interior and large
etched windows.

11-11 (12-10.30 Sun)

Angel 3
Kings Quay Street
Tel: (01255) 507241
Greene King IPA, Abbot Ale **H**

🍺 D 🍺 🛏 ⊨ ⇌

'U'-shaped bar, overlooking the
harbour and quay.

11-11 (12-10.30 Sun)

Billy 4
65 West Street (nr A120 &
B1352)
Tel: (01255) 502919
Tetley Bitter **H**

🍺 D ◀ ▶ ❀ ⇌

The only live music pub in
Harwich. Ideal for the young, or
the young at heart. Parking
difficult. Formerly the "Duke of
Edinburgh".

10.30-11 (12-10.30 Sun)

British Flag 5
56 West Street (nr A120 &
B1352)
Tel: (01255) 502717
Tetley Bitter **H**

🍺 D ◀ ▶ 🛏 ⇌

Typical town pub catering for all
types, with limited parking.

11-11 (12-10.30 Sun)

Classic (Haywain Hotel) 6
West Street (nr A120 & B1352)
Tel: (01255) 508300
Whitbread Boddingtons Bitter,
Flowers IPA **H**

🍺 D ◀ ▶ 🍺 🛏 ⇌

Modern pub/hotel offering
facilities for all.

East Coast Rock Cafe 7
Church Street
Free-house - No Real Ale.
Formerly the "Rendezvous".

Globe 8
Kings Quay Street
Allied Domecq - No Real Ale.

10.30-2; 6.30-11 (12-3; 7-10.30
Sun)

Hanover Inn 9
65 Church Street
Tel: (01255) 502927
Ridleys IPA, Witchfinder
Porter; **Tolly Cobbold** Mild,
Old Strong (Winter) **H**
Addlestone's Cider H

🍺 🛏 ⊨ ⇌

One of Harwich's historic buildings - Grade II listed with a
buried well in the cellar and a
nautical theme in the public bar.
Darts, pool and quiz teams.
Associations with the RNLI.

HARWICH

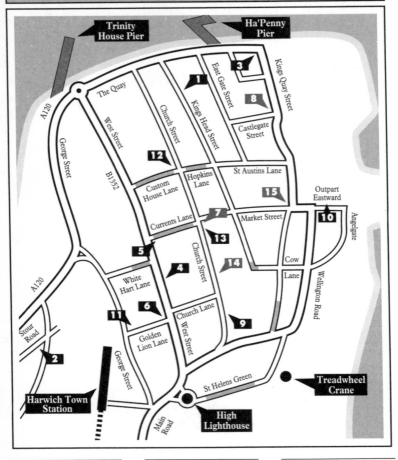

11-3; 7-11 (12-3; 7-10.30 Sun)

New Bell Inn   **10**
Outpart Eastward
Tel: (01255) 503545
S&N Courage Best Bitter,
Directors **H**
◖ ◖ **R** 🍴 🐾 ⇌
A pub since 1737, well-kept,
split-level with oak beams.
Friendly and inviting.

11-3; 6.30-11 (12-3; 7-10.30 Sun)

Sam's Wine Bar   **11**
31 Church Street / West Street
Tel: (01255) 503857
S&N John Smiths Bitter **H**
◖ ◖ ◖ **R** 🍴 🐾 ⇌
Comfortably furnished, friendly
wine bar.

Smugglers Inn   **12**
17 George Street / Golden Lion
Lane
'House Beer' H
◖ ◖ ◖ ⇌
Reopened as a free-house after a
period as a restaurant. Formerly
"Blazers" and the "Golden Lion".

10.30-11 (12-10.30 Sun)

Stingray   **13**
56 Church Street
Tel: (01255) 503507
Greene King IPA **H**
◖ ◖ ◖ **R** 🍴 🐾 ⇌
Town-style pub with discos at
weekends - held in the restau-
rant area.

Three Cups   **14**
64 Church Street
Tel: (01255) 553368
Pubmaster - Pub closed.

Wellington Inn   **15**
Kings Quay Street / Wellington
Road
Pubmaster - Pub closed.

Hastingwood   A3

Bull & Horseshoes
London Road (B1393), by
A414/M11 Jcn 7)
Allied - Pub closed - future
uncertain.

66

"The Cock Inn", Hatfield Broad Oak

11-3; 5.30-11 (12-3; 7-10.30 Sun)
Rainbow & Dove
Hastingwood Road,
Hastingwood Common (nr
A414/M11 Jcn 7)
Tel: (01279) 415419
Bass Draught Bass; **Ind Coope**
Friary Meux BB; **Guest Beer H**
◑ ◗ ◐ ▐ ☺ ❀
Small, friendly country pub, with
open log fire. Food is freshly
prepared and cooked. Worth
finding.

Hatfield Broad Oak B3

Typical, pleasant Essex village.

12-3; 6-11 (12-3 (or later); 7-10.30
Sun)
Cock Inn
High Street (B183)
Tel: (01279) 718273
Fullers London Pride; **Greene
King** IPA; **Guest Beers H**
Addlestones Cider H
◑ ◗ ◐ **R** ▐ ▭
Attractive, friendly village local,
with bare floorboards and
ancient beams. Guest beers
from independent breweries.
Imaginative menu of good quali-
ty food, the snacks include
'Essex Huffers'. No food Sunday
evenings. Bar billiards. Well-
worth a visit.

10.30-2.30; 5.30-11 (10.30-11 Sat;
12-10.30 Sun)
Dukes Head
High Street/Broad Street (B183)
Tel: (01279) 718283
S&N Courage Best Bitter,
Directors, Trumans IPA;
Guest Beers H
◑ ◗ ◐ **R** ▐ ☺ ❀
Popular, friendly, family pub,
ideal for children. Long-estab-
lished landlord.

Hatfield Heath B3

*Picturesque village on expansive
common with cricket pitch.*

Fox & Hounds
The Heath, Chelmsford Road
(A1060)
Greene King - Pub closed soon
after GK took over. It was then
sold without a licence, and
converted to a private house.

11-3; 5.30-11 (11-11 Fri/Sat; 12-
10.30 Sun)
Stag
The Heath, Chelmsford Road
(A1060)
Tel: (01279) 730404
Morlands Old Speckled Hen;
S&N Courage Best Bitter,
Directors; **Guest Beer H**
◑ ◗ ◐ ⊞ ❀
Traditional, two-bar, 17th
century pub - the only one on
the heath with adequate parking
(at the rear). Renowned for its
fish dishes - delivered fresh from
Cornwall twice a month.
Motel-type chalets expected at
the rear. Live music is popular
on Sunday evenings.
Wheelchair ramps available.
Patio at rear.

11.30-3; 6-11 (12-3; 7-10.30 Sun)
Thatchers
Stortford Road (A1060)
Tel: (01279) 730270
Bass Draught Bass; **Greene
King** IPA; **Guest Beer H**
◑ ◗ ◐ **R** ❀
Comfortable, modernised, 500
year old thatched inn, located
just off the heath. Guest beer
includes local microbreweries.
Open-plan interior, with eating
area to rear.

11.30-11 (12-10.30 Sun)
White Horse Inn
The Heath (A1060)
Tel: (01279) 730351
Greene King IPA, Abbot Ale,
Seasonal beers (occasional) **H**
◑ ◗ ◐ ⊞ ❀
Friendly, old, timbered pub with
deceptively large interior, large
garden and children's play area
to the rear. 'A la carte' restaurant
in the evenings. Believed to
have a 'cask breather' on the
IPA. Limited parking.

Hatfield Peverel C3

Useful stop-off point on the A12.

10-2.30; 5.30-11 (12-3; 7-10.30
Sun)
Cross Keys
The Green (nr B1019)
Tel: (01245) 380455
Greene King IPA, Abbot Ale;
Guest Beers G
◑ ◗ ▐ ❀ ♿
Friendly, one-bar, Gray and
Sons local.

11-11 (12-10.30 Sun)
Duke Of Wellington
The Street (B1137, jcn with
B1019)
Tel: (01245) 380246
Ridleys IPA, ESX, Rumpus **H**
◑ ◗ ▐ ❀ ⇌
Roadhouse, with regular
karaoke.

11-3; 6-11 (12-3; 7-10.30 Sun)
Swan Inn
The Street (B1137)
Tel: (01245) 380238
Bass Draught Bass; **Greene
King** IPA, seasonal beers **H**
◑ ◗ ◐ ⋈ ❀ ⇌
Popular, one-bar village local.

67

11-3 (4 Sat); 6-11 (12-4; 7-10.30 Sun)

Wheatsheaf
Maldon Road (B1019)
Tel: (01245) 380330
Ridleys IPA, ESX **H**
⓪⏻ⓛ⏻🍴 ⊞ **H**
Friendly local, with good food
served throughout the week.
Beware beer served on
'sparklers'.

11-3.30; 6-11 (12-3; 7-10.30 Sun)

William Boosey
The Street (B1137)
Tel: (01245) 380205
Marstons Pedigree; **Ridleys**
ESX; **Whitbread** Boddingtons
Bitter, Flowers IPA, Original **H**
⓪⏻ⓛ⏻ **R** 🍴 🐴 ❀
Ladies and Gents darts teams,
singles club on Tuesdays, quiz
nights Wednesdays.

Havering-Atte-Bower   A4

*Delightful village with green and
stocks. Fine views towards the
Thames and the City of London.*

11-11 (12-10.30 Sun)

Orange Tree
Orange Tree Hill (B175)
Tel: (01708) 740471
Tetley Bitter; **Guest Beer H**
⓪⏻ⓛ⏻ **R** ⊞ ❀
Refurbished and converted into
a 'Big Steak' pub. Guest beer
from the 'Tapsters' Choice'
range. Fine views over Romford
towards North Kent from the
beer garden.

11-3; 6-11 (12-3; 7-10.30 Sun)

Royal Oak
North Road (B175)
Tel: (01708) 744523
Greene King IPA **H**
⏻ⓛ⏻ **R** ❀ ♿
Refurbished pub with a patio at
the front, and a garden and
restaurant at the rear. Real Ale
not always available. Back with
its original name after a while as
the "Willows".

Hawkwell   D4

11-11 (12-10.30 Sun)

White Hart
White Hart Lane / Main Road (by
B1013)
Tel: (01702) 203438
S&N Courage Best Bitter,
Directors, Theakstons XB,
Websters Yorkshire Bitter **H**
⓪⏻ ⓛ **R** ❀
Friendly local overlooking small
recreation park area.

Hazel End (Farnham)   A2

12-11 (Closes Mon-Thu afternoons: 12-3; 7-10.30 Sun)

Three Horseshoes
On the road from Bishop's
Stortford to Manuden
OS: TL496243
Tel: (01279) 813429
S&N Courage Directors; **St
Austell** Dartmoor BB; **Tetley**
Bitter **H**
⓪⏻ ⓛ⏻ ❀
Popular country pub with
amazing matchbox collection.
No meals Sunday to Tuesday
evenings.

Hazeleigh   D4

11-4; 6-11 (12-10.30 Sun)

Royal Oak
Fambridge Road (B1018)
OS: TL849047
Tel: (01621) 853249
Greene King XX Mild **H**, IPA **G**
⓪⏻ ⓛ⏻ **R** ⊞ ❀
Popular, country Grays pub, one
mile south of Maldon, with well-
kept beer. Camping nearby.

Heckfordbridge (Birch)   D2

*Less than a mile South-West of
the much-improved Colchester
Zoo.*

11.30-2.30; 6-11 (12-3; 7-10.30
Sun)

Angel Inn
Maldon Road (B1022)
Tel: (01206) 330225
S&N Courage Best Bitter,
Trumans IPA **H**
⓪⏻ ⓛ⏻ **R** ⊞ ❀
Pleasant, multi-beamed pub
with duck pond and large safe
garden - ideal for children.
Plenty of pictures on the walls,
note the unusual seats in the
fireplace, and the 'Bowler &
Sons of Colchester' clock.

Helions Bumpstead   C1

11.45-2.30; 7-11 (12-2.30; 7-10.30
Sun)

Three Horseshoes
Water Lane
OS: TL650414
Tel: (01440) 730298
Greene King IPA, Abbot Ale;
Guest Beer H
⓪⏻ ⓛ⏻ **R** ⊞ ❀
Fine old pub in remote setting,
with jovial landlord and prize-
winning gardens. No meals on
Sundays, no evening meals
Mondays or Tuesdays. Worth
finding.

Hempstead   B1

*Birthplace of Dick Turpin and
blood circulation discoverer
William Harvey.*

11.30-3; 6.30-11 (12-4; 7-10.30
Sun)

Bluebell Inn
High Street (B1054)
Tel: (01799) 599486
Greene King IPA; **Ruddles**
County; **S&N** Courage Directors;
Guest Beers H
⓪⏻ ⓛ⏻ **R** 🐴 ❀ ❀
Friendly atmosphere, in the
comfortably-refurbished, 16th
century, listed village local.
Turpins' Restaurant. No food
Sunday evenings. Formerly the
"Rose & Crown".

Henham   B2

*Attractive village with greens,
thatch and duck ponds.*

12-3; 6-11 (12-3; 7-10.30 Sun)

Cock
Church End (nr B1051)
OS: TL545286
Tel: (01279) 850347
Adnams Bitter; **Greene King**
IPA; **Marstons** Pedigree **H**
⓪⏻ ⓛ⏻ **R** ❀
Attractive village pub with oak
beams, open studwork and
inglenook fireplace.

Henny Street (Gt Henny)   D1

11-3; 6-11 (12-3; 7-10.30 Sun)

Swan
Henny Street (2 miles South of
A131)
OS: TL879385
Tel: (01787) 269238
Greene King IPA, Abbot Ale **H**
⓪⏻ ⓛ⏻ **R** ⊞ 🍴 ❀ ♿
Traditional, rural, country pub,
on the banks of River Stour, with
fishing rights. Immaculately
kept. Large riverbank drinking
area, very popular in Summer.
Vast, ever-changing menu, of
home-made food. Huge pig
roasts in Summer, full a-la-carte
menu.

Herongate   B4

*Small village with attractive vil-
lage sign. Greatly improved
since by-passed by M25.*

11-11 (12-10.30 Sun)

Boars Head Tavern
15 Billericay Road (nr A128)
Tel: (01277) 810324
S&N Courage Directors, Johns
Smiths Bitter, Theakstons BB **H**
⓪⏻ ⓛ⏻ ❀
Picturesque, food-oriented pub,
with small lake in garden. Pub
dates from the 16th century.
Limited parking.

68

11-3; 6-11 (12-10.30 Sun)

Green Man
11 Cricketers Lane (nr A128)
Tel: (01277) 810292
Adnams Bitter; **Ind Coope**
Burton Ale; **Marstons** Pedigree;
Tetley Bitter; **Guest Beer H**
🛇🍴🛇🖕🐕✂
Well-decorated, with real fire.
Guest beers from the "Tapsters
Choice" range. Shove Ha'penny
- ask for board. Occasional live
music and beer festivals.
Children's play area in the
garden.

Herongate Tye B4

11 (12 Sat)-2.30; 6-11 (12-3.30; 7-
10.30 Sun)

Olde Dog Inn
Billericay Road, Herongate Tye
(1 mile East of A128)
OS: TQ641910
Tel: (01277) 810337
Greene King IPA, Abbot Ale;
Nethergate Golden Gate;
Ridleys IPA, Spectacular;
Guest Beers H/G
Westons Old Rosie **G**
🛇🍴🛇🅁🛋🖕🐕♿🏵
Friendly, old country pub, now
popular for its large selection of
Real Ales and home-cooked
food. Guest beers include the
Mauldon's and Mighty Oak
range, many straight from the
cask.

Heybridge D3

*Once a thriving canalside com-
munity, now an extension of
Maldon.*

*(See Maldon map for location of
pubs).*

10.30-3; 5.30-11 (10.30-11.30
Fri/Sat: 12-10.30 Sun)

Anchor H1
The Square (B1019)
Tel: (01621) 853448
Greene King IPA, Abbot Ale;
Nethergate IPA **H**
🛇🍴🏵
Refurbished eighteenth century
village pub. Meals available
every lunchtime - including
Sunday Roasts, evening meals
may be available by prior
arrangement.
Quiz nights or live music every
Friday. Beware 'Scrumpy Jack'
on handpump.

12-11 (10.30 Sun)

Benbridge Hotel H2
The Square (B1019)
Tel: (01621) 857666/8
Ridleys IPA, Rumpus **H**
🛇🍴🛇🅁🛋🖕🛏🚗
Smart hotel and restaurant,
dating from 1735. Real Ale not
always available.

11-11 (12-10.30 Sun)

Half Moon H3
The Square (B1019)
Tel: (01621) 854215
Greene King IPA **H**
🛇🍴🛇🖕
Large, single bar divided into
two distinct areas by central
servery. Occasional live music at
weekends, pool table - note
unusual pool clock.
May be closed for conversion to
OAP residential home.

11.30-3; 5-11 (11.30-11 Fri: 12-3;
7-10.30 Sun)

Heybridge Inn H4
34 The Street (B1022)
Tel: (01621) 853545
Greene King IPA; **S&N** Courage
Directors; **Guest Beers H**
🛇🍴🛇🅁
One of the oldest buildings in
Heybridge, which was a mill in
times gone by. Regularly-chang-
ing guest beers. Formerly the
"Queens Head".

11.30-3.30; 6.15-11 (12-3; 7-10.30
Sun)

Maltsters Arms H5
Hall Road (nr B1022)
Tel: (01621) 853880
Greene King IPA, Abbot Ale **G**
🏵
Friendly, discreetly-lit Grays
local - a drinkers pub. The formi-
ca-topped counter and elderly
till help create a 1960s 'feel'.
Limited parking.

Heybridge Basin D3

*Interesting village where
Chelmer-Blackwater canal meets
the sea.*

11.30-3(ish); 6-11 (11-11 Sat: 12-
10.30 Sun)

Jolly Sailor
The Basin
Tel: (01621) 854210
Greene King IPA **H**
🛇🍴🛇🅁🛏🏵♿
A pub since 1798, then serving
Wells and Perry beers delivered
by canal from Chelmsford.
A traditional, popular riverside
inn - recently refurbished.
Gigantic sandwiches!

"The Jolly Sailor", Heybridge Basin

11-3; 6-11 (11-11 Sat: 12-10.30 Sun)

Old Ship
Lock Hill, The Basin
Tel: (01621) 854150
Adnams Broadside; **Nethergate**
IPA; **Tetley** Bitter **H**
◑ ◐ ◑ ◗ 🍺
Pleasant and friendly pub with fine views over estuary to Northey Island. Unique, carved handpump handles commemorating the Maldon Millennium. Occasional sea-song festivals.

High Beach   A4

In the heart of Epping Forest.

11-11 (12-3.30; 7-10.30 Sun)

Duke Of Wellington
Wellington Hill (nr A104 & A121)
OS: TQ407985
Tel: (0181) 508 1566
Ind Coope Burton Ale;
Marstons Pedigree; **Tetley**
Bitter **H**
◑ ◐ ◑ ◗ 🍺
Friendly one-bar pub on the fringe of Epping Forest, with horse brasses, plates and brass cask taps. Bar billiards played. Camping nearby. Summer barbecues.

12-11 (12-3; 7-10.30 Sun)

Kings Oak
Nursery Road/Wake Road
(½ mile off A104)
Tel: (0181) 508 5000
Morlands Old Speckled Hen;
S&N Courage Best Bitter,
Directors **H**
◑ ◐ ◑ ◫ 🛏 🍴 🍺
Family pub, with entertainment for the kids, pool tables and a good function room. Good views of sunsets outside. Can be busy at weekends.

11-11 (12-3; 7-10.30 Sun)

Robin Hood
Epping New Road (A104)
Tel: (0181) 508 1104
S&N Courage Best Bitter,
Directors; **Guest Beers H**
◑ ◐ ◑ ◗ 🛏 🍺 ♿
Large roadhouse in the heart of Epping Forest, with plans for a garden bar. Guest beers include Marstons Pedigree and Ruddles County. Jazz on Fridays, and occasional discos.

High Easter   B3

Unspoilt village.

12-3; 7-11 (10.30 Sun)

Cock & Bell Inn
The Street
Tel: (01245) 231296
Guest Beers H
◑ ◐ ◑ **R** 🍴 🚂
14th century, grade 2 listed building, steeped in history and retaining many original features. Good beer, good food - full 'a la carte' menu - and a friendly welcome await. Try the recommended walk - a map is available from the pub.

High Garrett   C2

11-3; 7-11 (closed Mon: 11-11
Sat: 12-10.30 Sun)

Hare & Hounds
Grange Hill Road (A131)
Tel: (01376) 324430
Greene King IPA, Abbot Ale **H**
◑ ◐ ◑ **R** 🍴
Friendly, renovated 'stripped-pine' pub. B&B.

High Ongar   B3

11-3.30 (flexible); 6-11 (11-11 Sat:
12-10.30 Sun)

Foresters Arms
The Street (off A414)
Tel: (01277) 363626
Adnams Bitter; **Greene King**
IPA, Abbot Ale; **Guest Beer H**
◑ ◐ ◑ 🍺
Friendly and comfortable freehouse. No food Sunday and Tuesday evenings.

Red Lion
The Street (off A414)
Tel: (01277) 362733
Sycamore Taverns - No Real Ale. The landlord admitted that the handpumped 'Websters' was on 'Top Pressure'.

High Roding   B3

Linear village with fine half-timbered thatched cottages.

11-3; 6-11 (12-3; 7-10.30 Sun)

Black Lion
The Street (B184)
OS: TL602171
Tel: (01279) 872847
Ridleys IPA, ESX **G**
◑ ◐ ◑ **R** ◫ 🍺 ♿
Splendid, 15th century, timber-framed pub with a lot of character. The handpumps are 'ornamental' - the beer is on gravity from the cellar.

Old Lamb
The Street (B184)
Free-house - Pub closed.

Hockley   D4

11-11 (12-10.30 Sun)

Bull Inn
99 Main Road (B1013)
Tel: (01702) 203122
Morlands Old Speckled Hen;
S&N Courage Best Bitter,
Directors; **Guest Beers H**
◑ ◐ ◑ 🍺
Olde worlde and friendly, with a wealth of beams and a separate enclosed garden for kids and dovecote. The marquee in the grounds is available for weddings, etc.
Sadly, this Grade II listed traditional building was threatened with conversion into yet another pub/restaurant by Scottish Courage.
A CAMRA-supported campaign called 'STOP' (Save The Original Pub) has been set up to try to save as much of the original structure as possible.

11-11 (12-10.30 Sun)

Dome
Dome Country Club and Caravan Park, Lower Road
Tel: (01702) 230278
Greene King IPA **H**
◑ ◐ ◑ 🍺
Caravan & Country Club bar, now open to the public, with late licence on Fridays and Saturdays. Children's Certificate. Live music, including Rock & Roll, and Country & Western. Food, such as scampi or burgers, now available all sessions.

10-11 (12-10.30 Sun)

Spa
60 Southend Road (B1013)
Tel: (01702) 202173
Ind Coope 'House' Bitter;
Tetley Bitter **H**
◑ ◐ ◫ 🍺 ⇌
Imposing split-level town centre pub. 'Hasty-Tasty' menu.

Holland-on-Sea F3

The quieter end of Clacton, now one giant retirement home! Note that despite appearances, "The Tavern" at 55/57 Frinton Road, is a club.

11-3; 7-11 (12-3; 7-10.30 Sun, 12-10.30 Sun after Easter)

Flamingo
Queens Court, Kings Parade
OS: TM197159
Tel: (01255) 812239
Ridleys IPA **H**
◑ ◐ ◑ **R** 🚂
Modern-style, seafront bar-cum-restaurant, opposite the "King's Cliff Hotel"

11-3; 5.30-11 (11-11 Sat: 12-3; 7-10.30 Sun, 12-10.30 Sun after Easter)

King's Cliff Hotel
55 Kings Parade
Tel: (01255) 812343
Greene King IPA, Abbot Ale **H**
◑ ◐ ◑ **R** 🍴 🛏 🍺
Stylish, Regency hotel bar, Greene King's original flagship in the area.

11-3 (Not Mon/Tue); 6.30-12 (12-7 Sun)

Maffias
143 Frinton Road (B1032)
Tel: (01255) 812151
Free-house - No Real Ale.

11-3; 6-11 (12-3; 7-10.30 Sun)

Oakwood Inn
175 Frinton Road (B1032)
Tel: (01255) 813804
Ruddles Best Bitter; **S&N**
Websters Yorkshire Bitter H
⊄ D ⊄ ▶ ❀
Large 15th century inn, now
enveloped by Holland-on-Sea.

11-11 (12-10.30 Sun)

Roaring Donkey
316 Holland Road (B1032)
Tel: (01255) 812104
Greene King IPA; **Guest Beers** H
⊄ D ⊞ ❀ ⅊
Greene King's flagship family
pub, now converted to a
'Hungry Horse' theme
pub/restaurant following refur-
bishment in Spring 1998.

Hornchurch   B5

*A town of contrasts with ter-
races and detached houses.
Langtons house and gardens is
nice.*

11-11 (11-3; 5.30-11 Fri/Sat: 12-4;
7-10.30 Sun)

Chequers
North Street (nr A124)
Tel: (01708) 442094
Ind Coope 'House' Bitter,
Friary Meux BB; **Youngs**
Bitter; **Guest Beers** H
⊄ D ⅊ ⇌
Small, traditional and very popu-
lar, community locals pub on
traffic island, with excellent
value beers. The guest beer is
from the 'Tapsters Choice'
range. Keen darts following -
several teams. Local CAMRA
'Pub-of-the-Year' 1997 and 1998.
No meals at weekends. Limited
car parking.

11-3; 5-11 (11-11 Sat: 12-10.30
Sun)

Compasses
125 Abbs Cross Lane (nr A124)
Tel: (01708) 450240
Bass Draught Bass H
⊄ D ⊄ ▶ R ❀ ⅊
Suburban pub almost opposite
to Harrow Lodge Park, now con-
verted to a 'Harvester'.

11-11 (12-5; 7-10.30 Sun)

Cricketers
64-68 High Street (A124)
Tel: (01708) 442168
Hardys Popes Bitter; **Ruddles**
County; **S&N** Websters
Yorkshire Bitter H
⊄ ▶ R ⊨ ⟺ ⅊
Friendly pub with carvery, live
music and charity quizzes.

11-11 (12-10.30 Sun)

Crown
360 Hornchurch Road (A124)
Tel: (01708) 447656
S&N Theakstons BB, XB H
⊄ D ⊄ ▶ R ⊞ ❀
Large pub with patio. Quiz
nights on Tuesday, regular disco
nights.

11-11 (12-10.30 Sun)

Fatling & Firkin
109 High Street (A124)
Tel: (01708) 442125
Ford & Firkin Bully Bitter,
Fatling Ale, Rodeo Ale,
Dogbolter; **Guest Beer**
(occasional) H
⊄ D ⊄ ▶ ⌁
Tasteful conversion of the old
"Bull" pub into a non-brewing
'Firkin', although retaining some
connection with its historic past.
Beers come from the new "Ford
& Firkin" brewpub in Romford.
Loud music, particularly in the
evenings, and Sky Sports on a
large screen. Games and events!
Beware 'Addlestones' Cider may
be on CO2 pressure.
Tight 'sparklers' used - ask for
them to be removed when
ordering. Limited parking.

11.30-11 (12-10.30 Sun)

Harrow
130 Hornchurch Road (A124)
Tel: (01708) 449271
Tetley Bitter; **Guest Beer** H
⊄ D ⊄ ▶ R ⊞ ❀ ⅊
Much-enlarged 'Big Steak' pub,
with fish stall outside.

11-11 (12-10.30 Sun)

JJ Moons
Unit 3, 48-52 High Street (A124)
Tel: (01708) 478410
Greene King IPA, Abbot; **S&N**
Courage Directors, Theakstons
BB, **Guest Beers** H
⊄ D ⊄ ▶ ⅊ ⌁ ✂
A 'JD Wetherspoon' pub,
initially built in a single, long and
narrow, new shop unit. It was
extended into the adjacent unit
as trade built-up. Plenty of
framed photos of old
Hornchurch.
Improved range of guest beers.
Beer festivals in April and
November. Tight 'Sparklers'
sometimes used - so check
when ordering, and ask for them
to be removed if you are choos-
ing a 'Southern' beer.

10-11 (12-10.30 Sun)

Kings Head
189 High Street (A124)
Tel: (01708) 443934
Morlands Old Speckled Hen;
S&N Courage Directors,
Websters Yorkshire Bitter;
Guest Beer H
⊄ D ⊨ ⇌ ⊖
Popular, town centre pub, espe-
cially with youngsters. Meals on
weekdays, only snacks on
Saturdays.

11-11 (12-10.30 Sun)

Newt & Cucumber
168 High Street (A124)
Tel: (01708) 472962
Morlands Independents IPA,
Old Speckled Hen; **Ruddles**
County; **S&N** Theakstons BB;
Tetley Bitter H
⊄ D ⊄ ▶ ⊨ ⇌ ⊖
Converted in 1997, from one
'theme' - Allied Domecq's
'Exchange' - into another -
Morland's 'Newt and
Cucumber'!
Not all the beers are always 'on'
at the same time. Formerly
"Madison Exchange" and the
"White Hart".

12-3; 6-11 (12-3; 7-10.30 Sun)

Queens Theatre (Greene Room Bar / Pit Bar)
Billet Lane (nr A124)
Tel: (01708) 456118
Greene King IPA, Abbot Ale,
seasonal ales (occasional) H
Guest Beers G
⊄ D ⊄ ⊱ ⇌
Modern, theatre pub with jazz on
Sunday lunchtimes. Interesting
range of guest beers straight
from the cask - look for the
'Guest List'. Food available until
7pm. Closed Sunday evenings if
no performance.

11-11 (11-4; 6-11 Fri: 12-4;
7-10.30 Sun)

Railway Hotel
Station Lane
Tel: (01708) 476415
Tetley Bitter H
⊄ D ⊄ ▶ ⊞ ⋈ ⊨ ⊱ ❀ ⅊ ⊖
Comfortable, traditional and a
little expensive, two-bar pub,
with accommodation. No meals
at weekends or Friday evenings.

11-11 (12-10.30 Sun)

Spencers Arms
122 Ardleigh Green Road
(½ mile South of A127)
Tel: (01708) 442550
Taylor Walker - No Real Ale.

Horndon-on-the-Hill   B5

*Quiet, hill-top village with half-
timbered Guildhall. Much-
relieved by by-pass.*

10 (11 Sat)-2.30 (3 Sat); 6-11 (12-
3; 7-10.30 Sun)

Bell Inn
High Road (nr B1007)
Tel: (01375) 672451
Bass Draught Bass G; **Fullers**
London Pride; **Mighty Oak**
Burntwood Bitter; **Guest Beers**
H/G
⊄ D ⊄ R ⋈ ⊨ ❀ ⅊
Busy, 15th century coaching inn
with hot cross bun collection on
beams, started in 1900 and still
going strong! No live or canned
music and no games machines.
The award-winning restaurant is
Egon Ronay listed.

11-3 (5 Sat); 6-11 (12-5; 6-10.30 Sun)

Swan
High Road (nr B1007)
Tel: (01375) 640617
Adnams Bitter; **Tetley** Bitter;
Guest Beers H
🍺 🍴 R ⊞ ⊫ ❀
'Tapsters Choice' range of guest beers. Home-cooked food, book for Sunday lunches. Background music. Football, cricket and golf teams.

Horsley Cross   E2

11-11 (12-10.30 Sun)

Cross Inn
Clacton Road (A120)
Tel: (01206) 396391
Greene King IPA; **Guest Beer H**
🍺 🍴 R ⊞ ❀
Pleasant, 'beamed' roadside pub and eating place, an ideal introduction for visitors to Britain from the continent, after landing at Harwich.

Horsleycross Street   E2

11-3; 6-11 (12-3; 6-10.30 Sun)

Hedgerows
Clacton Road (B1035)
Tel: (01206) 395585
Bass Draught Bass; **Ridleys** IPA, ESX **H**
🍺 🍴 R ⊫ ❀
Mock-Tudor interior is balanced by wrought iron furniture. A fine rural setting.

Howe Street   C3

12-3; 5.30-11 (11.30-11 Sat: 12-10.30 Sun)

Green Man
Dunmow Road (nr A130)
Tel: (01245) 360203
Ridleys IPA, ESX, seasonal beers **H**
🍺 🍴 R ⊞ ❀
Fine, 14th century building, and possibly the oldest pub in Essex. Log fire in the lounge bar. Good food. Licensed camping and caravan site.

Howlett End (Wimbish)   B1

12-2.30 (3 Sat); 6.30 (7 Sat)-11 (12-3; 7-10.30 Sun)

White Hart
Thaxted Road, Howlett End (B184)
OS: TL582348
Tel: (01799) 599203
Greene King IPA; **Guest Beer H**
🍺 🍴 ⊫ ⛾ ❀
Pleasant comfortable 300 year old Grade II listed free-house. Field with caravans. CAMRA members welcome. Beer range may increase.

Hullbridge   D4
Seriously underpubbed!

11-11 (12-10.30 Sun)

Anchor
284 Ferry Road
Tel: (01702) 230205
Greene King IPA; **S&N**
Theakstons BB, XB, Old Peculier **H**
🍺 🍴 ⛾ ❀ ⚓
Large, comfortable and friendly pub on the riverside, affording good views of South Woodham Ferrers - adventurous (foolhardy ?) drivers have crossed the river at low tide!.
Extensive gardens and 'designer' play area for children.

Hutton   B4

12 (11 Sat)-11 (12-10.30 Sun)

Chequers
213 Rayleigh Road (A129)
Tel: (01277) 224980
Bass Draught Bass; **Fullers** London Pride; **Guest Beer H**
🍺 ⦿ ⊞ ❀
Traditional local, dating back to the 18th century or earlier. The guest beer is usually from an independent brewery. Nice garden, extensive pub games with live music on Wednesdays.

11-11 (12-10.30 Sun)

Hutton
15 Rayleigh Road (A129)
Tel: (01277) 215240
S&N Courage Best Bitter, Directors, John Smiths Bitter, Theakstons BB **H**
🍺 🍴 ❀
Comfortable, beamed, suburban pub. Limited parking.

11-11 (12-10.30 Sun)

Maxwells (Hungry Horse)
Hanging Hill Lane / Hutton Drive (nr A129)
Tel: (01277) 222609
Bass Toby Cask; **Greene King** IPA, Abbot Ale **H**
🍺 🍴 ⦿ ⚓
Refurbished 'Magic' Pub with patio and much-expanded food operation. May be renamed. Formerly the "Woodpecker".

12-3; 5.30-11 (12-11 Sat: 12-10.30 Sun)

Plough
570 Rayleigh Road (A129)
OS: TQ648948
Tel: (01277) 210255
Morlands Old Speckled Hen; **S&N** Courage Best Bitter **H**
🍺 🍴 ⦿ R ⊞ ⊫ ❀
Much-improved pub at the edge of Hutton. Regular live music, including jazz on Thursdays. Quizzes Wednesdays. Sunday lunches, no food Sunday evenings. Formerly the "Sir Winston Churchill".

Ilford   A5
Old style town, gradually being rejuvenated by new development. Valentines park is very pleasant.

11-11 (12-10.30 Sun)

Bell
308 Ley Street (nr A123)
Tel: (0181) 478 1302
Greene King Abbot Ale; **S&N** Theakstons BB, Websters Yorkshire Bitter **H**
🍺 🍴 ⦿ ⚓
Spacious 'Barras & Co.' pub with an all day menu, including many sausage specialities. Regular promotions. Occasional live music. Limited parking.

11-11 (12-10.30 Sun)

Black Horse
1 Chapel Road (A123)
Tel: (0181) 478 7060
Whitbread - No Real Ale.

11-11 (12 Wed-Sat: 12-10.30 Sun)

Cauliflower
553 High Road (A118)
Tel: (0181) 478 0627
S&N Courage Best Bitter **H**
🍺 🍴 ⦿ ⊞ ⚓ ⚞
Massive, well-known Victorian pub, with regular live music. Limited parking. No food on Sundays.

11-4 (8 Wed,11 Thu-Sat) Closed Sun.

Copperfields
229/231 Cranbrook Road (A123)
Tel: (0181) 554 8884
New free-house - No Real Ale.

11-11 (12-10.30 Sun)

Cranbrook
182 Cranbrook Road (A123)
Tel: (0181) 554 7326
S&N John Smiths Bitter, Theakstons BB, Websters Yorkshire Bitter **H**
🍺 🍴 ⦿ ⚓
At the end of the Ilford shopping area and close to Valentines Park. Live music on Fridays. Pool room separate from the rest of the pub. Real Ale not always available.

11-11 (12-10.30 Sun)

General Havelock
229 High Road (nr A118)
Tel: (0181) 478 0512
Ind Coope 'House' Bitter;
Tetley Bitter **H**
🍺 🍴 ⦿ ⊫ 🚻 ⚞
Converted to a comfortable 'Salmon & Hare' theme town-centre pub, serving a good variety of food. An improvement on previous refurbishments - but sadly the initial range of guest beers have gone. Parking difficult. Formerly "Havelocks".

11-11 (12-10.30 Sun)

Great Spoon of Ilford
114/116 Cranbrook Road (A123)
Tel: (0181) 518 0535
Hop Back Summer Lightning;
Fullers London Pride; **S&N**
Courage Directors, Theakstons
BB, XB; **Guest Beers H**
❶ ◨ ◐ ◼ ❶ ⛧ ⇌
New 'Wetherspoon' in former
video shop, popular with all
ages. Friendly, relaxing and
good value. Meals include daily
specials.
Beer choice has improved considerably - usually three to four
guest beers available. No music.

11-11 (12-10.30 Sun)

Hogshead
74/76 Cranbrook Road (A123)
Tel: (0181) 478 7645
Greene King Abbot Ale;
Marstons Pedigree; **Whitbread**
Boddingtons Bitter, Flowers
IPA, Original, Abroad Cooper;
Wadworths 6X; **Guest Beers H**
❶ ◀ ❺ ⇌
New Whitbread 'Hogshead'
conversion of former building
society offices, which opened in
June 1997. Some beers are
expensive, and the range has
been uninspiring - compared to
other 'Hogsheads'.

11-3; 5-11 (11-11 Fri/Sat)

Hope (Mr Qs)
19/21 Chapel Road (A123)
Tel: (0181) 478 2161
Allied - No Real Ale. Formerly
the "Hope Revived".

11-11 (12-10.30 Sun)

Jono's Bar
37 Cranbrook Road (A123)
Tel:
Free-house - No Real Ale
(Handpumps sadly disused).
Opened in June 1997.

11-11 (1am Fri/Sat) (12-10.30
Sun)

O'Neill's
Station Road (nr A123)
Tel: (0181) 478 3297
Bass (O'Neill's) - No Real Ale.
Formerly the "Angel".

11-11 (12-10.30 Sun)

Papermakers Arms
57 Roden Street (nr A118/A123
& A406)
Tel: (0181) 478 0501
S&N Courage Best Bitter,
Directors, Websters Yorkshire
Bitter **H**
❶ ◀ ⇌
Back-street local, near
Sainsbury's and the town-centre. Darts league. No food
Sundays. Limited parking.

11-11 (12-10.30 Sun)

Plough
417 Ilford Lane (A123)
Tel: (0181) 553 4507
Bass - No Real Ale.

11-3; 5.15-11 (11-11 Fri/Sat: 12-
10.30 Sun)

Prince Of Wales
63 Green Lane (A1083)
Tel: (0181) 478 1326
Ind Coope Burton Ale; **Tetley**
Bitter **H**
❶ ◀ ◐ ⛧
Very pleasant pub, catering
mainly for locals. Three separate
bar areas, including a snug, and
a secluded split-level patio-garden. Excellent value food (not
weekends) and good beer.

11-11 (12-10.30 Sun)

Rat & Carrot
71 Ilford Hill (A118)
Tel: (0181) 478 0867
Bass Draught Bass; **Greene**
King IPA; **S&N** Courage
Directors, Whitbread
Boddingtons Bitter **H**
❶ ◀ ◐ ⛧
Lively, busy and popular theme
pub, close to the town-centre.
Regular discos, quiz nights and
other functions. Real Ale not
always available. Formerly
"Mainstreet" and the "Red Lion".

11-11 (12-10.30 Sun)

Red Cow
104 Ley Street (nr A123)
Tel: (0181) 478 4001
Tetley Bitter **H**
❶ ◀ ❺ ⛧
Back-street pub near the
Exchange shopping centre.
Comfortable saloon and a public
bar with pool, darts and TV. Beer
garden at rear, with occasional
barbecues.

11-11 (12-10.30 Sun)

Rose & Crown
16 Ilford Hill (A118, nr A406)
Tel: (0181) 478 7104
Ind Coope 'House' Bitter;
Marstons Pedigree; **Tetley**
Bitter; **Guest Beers H**
❶ ◀ ◼ ⇌
Friendly, split-level 'Festival Ale
House' near town centre, with
small patio at rear and consistently good beer. Up to five
guest beers from independents
and micro breweries. Occasional
quiz nights and discos. Parking
difficult.

Stop Out
291-293 High Road
Tel: (0181) 478 0451
Free-house - no longer a pub.

Ingatestone   B4

*Large village with very narrow
High Street, centre has been
spoilt.*

11-3; 5-11 (11-11 Fri/Sat: 12-3; 7-
10.30 Sun)

Bell
55 High Street (B1002)
Tel: (01277) 353314
Bass Hancocks HB, Draught
Bass; **Guest Beer H**
❶ ◨ ◐ ◼ ❺ ⛧ ⇌
Old coaching inn with interesting collection of jugs and
regularly changing guest beer.

12-11 (12-4; 7-10.30 Sun)

Crown Inn
High Street (B1002)
Tel: (01277) 353538
Greene King IPA **H**
❶ ◐ ⛧
One-bar pub with pool table in
separate room.

12-2.30 (3 Sat); 5 (6 Sat)-11 (12-
3.30; 7-10.30 Sun)

Newell's Bar
High Street (B1002)
Tel: (01277) 353339
Bass Hancocks HB, Brew XI **H**
❶ ❺ ⛧
Comfortable, street-corner pub.
Parking difficult. Formerly the
"Anchor".

11-2.30; 5.45-11 (12-3; 7-10.30
Sun)

Star
High Street (B1002)
Tel: (01277) 353618
Greene King IPA, Abbot Ale **G**
▆ ⛚ ⛧ ⇌
Cosy, old, Gray & Sons village
local with one bar. Live music,
country or folk, Monday and
Thursday evenings. Old renovated bakehouse at rear, used as
Meeting room. Huge log fire in
Winter.

Inworth   D3

12-2.30; 5-11 (12-11: 12-10.30
Sun)

Prince Of Wales
The Street / Kelvedon Road
(B1023)
Tel: (01376) 570813
Greene King IPA, Abbot Ale **H**
❶ ◐ ◐ ⇌ ❺ ▆ ⛧ ⛒
Refurbished and extended country pub with emphasis on food.

Ivy Chimneys   A4

11 (11.30 Sat)-3; 6-11 (12-3; 7-
10.30 Sun)

Spotted Dog
Ivy Chimneys Road (nr B1393)
Tel: (01378) 572612
Whitbread Boddingtons Bitter,
Flowers IPA **H**
❶ ◐ ◐ ◼ **R** ⛧ ⛒
A 'foody', family pub. The
restaurant is closed Sunday and
Monday evenings. Music
Monday evenings, disco Sunday
evenings. Barbecues. The pub is
screened from the M25 motorway at the rear.

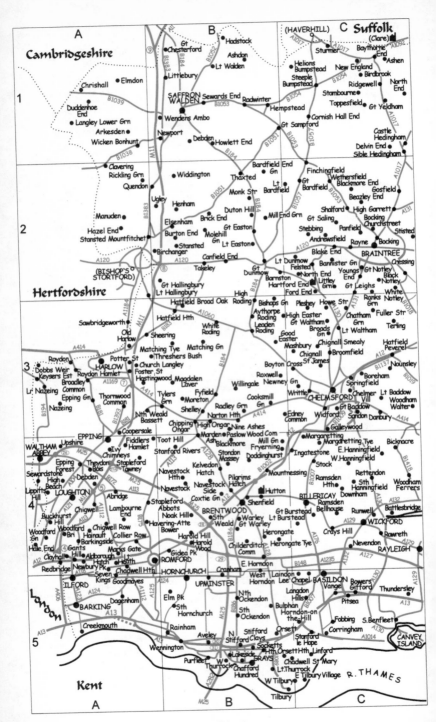

74

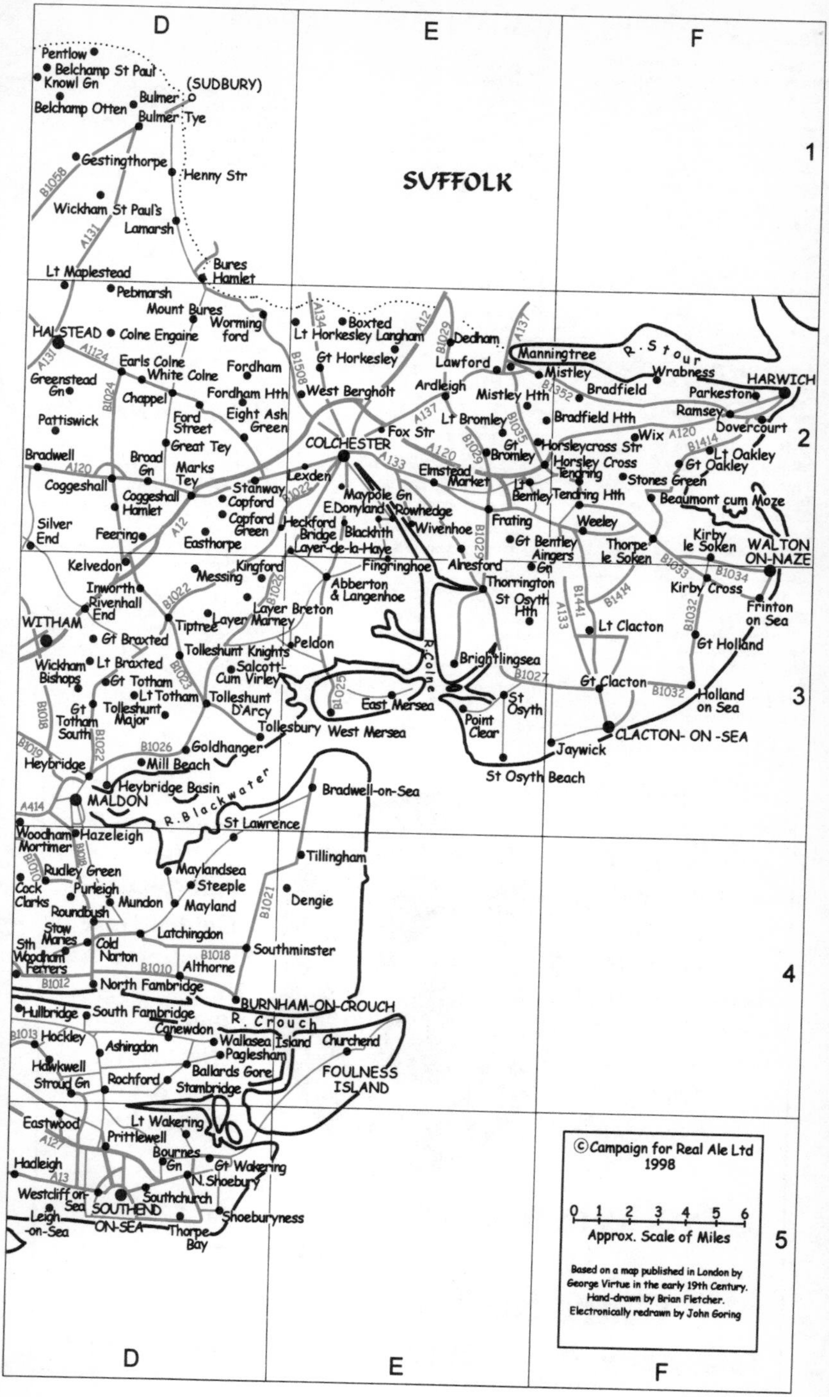
D
E
F
1
2
3
4
5
SUFFOLK
Pentlow
Belchamp St Paul
Knowl Gn
(SUDBURY)
Bulmer
Belchamp Otten
Bulmer Tye
Gestingthorpe
B1058
Henny Str
Wickham St Paul's
Lamarsh
A131
Lt Maplestead
Bures Hamlet
Pebmarsh
Mount Bures
Wormingford
HALSTEAD
Colne Engaine
A1124
Earls Colne
White Colne
Fordham
Greenstead Gn
B1024
Chappel
Fordham Hth
Pattiswick
Ford Street
Eight Ash Green
Great Tey
Bradwell
A120
Broad Gn
Marks Tey
Coggeshall
Coggeshall Hamlet
Stanway
Copford
Copford Green
Silver End
Feering
A12
Easthorpe
A134
Boxted
Lt Horkesley
Langham
B1029
Dedham
A137
Manningtree
R. Stour
Gt Horkesley
Lawford
Mistley
Wrabness
HARWICH
B1508
West Bergholt
Ardleigh
Mistley Hth
B1352
Bradfield
Parkeston
Ramsey
Lt Bromley
B1035
Bradfield Hth
Dovercourt
Fox Str
Wix
A120
B1414
COLCHESTER
A133
A120
Gt Bromley
Horsleycross Str
Lt Oakley
Horsley Cross
Gt Oakley
Lexden
Elmstead Market
Tendring
Stones Green
B1022
Maypole Gn
Lt Bentley
Tendring Hth
Beaumont cum Moze
E.Donyland
Rowhedge
Frating
Heckford Bridge
Blackhth
Wivenhoe
Weeley
Kirby le Soken
Layer-de-la-Haye
Gt Bentley
Aingers Gn
Thorpe le Soken
WALTON ON-NAZE
Kelvedon
Kingford
Fingringhoe
Alresford
B1033
B1034
Messing
B1026
Abberton & Langenhoe
Thorrington
Inworth
B1414
Kirby Cross
Rivenhall End
B1022
St Osyth Hth
B1441
Frinton on Sea
Layer Breton
A133
WITHAM
Tiptree
Layer Marney
Lt Clacton
B1032
Gt Braxted
Peldon
R. Colne
Gt Holland
Tolleshunt Knights
Wickham Bishops
Lt Braxted
Salcott-Cum Virley
Brightlingsea
B1023
Gt Totham
B1027
Gt Clacton
Lt Totham
Tolleshunt D'Arcy
B1025
St Osyth
B1032
Holland on Sea
B1018
Gt Totham South
Tolleshunt Major
East Mersea
Point Clear
Tollesbury
West Mersea
CLACTON- ON -SEA
B1019
B1022
B1026
Goldhanger
Jaywick
Heybridge
Mill Beach
St Osyth Beach
Heybridge Basin
Bradwell-on-Sea
A414
MALDON
R. Blackwater
St Lawrence
Woodham Mortimer
Hazeleigh
B1018
B1010
Tillingham
Rudley Green
Maylandsea
Cock Clarks
Purleigh
Steeple
Mundon
Mayland
Dengie
Roundbush
B1021
Stow Maries
Latchingdon
Sth Woodham Ferrers
Cold Norton
B1018
Southminster
B1010
Althorne
B1012
North Fambridge
BURNHAM-ON-CROUCH
Hullbridge
South Fambridge
R. Crouch
B1013
Hockley
Canewdon
Wallasea Island
Churchend
Ashingdon
Paglesham
Hawkwell
Ballards Gore
FOULNESS ISLAND
Stroud Gn
Rochford
Stambridge
Eastwood
Lt Wakering
A127
Prittlewell
Bournes Gn
Hadleigh
Gt Wakering
A13
N. Shoebury
Westcliff on-Sea
Southchurch
SOUTHEND ON-SEA
Leigh-on-Sea
Shoeburyness
Thorpe Bay
©Campaign for Real Ale Ltd 1998
0 1 2 3 4 5 6
Approx. Scale of Miles
Based on a map published in London by George Virtue in the early 19th Century. Hand-drawn by Brian Fletcher. Electronically redrawn by John Goring

Jaywick   E3

Classic, 1930s, shanty-town 'arcadia' built on low-lying flatlands near a nice beach. Many of the roads seem to have been named after the cars that brought London's 'Eastenders' here - many years ago.

11-11 (12-3; 7-10.30 Sun)

Mermaid Inn
24/26 Brooklands Gardens
Tel: (01255) 425687
Free-house - No Real Ale normally available. However, Bass beers are sometimes available in Summer.

12-5; 7-11 (12-11 Sat: 12-3; 7-10.30 Sun)

Never Say Die
24 The Broadway
Tel: (01255) 430994
Pubmaster - No Real Ale.

11-11 (12-10.30 Sun)

Sheldrake
1 Meadow Way
Tel: (01255) 430732
Guest Beer H
🍺 ♿
Well-maintained with a 1960s feel. Illuminated fish tanks.

11-11 (12-10.30 Sun)

Three Jays
1 Marlowe Road
Tel: (01255) 428440
S&N Courage Directors, Websters Yorkshire Bitter **H**
🍺🍷❁
Smart and pleasant pub with pensioners specials on lunchtime meals (not weekends). Sunday roasts.

12-2.30; 7-11

Wick Lodge
145 Jaywick Lane (nr B1027)
Tel: (01255) 427543
Guest Beers H
🍺🍷❁
Large and very popular pub, on the road into Jaywick, with squash club at rear. Two guest beers from the Whitbread 'stable'. Carvery Friday and Saturday evenings and on Sundays.

Kelvedon   D3

The longest of High Streets, and a haven for antique shops. Former junction for the Tollesbury light railway.

11-11 (12-10.30 Sun)

Angel
St Marys Square (B1024)
OS: TL859184
Tel: (01376) 570445
Whitbread Flowers IPA **H**
🍺🍷❁
Large and friendly pub with pool table.

12-11 (12-3; 7-10.30 Sun)

George
131 High Street (B1024)
OS: TL862189
Tel: (01376) 570839
Adnams Bitter; **Greene King** IPA **H**
❁♿
Local's pub with pool table. Parking difficult.

11-11 (12-10.30 Sat)

Railway Tavern
182 High Street (B1024)
OS: TL865192
Tel: (01376) 570293
Greene King IPA; **Marstons** Pedigree (occasional); **Tetley** Bitter **H**
🍺♿
On the west bank of the River Blackwater, which forms the boundary with Feering. Has a large riverside terrace. Petanque club and children's play area. Small restaurant area off the front bar.

White Hart
2 High Street (B1024)
OS: TL859185
Inntrepreneur - Pub closed and converted to an antiques shop.

Kelvedon Hatch B4

12-2.30 (3 Sat/Sun); 6-11 (10.30 Sun)

Dog & Partridge
Swan Lane (nr A128)
(off Blackmore Road)
Tel: (01277) 372565
Greene King IPA, Abbot Ale; **Guest Beer H**
🍺❁♿
Smart free-house, near village pond, with regularly-changing guest beers. Fresh fish Thursday and Friday. Formerly the "Swan"

11-2.30; 6-11 (12-10.30 Sun)

Eagle
Ongar Road (A128)
Tel: (01277) 373472
Ruddles Best Bitter; **S&N**
Courage Best Bitter, Directors **H**
⓵ Ð ◖ ▶ 🚃 ⅋

Friendly pub, set back from main
road. Large, award-winning garden with children's play area.
Fresh-fish night Thursdays.

11-3; 6-11 (12-10.30 Sun)

Shepherd Inn
Blackmore Road (nr A128)
Tel: (01277) 372389
Greene King IPA, Abbot Ale;
Shepherd Neame Master Brew
H
⓵ Ð ◖ ▶ ❀ ⅋

Small, friendly, 15th century
Gray & Sons pub. Neat and tidy.
No meals served on Sunday
evening.

Keysers Estate
(Nazeing)   A3

11-3; 5.30-11 (11-11 Fri/Sat: 12-
10.30 Sun)

Crown
Old Nazeing Road (nr A1170)
OS: TL374067
Tel: (01992) 468078
Bass Draught Bass **H**
⓵ Ð ◖ ▶ R ❀

A 'Toby Grill'. Is this a pub with
a restaurant, or a restaurant with
a bar ?

Kingsford   D3

12-3 (4 Sat); 7-11 (12-3; 7-10.30
Sun)

*King's Ford Park Hotel
(Regency Bar)*
Layer Road
Tel: (01206) 734301
Free-house - No Real Ale.

Kirby Cross   F3

11-3; 6.30-11 (12-3; 7-10.30 Sun)

Hare & Hounds
114 Thorpe Road (B1033)
Tel: (01255) 674270
Greene King IPA **H**
⓵ Ð ◖ ▶ ❀ ⇌

Comfortable country pub with
plush bar and parrot. Sunday
lunches.

Kirby Tavern
37 Thorpe Road (B1033)
Greene King - Pub closed.

Linnets
Thorpe Road (B1033)
Free-house - Pub closed.

Kirby-Le-Soken   F2

*Inland village, but with a small
ancient quay, off Walton
Backwaters. The 'Goblin Creek'
of Arthur Ransome's 'Secret
Water'.*

11-11 (12-3; 7-10.30 Sun)

Red Lion
The Street (B1034)
Tel: (01255) 674832
Adnams Bitter; **Morlands** Old
Speckled Hen; **S&N** Websters
Yorkshire Bitter; **Guest
Beer H**
⓵ Ð ◖ ▶ R ❀

Popular, 14th century, olde-
worlde, one-bar, food pub, with
old priest-hole. The continental
keg fonts look rather incongru-
ous.

11-11 (12-10.30 Sun)

Ship Inn
Walton Road (B1034)
Tel: (01255) 674256
Whitbread Boddingtons Bitter,
Flowers IPA, Original;
Tetley Bitter **H**
⓵ Ð ◖ ▶ R 🍴 ❀

Mellow, 17th century local with
exposed beams, and an
emphasis on food. Smart ladies
facilities.

Knowl Green
(Belchamp
St Paul)   D1

12-3; 7-11 (closed Tue, 12-11 Sat:
12-3; 7-10.30 Sun)

Cherry Tree Inn
Knowl Green
OS: TL784413
Tel: (01787) 237263
Adnams Bitter; **Greene King** IPA;
Guest Beers H
⓵ Ð ◖ ▶ R 🍴 🛏 ⊫ ❀ ⬚

Comfortable, isolated 16th century pub with good play area for
children. Good value beer and
food.

Laindon   C4

*Expanding town on the west
side of Basildon!*

*The remnants of the 'Fortune of
War' roundabout, on the A127,
still delay many thousands of
motorists every day, several
years after it was replaced by a
new bridge and closed.*

*(See Basildon map for the loca-
tion of the pubs).*

11-3; 6-11 (11-11 Thu-Sat: 12-
10.30 Sun)

Fortune of War   L1
Southend Arterial Road (A127)
OS: TQ681901
Tel: (01268) 543607
Youngs Special **H**
⓵ Ð ◖ ▶ ⬚

Very large roadhouse, with
emphasis on darts, pool, Sky TV,
discos and karaoke. Known to
many for the roundabout outside. Back to its original name
after a few years as "Hustlers".

11-3; 6-11 (12-3; 7-10.30 Sun)

Four Seasons   L2
Fenton Way, Laindon West
Tel: (01268) 540051
Greene King IPA, Abbot Ale **H**
⓵ Ð ◖ ▶ R ⊫ 🛒 ❀ ⅋

Looks likes it was designed and
built by a mad professor, with a
giant 'Lego' set. Drinkers are
confined to a small area close to
the bar.
Stern notices warn that most of
the seating area is for diners
only. Children's playroom. A
Greene King "King's Fayre"
pub-restaurant. Formerly
"Springfields".

11-11 (12-10.30 Sun)

Joker   L3
25 Laindon Centre
Tel: (Ex-Directory)
S&N Courage Best Bitter **H**
⓵ Ð ⇌

Modern, multi-level pub in the
middle of a dismal concrete
shopping centre. Pool room in
the basement. A recent convert
to Real Ale. Parking difficult.

11-3; 5.30-11 (11-11 Fri/Sat:
12-10.30 Sun)

Prince Of Wales   L4
Wash Road (nr A176)
OS: TQ691906
Tel: (01268) 413004
Ind Coope Burton; **Tetley**
Bitter; **Youngs** Bitter;
Guest Beer H
⓵ ◖ ▶ ⬚ 🛒 ❀ ⅋

Large, 1930s-style roadhouse,
that is attractive and comfortable, with 'Big Steak' menu -
worth finding. Occasional barbecues and live entertainment.

Lakeside (West
Thurrock)   B5

*Vast new shopping complex in
former quarry pits.*

10-11.30

Mamma Amalfi
The Pavilion, Lake Shopping
Centre, West Thurrock Way
(A126)
Tel: (01708) 861212
Free-house - No Real Ale.
Formerly "Capones".

12-11 (10.30 Sun)

*Old Orleans
(Mississippi Queen)*
The Pavilion, West Thurrock
Way (A126)
Tel: (01708) 868454
S&N bar in replica paddle
steamer - No Real Ale.

12-11.30 (11-11.30 Sat: 11-11
Sun)

T.G.I. Friday's
West Thurrock Way (nr B186)
Tel: (01708) 861123
Whitbread (T.G.I. Friday's) - No
Real Ale.

Lamarsh D1

Attractively set deep in the Stour Valley. The Norman church has a round flint tower.

11-3; 6-11 (12-3; 7-10.30 Sun, 12-10.30 Summer Sun)
Red Lion
Bures Road
OS: TL892355
Tel: (01787) 227918
Greene King IPA; **Mauldons** Suffolk Punch; **S&N** Courage Best Bitter; **Wadworths** 6X **H**
◖◗ ◉ **R** ⊨ ⮞ ❀ ᕹ
Interesting, remote pub with fine views. Good food.

Lambourne End A4

11-11 (12-10.30 Sun)
Camelot
Manor Road
OS: TQ478944
Tel: (0181) 500 7712
Morlands Old Speckled Hen; **Wadworths** 6X; **Whitbread** Boddingtons Bitter, Flowers Original; **Guest Beer H**
◖◗ ◉ **R** ❀ ᕹ
Large, one-bar pub with separate 'Beefeater' restaurant.

Langdon Hills (Laindon) C5

(See Basildon map for the location of the pub.)

11-11 (12-10.30 Sun)
Crown LH1
High Road, Langdon Hills (B1007)
Tel: (01268) 414233
Morlands Old Speckled Hen; **Tetley** Bitter **H**
Addlestones Cider H
◖◗ ◉ **R** ⮞ ❀ ᕹ
Pleasant pub on the edge of a country park. The 1995 refurbishment increased the restaurant area, but reduced the bar area.
Indoor children's area with entertainment and games.

Langham E2

11-3; 5.30 (6 Sat)-11 (12-3; 7-10.30 Sun)
Shepherd & Dog
Moor Road (nr A12)
OS: TM019318
Tel: (01206) 272711
Greene King IPA, Abbot Ale; **Nethergate** Old Growler; **Guest Beers H**
◖◗ ◉ **R** ❀ ᕹ
Busy, food-oriented, country pub.

Langley Lower Green A1

An attractive country village, set on the edge of the eastern continuation of the Chiltern Hills.

12-2.30; 6-11 (12-3; 7-10.30 Sun)
Bull
OS: TL437345
Tel: (01279) 777307
Adnams Bitter, Broadside; **Greene King** IPA **H**
🍺 ❀
A classic, rural, Victorian pub - the village's social centre. Pitch-Penny game concealed under the bench seat in saloon bar, darts and crib also played. No music or machines.
Friendly and well-worth finding.

Latchingdon D4

11-11 (12-10.30 Sun)
Latchingdon Lion
The Street (B1010)
Tel: (01621) 740298
Greene King IPA, Abbot Ale; **Guest Beers H**
◖◗ ◉ **R** ❀ ᕹ
Refurbished, village pub with a wide variety of food. New housing development built alongside.

Waggon & Horses
Burnham Road (B1010)
Free-house - Pub closed and converted to a private house.

Lawford E2

Large spread-out village.

11-3; 7-11 (12-3; 7-10.30 Sun)
Kings Arms
Wignall Street (A137)
Tel: (01206) 392758
Adnams Bitter; **Greene King** IPA **H**
◖◗ ◉ **R** 🛏 ❀
16th century pub with good-value food and a strong games following - particularly food and darts.

10.30-11 (12-3 Sun, closed evening)
Station Buffet
Manningtree Railway Station, Station Road (nr A137)
Tel: (01206) 391114
Adnams Bitter; **Marstons** Pedigree; **Shepherd Neame** Spitfire; **Guest Beers H**
◖◗ ◉ **R** ❀ ⇌
Small, one-room pub, with a marble bar, on the 'London' platform of the listed, 19th century, Manningtree railway station. Widespread and international clientele.
Breakfasts served from 8am until lunchtime, during the week. Home-cooked food. Regular guest beers (usually 3 or more). A gem!

Layer Breton D3

11-11 (12-10.30 Sun)
Hare & Hounds
Birch Green (1 mile off B1022)
OS: TL944189
Tel: (01206) 330459
Adnams Bitter; **Greene King** IPA; Abbot Ale **H**
◖◗ ◀ ⮞ ❀ ᕹ
Well-beamed local, with large fire in the main bar.

Layer Marney D3

Small village with magnificent 16th century house and towers which contain early examples of moulded terracotta - the moulds for which came from Italy.

White Horse
Smyth's Green (B1022)
Tel: (01206) 330340
Free-house - Pub temporarily closed.

Layer-de-la-Haye E2

11-2.30 (3 Sat); 5-11 (12-3; 7-10.30 Sun)
Donkey & Buskins
High Road (B1026)
Tel: (01206) 734774
Whitbread Boddingtons Bitter, Flowers IPA **H**
◖◗ ◉ **R** 🍺 ❀ ᕹ
Lovely garden. Muirs (of Edinburgh) mirror in public bar. All beers believed to be on 'Blanket' CO2 pressure.

11-3; 6-11 (12-3; 7-10.30 Sun)
Fox Tavern
Malting Green Road (B1026)
Tel: (01206) 734351
Greene King IPA; **Marstons** Pedigree **H**
◖◗ ◉ **R** ❀
Smart, split-level pub with lots of beams and friendly staff. Large fire in the restaurant. Large menu, no food Sunday evenings.

Leaden Roding B3

King William IV
Stortford Road (A1060)
Free-house - Pub closed and converted to a private house.

Lee Chapel (Basidon)   C4

(See Basildon map for the location of the pubs).

11-11 (12-10.30 Sun)

Castle Mayne   **LC1**
The Knares/Sporhams, Lee Chapel South (nr A176 & B1036)
Tel: (01268) 542599
S&N John Smiths Bitter **H**
⊄ D ◖ ⊟ ▭
Friendly, modern local, with live bands Friday to Sunday.

Leigh-on-Sea   D5

Quaint end of Southend, famous for cockles. Leigh old town is a gem, beer prices reflect this. An amazing number of new bars have sprung up since our 8th edition.

11-11 (12-10.30 Sun)

Bellini
1008-1012 London Road (A13)
Tel: (01702) 713996
Greene King IPA; **S&N** Courage Directors, John Smiths Bitter;
Tetley Bitter **H**
⊄ D ◖ ▶ R ▙ ▄ ▭
'Posh' style-bar with strict dress code - no trainers, jeans, football shirts or hats allowed! Over 21s only. Formerly "TGF Churchills".

11-3; 6-11 (12-3; 7-10.30 Sun)

Broker
213-217 Leigh Road
Tel: (01702) 471932
Shepherd Neame Spitfire;
Tolly Cobbold Original;
Guest Beers H
⊄ ◖ ▶ R
Comfortable, newish free-house, featuring guest beers from small independent breweries. An area in the bar is available for children (until 7.30pm) and non-smokers. No meals Sunday evenings.
Formerly "Mozarts Bar".

11-11 (12-10.30 Sun)

Carlton
12 Broadway
Tel: (01702) 476221
Greene King IPA; **S&N**
Theakstons BB, Websters Yorkshire Bitter; **Guest Beers H**
⊄ D ◖ ▶ ❀
Comfortable 'locals' pub offering reasonable meals. Part of S&N's John Barras chain. Sky TV, pool. Parking limited.

12-11 (10.30 Sun)

Crooked Billet
51 High Street (Old Town)
Tel: (01702) 714854
Adnams Bitter; **Ind Coope**
Friary Meux BB, Burton Ale;
Guest Beers H
⊄ ◖ ⊟ ▙ ▭ ▭
Excellent, unspoilt, listed, 16th century pub, situated between the railway and the cockle sheds. Real fire. Live music - jazz/blues/folk on Saturdays. The atmosphere is redolent of fishermen and smugglers in this well-preserved 'Heritage' pub. No food on Sundays. Limited parking.

10-11 (12-10.30 Sun)

Elms
1060 London Road (A13)
Tel: (01702) 474687
S&N Courage Directors,
Theakstons BB; **Guest Beers H**
⊄ D ◖ ▶ ❀ ⅙ ⊟ ⅍
A welcome refurbishment, after many years of closure. A typically vast 'Wetherspoon' interior, but more like a local than usual. Clean and comfortable.

11-11 (12-10.30 Sun)

Grand Hotel
131 The Broadway
Tel: (01702) 710768
S&N Courage Best Bitter,
Directors, Theakstons BB **H**
⊄ D ◖ ▶ ▙ ❀
Large and well-furnished, with three bars and regular live music. Open at 10am for breakfasts. Beware 'Scrumpy Jack' Cider on fake handpump!

12-3; 5-11 (12-11 Sat)

Harry
1517 London Road (A13)
Tel: (01702) 476634
Adnams Bitter; **Tetley** Bitter;
Guest Beers H
⊄ ▙ ❀
Formerly the "Black Rose" restaurant, converted into a traditional-style locals pub, in a previously 'dry' area of Leigh. Guest beers feature the small independent breweries. Twice-yearly beer festivals. Children's Certificate. Limited parking.

11-3; 5-11 (12 Fri) 11-12 Sat (12-3; 7-10.30 Sun)

Monty's Bar & Bistro
1595 London Road
Tel: (01702) 712910
Free-house - No Real Ale.
Formerly "Wolf's Wine Bar"

11-11 (12-10.30 Sun)

Peter Boat
27 High Street (Old Town)
Tel: (01702) 475666
S&N Courage Best Bitter,
Directors, Theakstons BB, XB,
Old Peculier **H**
⊄ D ◖ ▶ R ❀ ▙ ❀
Fine views of the estuary. Good food at reasonable prices. No meals Sunday evenings.

11-11 (12-10.30 Sun)

Ship
1 New Road / Leigh Hill
Tel: (01702) 478465
Ridleys IPA; **S&N** Websters Yorkshire Bitter; **Wadworths** 6X **H**
⊄ ◖ ▱ ▭ ⇶
Faces the old town across busy railway line. The 'Hoy at Anchor' folk club meets upstairs every Tuesday. Darts tournaments held. Limited parking.

11.30-11 (12-10.30 Sun)

Watermans Arms
1743 London Road (A13)
Tel: (01702) 475549
Bass Draught Bass **H**
⊄ D ◖ ▭
New, single, split-level bar, that was previously a wet-fish shop. The licensee is a 'Thames Waterman', and nautical items, photos, certificates etc. are on display.
Parking difficult - there is a small public car park nearby.

11-11 (12-10.30 Sun)

Ye Olde Smacke
High Street (Old Town)
Tel: (01702) 476765
Greene King IPA; **S&N** Courage Directors **H**
⊄ D ◖ ▶ ▱ ❀ ▙ ⇶
Refurbished 'Old Town' pub with riverside terrace, and fine old brewery window. Pool played. Parking difficult, particularly in summer. Formerly the "Smack Inn".

Lexden (Colchester)   E2

(See Colchester map for location of pubs)

Brights   **L1**
54 Straight Road (nr A1124)
The first '**Grand Met.**' 'Pub 80' theme pub in Essex - closed in February 1996, and demolished for new housing. Formerly the "Star".

11.30-3; 6-11 (11-11 Sat: 12-3; 7-10.30 Sun)

Crown Inn   **L2**
235 Lexden Road (A1124)
Tel: (01206) 572071
S&N John Smiths Bitter,
Trumans IPA; **Guest beers H**
⊄ D ◖ ▶ R ▙ ▱ ❀
Popular, comfortable pub, with live music (solo). Bar billiards, darts, boules and quiz nights. Extensive Sunday menu. Split-level bar.

12-2; 6-11 (12-11 Fri/Sat: 12-10.30 Sun)

Sun Inn   **L3**
112 Lexden Road (A1124)
Tel: (01206) 574327
Greene King IPA; **Guest Beers H**
⊄ D ◖ ▙ ▭ ❀
Busy pub on hill, with real beams. Two guest beers. Pool, Sky TV, Karaoke, barbecues.

79

Linford B5

11-3; 6-11 (11-11 Fri/Sat: 12-3; 6-10.30 Sun)

George & Dragon
Princess Margaret Road
Tel: (01375) 673177
Adnams Bitter; **Youngs** Special **H**
◑ ◐ 🍴 ☙ ⧺
Comfortable small saloon and a larger public bar which attracts a lively crowd. The large garden has a climbing frame for children and is fenced off from the main road. Near East Tilbury Station.

Lippitts Hill (High Beach) A4

11-3; 6-11 (12-3; 7-10.30 Sun)

Owl
Lippitts Hill (1½ miles off A112)
Tel: (0181) 502 0663
McMullens Original AK, Country, Gladstone **H**
◑ ◐ ◑ 🐾 ☙ ♿
Modernised, family pub, with barbecues in Summer and Mexican food in Winter. Ideal for walkers and ramblers. Extensive views. Celebrated its centenary as a McMullen pub in June 1998.
Beware keg 'Scrumpy Jack' cider on handpump.

Little Baddow C3

Delightfully set in Silver Birch woods on open common land.

11-3; 6 (12-3 (4 Jazz days); 7-10.30 Sun)

General's Arms
The Ridge (nr A414)
OS: TL781071
Tel: (01245) 222069
S&N Courage Directors; (all beers on Top Pressure)
Wadworths 6X; **Guest Beers H**
◑ ◐ ◑ **R** ☙ **⊫** ☙
Rural pub named after Major General Strutt, whose interesting history can be read in the lounge. Reputedly haunted. Jazz alternates between Sunday lunchtimes and Friday evenings.

11.30-2.30 (3 Sat); 6-11 (12-10.30 Sun)

Rodney
North Hill
OS: TL778080
Tel: (01245) 222385
Greene King IPA, Abbot Ale; **Guest Beer H**
◑ ◐ ◑ ☙ ☙
Comfortable, small village pub, near the Chelmer-Blackwater Navigation. Weekly changing guest beer. Separate pool room. Food always available all on Sundays and bank holiday Mondays.

Little Bentley E2

12-3; 6.30-11 (12-3; 7-10.30 Sun)

Bricklayers Arms
Rectory Road (nr A120)
Tel: (01206) 250405
Greene King IPA **H**; **Mauldons** Squires Bitter **G**
◑ ◐ ◑ **R ⊫** ☙
Cosy, comfortable, country pub, serving first-rate, home-made food. Interesting plate rack and artefacts.

Little Braxted D3

Quiet colourful village - that can be hard to find.

11-3; 6-11

Green Man
Kelvedon Road/Little Braxted Lane (1½ miles South East of village)
OS: TL849130
Tel: (01621) 891659
Ridleys IPA, Witchfinder Porter (Winter), Rumpus **H**
◑ ◐ ◑ ☙ ☙
Set in delightful rural surroundings, this pretty, country pub has hanging baskets of flowers and a cosy traditional lounge. Unusual handpumps! Framed models of commercial vehicles. Good value food - 'Egon Ronay' recommended. Trophy-winning darts team.

Little Bromley E2

12-3; 7-11 (10.30 Sun, 12 Wed, 1 Fri/Sat)

Fox & Hounds
Bentley Road
Tel: (01206) 397415
Adnams Bitter **H**
◑ ◐ ◑ **⊫** ☙
Re-opened as a pub, with extensive plans for the future. Low-lit, low-ceilinged bar with first floor conservatory! May not open lunchtimes in future - check first. A vibrant 'Gay' venue.

Wheatsheaf
Shop Road
OS: TM095286
Tel: (01206) 392891
Free-house - Pub closed.

"The Flitch of Bacon", Little Dunmow

Little Burstead C4

Small village with fine old church on ridge.

11-11 (12-10.30 Sun)

Burstead Village Inn
Laindon Common Road (nr A176)
OS: TQ672928
Tel: (01277) 651333
Bass Hancocks HB, Draught Bass **H**

◁ ◖ ● **R** ❀ ⊑ ➳ ♿

Pleasantly situated on the common, with a conservatory at the front, a duckpond, a patio and a garden. Now is an 'Innkeepers Fayre' restaurant. Quite unlike a village inn! Formerly the "Dukes Head".

Little Clacton F3

11-11 (12-10.30 Sun)

Apple Tree
The Street (B1441)
Tel: (01255) 861026
Fuller ESB ; **Wells** Eagle;
Guest Beers H

◁ ◖ ● ➳ ➡ ♿

A Real Ale oasis, with beams, brass and bare-brick interior. A leading, live music pub in the area at weekends. Frequent guest beers. Beer festivals.

11-11 (12-3; 7-10.30 Sun)

Blacksmith's Arms
20 The Street (B1441)
Tel: (01255) 860888
Bass Worthington BB, Draught Bass; **Ind Coope** Burton Ale;
Tetley Bitter; **Guest Beer H**

◁ ◖ **R** ⊞ ❀

A 'village' pub on the outskirts of Clacton. Friendly, with lots of sports teams, charity fundraising and even has its own beer club which visits festivals.

Little Dunmow C2

Famous for the 'Dunmow Flitch Trials', in which a man and his wife who can prove that they had not quarrelled for a year and a day, are awarded a flitch of bacon, and carried through the streets of Dunmow in special chairs.

12-3; 6-11 (12-6 Sun)

Flitch of Bacon
The Street (off A120)
Tel: (01371) 820323
Greene King IPA; **Woodfordes** Wherry; **Guest Beer H**

◁ ◗ ● ➳ ⊑ ❀

17th century, single-bar village local, with a comfortable feel. English country cooking, with seasonal ingredients. Used as a polling station. Beware keg 'Scrumpy Jack' cider on fake handpump!

Little Easton B2

Adjacent to Easton Lodge, where the Warwick family (particularly Countess Daisy), entertained Edward VII, Prince of Wales.

11-2.30 (or later); 6-11 (12-3; 7-10.30 Sun)

Stag
Duck Street/Butchers Pasture (1 mile West of B184)
OS: TL608241
Tel: (01371) 870214
Ridleys IPA **H**

◁ ◗ ● ❀

Restored village local with large garden area.

Little Hallingbury A2

11.30-3; 5.30-11 (12-3; 7-10.30 Sun)

George
George Green, Stortford Road (A1060)
Tel: (01279) 653900
Whitbread Flowers IPA; **Guest Beers H**

◁ ◗ ● ❀

Compact, roadside local with two guest beers. No food Sundays.

11-2.30; 6-11 (12-11 Sat: 12-10.30 Sun)

Sutton Arms
Bishop's Stortford Road, Hall Green (by A1060)
OS: TL510162
Tel: (01279) 730460
B&T Shefford Bitter; **Ind Coope** Burton Ale; **Tetley** Bitter; **Guest Beers H**

◁ ◗ ● ⊞ **R** ➳ ❀

Deservedly-popular for its daily-changing menu of fresh food. Snug bar. Excellent beer - keen landlord. Guest beers from the 'Tapsters Choice' range.

Little Heath A4

11-11 (12-10.30 Sun)

Haw Bush
205 Barley Lane (B177, nr A12)
Tel: (0181) 590 2979
Bass Draught Bass **H**

◁ ◖ ⊞ ❀

Reasonable, roadside pub, mainly catering for local clientele. Separate, more basic public bar has pool table and darts.

Little Horkesley E2

12-2 (or later); 7-11 (12-3; 7-10.30 Sun)

Bee Hive
At Village Cross Roads (nr A134)
Tel: (01206) 271610
Greene King IPA, Abbot Ale **H**

◁ ◗ ● **R** ⊑ ⊞ ❀

Quiet, friendly country pub that was hit by a bomb in 1940, and rebuilt in 1954. Quoits played here.

Little Maplestead D2

11.30-2.30; 6.30-11 (12-3; 6.30-10.30 Sun)

Cock
Cock Inn Corner, Sudbury Road (by A131)
Tel: (01787) 472243
Greene King IPA; **Tetley** Bitter **H**

◁ ◗ ● **R** ❀

Typical, large, modernised roadside establishment, with large garden.

Little Oakley F2

11-2.30; 5-11 (12-3; 7-10.30 Sun)

Ye Olde Cherry Tree
Clacton Road (B1414)
Tel: (01255) 880333
Adnams Bitter, Broadside; **Bass** Draught Bass; **Wells** Eagle; **Guest Beers H**

◁ ◗ ● **R** ⊑ ➳ ➡

Friendly, 17th century freehouse, on 'Domesday' site, overlooking the Naze. Regular guest beers, value-for-money meals and a large wrought-iron fire make this a popular pub. Visited by fuschia lovers and aero modellers. Excellent Christmas decorations.

Little Thurrock B5

11-11 (12-5; 7-10.30 Sun)

Bull
98 Dock Road (A126)
Tel: (01375) 373979
S&N Courage Best Bitter, Directors; **Youngs** Special **H**

◁ ◗ ❀

Family pub, with canvas covered outdoor drinking area.

11-3; 5-11 (11-11 Thu-Sat: 12-10.30 Sun)

Half Moon
42 Broadway (A126)
Tel: (01375) 372628
S&N - No Real Ale.

"The Swan", Little Totham

11-11 (12-10.30 Sun)

Ship
16 Dock Road (A126)
Tel: (01375) 371121
Ruddles County; **S&N** John
Smiths Bitter, Theakstons BB **H**
◖◗ ◖◗ **R** ❀
Large pub with young clientele.
Restaurant open in the evenings.

Little Totham   D3

11-3.30; 7-11 (11-11 Sat: 12-10.30
Sun)

Swan
School Road (nr B1022)
Tel: (01621) 892689
Adnams Bitter; **Greene King**
IPA; **Guest Beers H/G**
◖◗ ◖◗ ⊕ ❀
Pleasant and friendly, 16th
century, country cottage, near
village green and set back
behind pleasant walled-garden.
Comfortable, 'beamed' lounge,
contrasts with public bar that is
dominated by pool table and TV.
Real fire.
Constantly-changing range of
around five guest beers. Beer
festival held in June.

Little Wakering   D5

11-11 (12-10.30 Sun)

Castle Inn
181 Little Wakering Road (nr
B1017)
Tel: (01702) 219295
S&N Courage Best Bitter; **Guest
Beer H**
◖◗ ◖◗ 🚗
Friendly pub with one bar, a
pool table and dart board. In
need of redecoration! Beware
'Scrumpy Jack' on fake hand-
pump!

Little Walden   B1

Derelict wartime airfield nearby.

11.30-2.30; 6-11 (12-10.30 Sun)

Crown
(B1052)
OS: TL546415
Tel: (01799) 552475
Bass Draught Bass,
Worthington BB, **Greene King**
IPA, Abbot Ale; **Wadworths**
6X; **Guest Beers H**
◖◗ ◖◗ ❀
Comfortably, refurbished village
local, with excellent menu of
good food. No food Sunday
evenings.

Little Waltham   C3

*Much improved by the addition
of a by-pass.*

11-11 (12-10.30 Sun)

Bell
32/34 The Street (nr A131)
Tel: (01245) 362224
Greene King IPA; **Guest Beer H**
◖◗ ◖◗ ⊕ 🚗 ❀
A lounge bar and larger public
bar, split into separate seating
areas, together with a pool table.
Popular with younger drinkers.

11-3; 6-11 (11-11 Sat: 12-10.30
Sun)

White Hart
107 The Street (nr A131)
Tel: (01245) 360487
Ridleys IPA, ESX **G**
◖◗ ◖◗ **R** ⊕ 🚗 ❀
Old village inn which used to be
a country hotel. Now has a
lounge with adjoining dining
area, and a large public bar with
games and music.

Littlebury   B1

11-11 (12-10.30 Sun)

Queens Head Inn
High Street (B1383)
Tel: (01799) 522251
Banks Mild; **Marstons** Bitter,
Pedigree **H**
◖◗ ◖◗ **R** 🛏 🍴 🚗 ❀
600 year old village local with
traditional features and good
accommodation. No food
Sunday evenings. Formerly a
free-house, but now taken over
by Marstons.

Littley Green   C3

*Quiet hamlet near Ridley's brew-
ery and the River Chelmer.*

11.30-3; 6-11 (12-3; 7-10.30 Sun)

Compasses
Littley Green (1 mile East of
B1417, turn off at Ridleys
Brewery)
OS: TL699172
Tel: (01245) 362308
Ridleys XXX Mild, IPA, ESX,
Witchfinder Porter, Rumpus,
Winter Winner **G**
◖◗ ◖◗ ⊕ 🍴 🚗 ❀
Remote, cottage-style, country
pub, retaining traditional village
atmosphere. Many times win-
ners of local CAMRA 'Pub of the
Year' awards - East Anglian 'Pub
of the Year' in 1990.
Difficult to find - but well-worth
the effort. Food speciality is the
'Essex Huffer' - a very large bap.
A gem!

LOUGHTON
& Debden

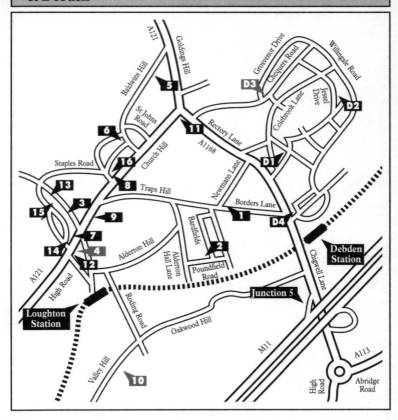

Loughton   A4

Classy suburban town near Epping Forest.

11-11 (12-4; 7-11 Sat: 12-3; 7-10.30 Sun)

Bentleys Bar   **1**
Borders Lane
Tel: (0181) 532 1101
S&N Websters Yorkshire
Bitter **H**

◖ ◖ (Sun only)
Bouncy castle and slide for the kids, barbecues in Summer. Formerly the "Golden Lion" & "Spencers", likely to change again!

11-11 (12-10.30 Sun)

Black Deer   **2**
Poundfield Road
Tel: (0181) 508 2731
S&N John Smiths Bitter,
Websters Yorkshire Bitter;
Guest Beer H

🚃

Estate pub with music and dancing licence, live music monthly

---

11-11 (12-10.30 Sun)

Carpenters Arms   **3**
99 Smarts Lane (nr A121)
Tel: (0181) 502 1382
Adnams Bitter; **Marstons**
Pedigree; **Whitbread**
Boddingtons Bitter, Flowers
IPA; **Guest Beer H**

◖ ◗ ◖ ◗ ◗ 🐾 ⊖
The pub dates back to 1852, and is named after the original inhabitants of Smarts Lane. Handy for Epping Forest and popular with walkers.

Dry Bar   **4**
167 High Road
Free-house - No Real Ale.

11-3; 5.30-11 (11-11 Sat: 12-10.30 Sun)

Foresters Arms   **5**
Baldwins Hill (nr A121)
OS: TQ428977
Tel: (0181) 508 1313
Adnams Bitter; **Greene King**
IPA; **Marstons** Pedigree;
Youngs Bitter **H**

◖ ◖ 🐾
One of the better locals in Loughton, with fine views of Epping Forest. Limited parking.

Gardeners Arms 6
103 York Hill (nr A121)
OS: TQ426971
Tel: (0181) 508 1655
Adnams Bitter; **Ruddles** County;
S&N John Smiths Bitter,
Websters Yorkshire Bitter **H**

◑ ◐ ⊨ ⊖
A very old unusually-designed
hillside pub, in a modern estate.

10-11 (12-10.30 Sun)

Holly Bush 7
140 High Road (A121)
Tel: (0181) 508 1156
McMullens Original AK,
Country, Gladstone **H**

◑ ◐ ⊖
Large friendly and comfortable
pub with conservatory. No
meals Sunday & Monday
evenings.

11-3; 5.30 (6.30 Sat)-11 (12-3; 7-
10.30 Sun)

Kings Head 8
2 Church Hill (by A121)
Tel: (0181) 508 4085
Ruddles Best Bitter; **S&N**
Websters Yorkshire Bitter **H**

◑ ◐ ◑ **R** ⊨
Comfortable, pub with live
music fortnightly, DJ Fri/Sat
nights (easy listening). Smart
dress code at weekends.
11-11 (12-10.30 Sun)

Last Post 9
227 High Road (A121)
Tel: (0181) 532 0751
Marstons Pedigree; **S&N**
Courage Directors, Scotch
Bitter, Theakstons BB, XB;
Guest Beers H
Westons Old Rosie Cider **H**

◑ ◐ ◑ ⊨ ⬚ ⚲ ⊔ ⊖
Wetherspoon conversion of the
former post office.

Mother Hubbard 10
Valley Hill / Loughton Way
Tel: (0181) 502 5760
Whitbread - No Real Ale.

11-11 (12-10.30 Sun)

Plume of Feathers 11
123 Church Hill (A121)
Tel: (0181) 508 3618
Hardys Royal Oak; **Ind Coope**
Burton Ale; **Tetley** Bitter **H**

◑ ◐ ◑ **R** ⊛
A typical 'Big Steak' pub, with
standard fittings and decor, on
the main road at the north end
of Loughton.

11-11 (12-10.30 Sun)

Rat & Carrot 12
153 High Road (A121) / Old
Station Road
Tel: (0181) 508 0206
Bass Draught Bass; **Greene
King** IPA; **Whitbread**
Boddingtons Bitter; **S&N**
Websters Yorkshire Bitter **H**

◑ ◐ ◑ ⊕ ⬚ ⊖
Refurbished, corner pub with
large TV projection screen and
juke box. DJ Saturday nights,
pop quiz Wednesday nights.
Ladies toilets upstairs.
Formerly the "Crown".

11-3; 5-11 (12-3; 7-10.30 Sun)

Royal Oak 13
Forest Road (nr A121)
Tel: (0181) 508 7077
Whitbread Boddingtons Bitter,
Flowers Original; **Guest Beer H**

◑ ◐ ◑ **R** ⊛ ⬚ ⊖
Large pleasant local, close to the
forest, with various sports teams
- netball, sub-aqua, golf, cricket
and football. Amateur drama
group meet on Wednesdays.
Live music Saturdays, over 21s
only. The original pub stood in
the garden.

11-11 (12-10.30 Sun)

Royal Standard 14
124/126 High Road (A121)
Tel: (0181) 502 5645
Bass Hancocks HB, Draught
Bass; **Guest Beers H**

◑ ◐ ⊨ ⊛ ⊖
Comfortable local, over 125
years old, with upstairs function
room and striking green tile
exterior.

11-3; 5-11 (12-3; 7-10.30 Sun)

Victoria Tavern 15
165 Smarts Lane (nr A121)
Tel: (0181) 508 1779
Bass Draught Bass; **Guest
Beers H**

⊛ ⬚ ⊖
Gorgeous, unspoilt pub with
wood panelling, close to Epping
Forest.

11-11 (12-3; 7-10.30 Sun)

Wheatsheaf 16
15 York Hill (nr A121)
Tel: (0181) 508 9656
Bass Hancocks HB, Draught
Bass; **Fullers** London Pride;
Guest Beer H

◑ ◐ ◑ ⊛ ⬚
Well-decorated local, near the
High Road, with lots of fishing
paraphernalia.

Lower Nazeing A3

11-3; 5-11 (12-3; 7-10.30 Sun)

Crooked Billet
Middle Street
Tel: (01992) 893239
Tetley Bitter **H**

◑ ◐ ◑ ⊕ ⊨ ⊛
17th century, two-bar pub in
village setting.

Magdalen
Laver B3

11-3; 6-11 (12-3; 7-10.30 Sun)

Green Man
OS: TL508074
Tel: (01279) 411752
Greene King IPA, Abbot Ale **H**
Guest beer (Occasional) **H/G**

◑ ⚲
A gem of a pub, with many fine
exposed timbers and a revolving
pool table.

Maldon D3

*Fine old nautical town, famous
for 'Maldon Salt'. The new
bypass was built along the
course of part of the old railway
lines to Witham and Woodham
Ferrers.*

11-2.30 (3 Fri/Sat); 6-11 (12-3; 7-
10.30 Sun)

Blue Boar Hotel 1
Silver Street / Coach Lane (nr
A414)
Tel: (01621) 852681
Adnams Bitter; **Guest Beers G**

◑ ◐ ◑ **R** ⊕ ⚲ ⊨ ⍭ ⊛
⬚
Quiet and historic THF hotel.

10.30-4; 6-11 (12-10.30 Sun)

Borough Arms 2
Wantz Road (B1018)
Tel: (01621) 859481
Greene King IPA **H**

◑ ◐ ◑ ⊕ ⚲ ⊛
A 'Grays' local with two pleasant
bars. Darts, dominoes and
quizzes. Occasional Guest beers
and discos. Motel accommodation at rear.

10.30-3; 6-11 (11-11 Sat; 12-10.30
Sun)

Carpenters Arms 3
33 Gate Street
Tel: (01621) 853833
Greene King IPA; **Shepherd
Neame** Masterbrew **H**

◑ ◑ ⊕
Fine, Grays locals pub tucked
away behind the "Blue Boar",
which was once the brewery tap
of Grays Maldon brewery.
Convivial atmosphere with conversation, darts and dominoes
found here. Snacks only at
weekends. Limited parking.

11-3; 6-11 (11-11 Fri and
Summer: 12-3; 7-10.30 Sun, 12-
10.30 Summer Sun)

Clarkies Irish Bar 4
185 High Street (nr B1018)
Tel: (01621) 850122
Guest Beers H

⊛
Large, refurbished 19th century
free-house, which has now been
turned into another 'Irish' theme
pub. Unusually, this one has a
varying range of around four
Real Ales.
Formerly "Reflections" and the
"Warwick Arms", but originally
the "Queen Adelaide", until
acquired by the Earl of Warwick
from coal merchants in 1868.

11-3; 6-11 (12-3; 7-10.30 Sun)

Cups 5
214 Wantz Road
Tel: (01621) 853318
Greene King IPA **H**

◑ ◑ ⊛
Single-bar locals pub with a
good mix of customers. Pool,
darts and dominoes played.

MALDON
& Heybridge

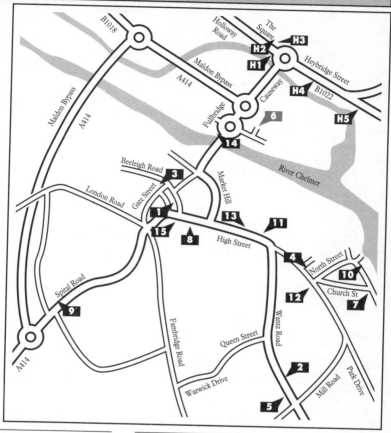

Great Eastern Motel   6
Station Road, Causeway
Tel: (01621) 856826
Free-house - Pub closed, future
uncertain.

11-11 (12-10.30 Sun)

Jolly Sailor   7
Church Street / The Hythe
Tel: (01621) 853463
Crouch Vale Millennium Gold;
Morlands Old Speckled Hen;
Guest Beers H
◖ ◗ ◖ ◗ **R** ✿

Classic Essex clapboard pub
with fine view of the Blackwater
estuary. Often hosts Morris
dancers. Large aviary in outdoor
drinking area. Good selection of
beers.

11-11 (12-10.30 Sun)

La Borsa   8
Kings Head Centre,
38 High Street
Tel: (01621) 850950
Guest Beers H
◖ ◗ ◖ ◗ **R** ✿

The 'Kings Head', once a fine
coaching inn, fell into a sad state
of decay in recent years.
Restored, though sadly as a
shopping arcade, rather than a
pub, it still caters for the drinker,
by way of 'La Borsa' - a small,
pleasant wine bar, tucked into a
corner of the building.
The interior retains some of the
original architectural features.
Guest beers, usually from
Crouch Vale.

10.30-3; 6-11 (12-3; 7-10.30 Sun)

Queen Victoria   9
Spital Road
Tel: (01621) 852923
Greene King XX Mild, IPA,
Abbot Ale **H**
◖ ◗ ⊞ ✿ ⅙

A comfortable refurbished Grays
pub.

10.30-11 (12-10.30 Sun)

Queen's Head   10
The Hythe
Tel: (01621) 854112
Greene King IPA, Abbot Ale;
Shepherd Neame Masterbrew **H**
◖ ⊞ ✿

Soak-up the strong nautical
atmosphere in this 3 bar Grays
pub, which overlooks the sailing
barge moorings, on the River
Blackwater.
Food availability increases in
Winter. Limited parking.

11-11 (12-10.30 Sun)
Rose & Crown 11
109 High Street
Tel: (01621) 854175
Whitbread Flowers IPA **H**
⊄ D ◑ ◑ ⊕ ❀

Imposing High Street pub with etched windows and low-beamed bars. Disco / live music Friday and Saturday. Big screen TV in one bar.
Good value food - barbecues in Summer. Limited beer range.

11-11 (12-10.30 Sun)
Ship & Anchor 12
188 High Street
Tel: (01621) 855706
Ruddles Best Bitter; **Guest Beers** include **Greene King** IPA; **Nethergate** Porters Suffolk Bitter; **S&N** John Smiths Bitter **H**
⊄ D ◑ ◑ R ⊫ ꒰ ❀

Very old, heavily beamed pub, opened out into one fairly rambling bar. Family area in conservatory. Popular meeting place for local clubs and organisations. Pool table and juke box.

11-11 (12-3; 7-10.30 Sun)
Swan Hotel 13
73 High Street
Tel: (01621) 853170
Greene King IPA, Abbot Ale; **Shepherd Neame** Masterbrew (Occasional) **H**
⊄ D ◑ ◑ ⊨ ⊫ ⅙

Friendly, old High Street local, with separate dining area, and small car park.

11-3; 7-11 (11-11 Sat: 12-10.30 Sun)
Welcome Sailor 14
1 Fullbridge
Tel: (01621) 852167
Greene King IPA, Abbot Ale **H**
⊄ ◑ R ⊕ ꒰ ❀

By the River Blackwater, with picturesque riverside terrace. Popular with the younger set, has pool, darts and various machines.

10.30-11 (closes 3-5.30 winter: 12-10.30 Sun)
White Horse 15
26 High Street
Tel: (01621) 851708
Guest Beers H
⊄ D ◑ ◑ ⊕ ꒰

Jazz night on Mondays and Rock night on Fridays. Small car park.

Manningtree E2

11-11 (12-10.30 Sun)
Crown Hotel
51 High Street (B1352)
Tel: (01206) 396333
Greene King XX Mild, IPA, Abbot Ale; **Guest Beer H**
⊄ D ◑ ◑ R ⊕ ꒰ ⊫ ꒰ ❀
⅙

A 16th century, three-bar, coaching inn, with a nautical theme in the restaurant, which also overlooks the River Stour and affords panoramic views. Reasonably priced food. No food Monday evenings.

11.30-3.30; 6-11 (12-3.30; 7-10.30 Sun)
Red Lion
42 South Street
Tel: (01206) 395052
Whitbread Boddingtons Bitter, Flowers IPA; **Guest Beers H**
⊄ ◑ ⊫ ❀

Friendly local, with single, split-level bar and 70 seater function room. Limited parking.

11-3 (4 Sat); 6-11
Skinners Arms
Station Road / High Street (B1352)
Tel: (01206) 393658
Tolly Cobbold Old Strong (Winter); **Whitbread** Flowers IPA **H**
⊄ ⊕ ❀

Two-bar locals boozer, with a keen games following.

11-11 (12-3; 7-10.30 Sun)
Swan
15 Brook Street
Tel: (01206) 392662
Free-house - No Real Ale.

11-3; 7-11 (11-11 Summer: 12-3; 7-10.30 Sun)
White Hart
9 High Street (B1352)
Tel: (01206) 392768
Greene King IPA; **Ind Coope** Burton Ale **H**
⊄ D ◑ ⊕ ꒰ ❀

Occasional live music. Limited parking, on-street.

Manuden A2

Delightful village with thatched cottages, some with overhanging storeys.

12-3; 6-11 (12-3; 7-10.30 Sun)
Yew Tree Inn
36 The Street
OS: TL492267
Tel: (01279) 812888
S&N Theakstons BB, Youngers No 3; **Wells** Fargo **H**
⊄ D ◑ ◑ R ꒰ ❀

Nice pub, but rather dominated by food. No food Sundays.

Marden Ash B4

Smallish village on the south eastern fringe of Ongar.

11-3; 5.30-11 (12-4; 7-10.30 Sun)
Stag
Brentwood Road (A128)
Tel: (01277) 362598
McMullens Original AK, Country, Gladstone **H**
⊄ D ◑ ◑

Cosy locals pub with real fire. A rare outlet for Macs beers. Very welcoming reception.

Margaretting C4

Salvaged by by-pass.

11-3; 6-11 (12-3; 7-10.30 Sun)
Black Bull
Main Road (B1002)
Tel: (01277) 353141
Ridleys IPA, Rumpus **H**
⊄ D ◑ ◑ ⊕ ⊫ ❀

Friendly, two-bar pub, dating from the 1880's. Good food.

Furze Hill Hotel
Ivy Barn Lane (nr A12)
Free-house - Bar closed.

11-3; 6-11 (12-10.30 Sun)
Red Lion
35 Main Road (B1002)
Tel: (01277) 352184
Ridleys IPA, ESX, Rumpus **H**
⊄ D ◑ ◑ ⊕ ❀

Fine old pub, with emphasis on food.

11-11 (12-10.30 Sun)
Spread Eagle
Main Road (B1002, nr A12)
Tel: (01277) 352052
Greene King IPA; **Guest Beers H**
⊄ D ◑ ◑ ❀

One large 'L' shaped bar with a pool table. Regular live music, Tuesdays and Fridays plus occasional Saturdays. Two guest beers.

Margaretting Tye C4

Pleasant hamlet with large common. Known locally as "Tiger's Island".

11-3; 6-11 (12-3; 6-10.30 Sun)
White Hart
Swan Lane
OS: TL684011
Tel: (01277) 840478
Adnams Bitter, Broadside; **Greene King** IPA; **Guest Beer H**
⊄ D ◑ ◑ ⊫ ꒰ ❀

Extended one-bar country pub, with wide menu. Substantial 'specials' board, changed frequently. Steaks and pork from a local farm - owned by the landlord.

Marks Gate A4
(Chadwell Heath)

11-11 (12-10.30 Sun)

Crooked Billet
Billet Road (nr A1112)
Tel: (0181) 590 0893
Ind Coope 'House' Bitter;
Tetley Bitter **H**
🍺 🍴 🚪
Comfortable panelled saloon
bar. Pub faces open fields. Darts,
dominoes, cribbage.

11-11 (12-10.30 Sun)

Harrow
Rose Lane / Billet Road (nr
A1112)
Tel: (0181) 590 1969
S&N Theakstons BB **H**
🍺 🍴 🚪
Recently refurbished, with views
out over farmland to the North.
Darts and pool, quiz night on
Mondays.

Marks Tey D2

11-12 (12-3; 6-11)

Marks Tey Hotel
Stanway Road (B1408, nr A12)
Tel: (01206) 210001
S&N Courage Best Bitter **H**
🍺 🍴 ⬤ **R** 🛏 ⬤ ≢
Plush hotel bar.

11-11 (12-10.30 Sun)

Prince Of Wales
86 London Road (nr A120/A12)
Tel: (01206) 210317
Ridleys IPA, Rumpus; **S&N**
Courage Directors, Theakstons
BB **H**
🍺 🍴 ⬤ 🍴 ⬤ 🛏 ⬤ ≢
Large roadhouse on the old A12,
with two bars, separate function
room and good garden for
children.

12-2.30; 6-11 (12-3; 7-10.30 Sun)

Red Lion
130 Coggeshall Road (A120)
Tel: (01206) 210293
Greene King IPA; **Whitbread**
Flowers IPA **H**
🍺 🍴 ⬤ **R** 🍴 ⬤
Converted 17th century farm-
house, with separate restaurant.
Beer cheaper in the public bar.

Mashbury B3

Fox
Fox Road / Mashbury Road
OS: TL650127
Ridleys - Pub closed summer
1997. Until recently a delightful
country pub, then allowed to
run-down.

Matching
Green B3

*Village surrounds large green
with cricket pitch and pond.*

11-3; 6-11 (11-11 Sat: 12-10.30
Sun)

Chequers Inn
The Green
OS: TL536110
Tel: (01279) 731276
Greene King IPA; **Guest Beers H**
🍺 🍴 ⬤ 🍴 **R** ⬤
The only pub on the green, with
three guest ales and jazz at
lunchtime on the last Sunday of
the month. Proud of its large
portions.

Matching Tye B3

12-3 (Not Mon); 7-11 (10.30 Sun)

Fox Inn
The Green / Newmans End
OS: TL516113
Tel: (01279) 731335
Bass Draught Bass; **Shepherd
Neame** Spitfire; **Guest Beers H**
🍺 🍴 🍴 ⬤
Cosy pub with three rooms and
a huge garden that includes a
boules pitch. Two guest beers,
occasional live music.

Hare & Hounds
The Green
Free-house - Pub closed and
converted to residential use.

Mayland D4

12-2.30; 5-11 (12-11 Summer:
12-10.30 Sun)

Mayland Mill
Steeple Road
OS: TL918016
Tel: (01621) 740998
S&N Courage Directors,
Theakstons Old Peculier **H**
🍺 🍴 ⬤ 🍴 **R** A
Fine old pub, dating from
around 1576, with regular enter-
tainment. Four bedrooms (two
en-suite).

"The Fox", Matching Tye

"The Old Crown", Messing

Maylandsea D4

Sprawling riverside development.

11-3 (4 Sat); 6 (5 Thu/Fri, 7 Sat)-11 (12-4; 7-10.30 Sun)

General Lee
36 Imperial Avenue
OS: TL905023
Tel: (01621) 740791
Bass Hancocks HB **H**

Lively community pub with large single bar.

11-3 5.30-11 (12-3; 7-10.30 Sun)

Silvers
Marine Parade, Blackwater Marina
Tel: (01621) 741073
Adnams Bitter; **Greene King** IPA; **S&N** Courage Directors, John Smiths Bitter **H**

New bar, well-situated for thirsty sailors. No snacks Monday Lunchtimes, and Thursday to Sunday evenings.

Maypole Green (Colchester) E2

(See Colchester map for location of pub)

11-11 (12-10.30 Sun)

Maypole **MG1**
131 Berechurch Hall Road
OS: TL986219
Tel: (01206) 578170
S&N John Smiths Bitter;
Guest Beer (occasional) **H**

Two-bar pub on the edge of town with large garden which has various activities for children.

Messing D3

Pleasant village, off the beaten track.

12-3; 6-11 (12-3; 7-10.30 Sun)

Old Crown Inn
Lodge Road (1 mile off B1022)
OS: TL898190
Tel: (01621) 815575
Ridleys IPA, ESX, Rumpus **H**

R

Traditional country inn with open fires. A sub post office on Mondays and Thursdays. Popular with walkers. No meals Sunday evening.

Mill End Green (Gt Easton) B2

12-3; 6-11 (12-3; 7-10.30 Sun)

Green Man
Mill End Green (1 mile East of B184)
OS: TL619260
Tel: (01371) 870286
Adnams Bitter; **Greene King** IPA **H** ; **Ridleys** IPA **G**

R

Very pleasant, 15th century country pub with oak studwork, low beams and an excellent garden. Good value food, but no meals Sunday evenings.

Mill Green B4

Small village full of large and expensive houses.

12-3; 6-11 (12-3; 7-10.30 Sun)

Cricketers
Mill Green Road
OS: TL639012
Tel: (01277) 352400
Greene King IPA, Abbot Ale;
Guest Beer (occasional) **G**

R

Popular, Gray & Sons pub on the green, with cricket theme. Public bar becoming increasingly smarter with the addition of carpet!. Beer direct from the cask. Popular with diners.

10-2.30 (3 Fri); 6-11 (12-3; 7-10.30 Sun)

Viper
Mill Green Road
OS: TL641019
Tel: (01277) 352010
Ridleys IPA; **Guest Beers** **H**

Unspoilt country pub with an award-winning garden, in a picturesque woodland setting. Traditional 'Tap room' public bar, with darts, dominoes, crib, etc., a 'Snug' bar, and a comfortable lounge.
Regularly changing range of two or three guest beers. The landlord is a beer enthusiast. A rural gem, believed to be the only pub with this name in the country! The local CAMRA branch 'Pub-of-the-Year' in 1997 and 1998.

"The Viper", Mill Green

Millbeach (Heybridge)   D3

Boating access to River Blackwater.

11-11 (12-10.30 Sun)

Millbeach
Goldhanger Road (B1026)
Tel: (01621) 852197
Guest Beers H
◖D ◖▶ R ⊫ ⛵ ✳
Two-acre garden with ornamental pond next to the river. Real Ale may not be available after October and before Easter. Formerly "Ellingtons".

Mistley   E2

Home of Edme Maltsters.

11-3 (Summer only); 5 (6 Sat)-11 (12-10.30 Sun)

Anchor
Harwich Road (B1352)
Tel: (01206) 393551
S&N Courage Directors, Theakstons BB; **Guest Beer H**
◖D 🍴 ⇌
Colonial-style, weather-boarded frontage. White-painted and totally refurbished.

11-3 (4 Sat); 7-11 (12-3; 7-10.30 Sun)

Lord Denman
Beckford Road/California Road (nr B1352)
Tel: (01206) 392944
Whitbread Flowers IPA **H**
⍟ ✳ ⇌
Back-street, two-bar local. Named after a 'hanging' judge, who made a short, but famous, speech in Parliament. Believed to be only three 'Lord Denman' pubs in the country. Parking difficult.

11.30-3; 6-11 (11-11 Fri/Sat: 12-3; 7-10.30 Sun)

Thorn Hotel
High Street (B1352)
Tel: (01206) 392821
Marstons Pedigree; **Ridleys** IPA; **Witchfinder** Porter (Winter); **S&N** Courage Directors **H**
◖D ◖▶ R 🍴 ⊫ ⇌
Popular, 18th Century coaching inn, with darts, pool and occasional live music. Resident ghost! No Sunday lunches in Winter.

12-3; 7-11 (10.30 Sun)

Waggon & Horses
New Road
Tel: (01206) 393411
Greene King IPA; **Whitbread** Flowers IPA **H**
✳ ⇌
Single-bar, locals boozer.

Mistley Heath   E2

Hamlet with 13 houses, one farm and the pub, near the earthworks of the partly-built Mistley Thorpe & Walton Railway.

12-3 (Sat/Sun only);7.30-11 (10.30 Sun)

Blacksmiths Arms & Heath Motel
Heath Road (nr B1352)
OS: TM128307
Tel: (01206) 397433
Greene King IPA (Summer only) **H**
◖D ◖▶ 🍴 🚍 ♿
Semi-rural pub, with large food menu, including Indian, Chinese and Thai. Real Ale in Summer only.

Molehill Green (Takeley)   B2

11-11 (12-10.30 Sun)

Three Horseshoes
Molehill Green
OS: TL563247
Tel: (01279) 870313
Greene King Abbot Ale; **Ind Coope** Aylesbury Duck, Burton Ale; **Tetley** Bitter **H**
◖D ◖▶ ⍟ ✳
Thatched, beamed pub with low sloping ceilings and an inglenook fireplace complete with stove. Fine garden, ideal for children.
Pool played. Beware of keg Cidermaster on handpump.

Monk Street (Thaxted)   B2

11.30-3; 6-11 (11.30-11 Sat: 12-10.30 Sun)

Farmhouse Inn
Monk Street (West of B184)
OS: TL614288
Tel: (01371) 830864
Adnams Bitter; **Greene King** IPA; **Shepherd Neame** Spitfire **H**
◖D ◖▶ R 🍴 ⊫ ✳
Smart and friendly with restaurant and hotel facilities - 11 rooms. No food Sunday evenings. Formerly the "Greyhound".

Moreton   B3

Previous winner of the 'Best Kept Small Village' competition.

12-3; 6.30-11 (closed Mon: 12-3; 6.30-10.30 Sun)

Nags Head
Church Road
Tel: (01277) 890239
Brakspears Bitter; **Hook Norton** Best Bitter; **Tolly Cobbold** Original; **Guest Beer H**

Comfortable, 16th century, split-level, listed building, where families are welcome. Good food. No music or machines. Has featured in the TV series 'Lovejoy'. Formerly the "Moreton Massey".

11-3; 5.30-11 (11-11 Sat: 12-10.30 Sun)

White Hart Inn
Church Road / Bridge Road
Tel: (01277) 890228
Adnams Bitter; **Belchers** Best Bitter; **S&N** Courage Best Bitter, Directors, Theakstons XB; **Shepherd Neame** Masterbrew **H**
16th century village free-house, cosy and little altered. A la carte menu Monday to Saturday evenings. Three or more guest beers. Regular venue for round table meetings. Occasional live music in the evenings.

Mount Bures   D2

12-3; 7-11 (12-3; 7-10.30 Sun)

Thatchers Arms
(1 mile off B1508)
OS: TL905318
Tel: (01787) 227460
Greene King IPA, Abbot Ale **H**
Smart country pub with restaurant. Popular with locals and steam railway enthusiasts alike. Panoramic views of the Stour Valley to the rear of the pub.

Mountnessing   B4

Attractive village with fine windmill.

11-11 (12-10.30 Sun)

George & Dragon
294 Roman Road (B1002)
Tel: (01277) 352461
Marstons Pedigree; **Whitbread** Boddingtons Bitter, Flowers Original **H**
Split-level 'Beefeater' with lots of nooks and crannies for eating In.

11-3; 5-11 (11-11 Sat: 12-3; 7-10.30 Sun)

Plough
Roman Road (B1002)
Tel: (01277) 352026
Marstons Pedigree; **Ruddles** Best Bitter; **Guest Beer H**
Friendly, country, family pub, with separate bar areas. Pool and darts. No food Sunday evenings.

11-3; 6-11 (12-3; 7-10.30 Sun)

Prince Of Wales
199 Roman Road (B1002)
Tel: (01277) 353445
Ridleys Champion Mild, IPA, ESX, Witchfinder Porter (Winter) **H**, Rumpus **G**
Popular, old, 'beamed' pub, opposite the windmill, the local CAMRA 'Pub-of-the-Year' in 1996. Patio.
Excellent Sunday Lunches with a good selection of vegetables. No food Monday evenings.

Mundon   D4

12-3; 6-11 (12-10.30 Sun)

White Horse
Main Road (B1018)
OS: TL870025
Tel: (01621) 740276
Greene King IPA; **Ind Coope** Ansells Mild, Friary Meux BB; **Guest Beer H**
Comfortable pub, popular with villagers. Live music (duo) on Fridays.

Navestock   B4

11-3; 6-11 (12-10.30 Sun)

Alma Arms
Horsemanside
OS: TQ544961
Tel: (01277) 372629
Greene King IPA, Abbot Ale; **Mighty Oak** Burntwood Bitter; **Guest Beers H**
Cosy and friendly country pub with the accent on food. New conservatory extension. A good selection of beers at reasonable prices.

King William IV
Tan House Lane
OS: TQ549964
Inntrepreneur - Pub closed, probably permanently. A missed opportunity!

Navestock Heath   B4

Isolated!

12-11 (10.30 Sun)

Plough Inn
Off Sabines Road
OS: TQ538970
Tel: (01277) 372296
Brakspears Bitter; **Fullers** London Pride; **Nethergate** Bitter; **Whitbread** Flowers IPA **H**
Bulmers Old Hazy **H**
Hard to find pub, that has changed much in recent years. Different landlord, different clientele, different atmosphere, pub now has a fruit machine. No food Sunday evenings or Mondays.
Usually two Guest Beers.

Navestock Side B4

The 'Essex County Cricket Club' was formed here in 1790.

11-3; 6-11 (11-11 Sat: 12-10.30 Sun)

Green Man
Navestockside
OS: TQ562975
Tel: (01277) 372231
Bass Draught Bass; **Ind Coope** Friary Meux BB; Burton Ale (occasional); **Tetley** Bitter **H**
Large and pleasant village pub with a friendly atmosphere, opposite the village green. Bargain 3-course lunches. Ask for the sparklers to be removed when ordering.

Nazeing   A3

Sprawling village with attractive but inaccessible common.

11-11 (12-10.30 Sun)

Coach & Horses
Waltham Road / St Leonards Road (nr B194)
OS: TL399041
Tel: (01992) 893151
Ind Coope Burton Ale; **Tetley** Bitter; **Whitbread** Flowers IPA **H**
Saloon was once a tea-room, public has old Christie's Brewery glasswork.
Open-plan pub, the carpet in the saloon marks the bar boundaries. Piano in saloon bar.

11-3; 5.30-11 (12-10.30 Sun)

King Harold's Head
Bumbles Green, Nazeing Gate
OS: TL412051
Tel: (01992) 893110
Ruddles Best Bitter; **S&N**
Courage Directors, John
Smiths Bitter **H**
🍺 🇩 ◖◗ Ⓡ 🍴
Comfortable pub on the edge of
Nazeing Common. The lounge
has a lot of brassware in it -
bring your own "Brasso"! There
is a collection of bank notes on
display behind the bar.

11-3; 5.30-11 (11-11 Sat; 12-10.30
Sun)

Sun Inn
Nazeing Common
OS: TL420066
Tel: (01992) 893257
McMullens Original AK,
Gladstone; **S&N** Courage
Directors **H**
🍺 🇩 ◖◗ Ⓡ 🍴 ♿
Formerly a free-house, but
acquired by McMullens in 1998.
Overlooks Nazeing Common.
Comfortable lounge, offering a
genuinely friendly welcome. The
large garden has a patio and a
children's play area. Children's
Certificate.

Nevendon
(Basildon)   C4

*Greenfringe North East of
Basildon.*

*(See Basildon map for the loca-
tion of the pubs).*

11.30-2.30; 5.30-11 (12-10.30
Sun)

Jolly Cricketers   N1
Southend Arterial Road (by
A127/A132)
Tel: (01268) 726231
Tetley Bitter; **Youngs** Bitter **H**
🍺 🇩 ◖◗ 🍺 ♨
Popular local on the edge of
town and industrial area. Has
become a friendly, family pub
since the A127 flyover bypassed
it. Sunday roast lunch a speciality.

Nevendon
(Wickford)   C4

*(See Basildon map for the
location of the pubs).*

11-11 (12-10.30 Sun)

Dick Turpin   N2
Southend Arterial Road (A127)
Tel: (01268) 478033
Morlands Old Speckled Hen;
Whitbread Boddingtons Bitter,
Flowers Original; **Guest Beer H**
🍺 🇩 ◖◗ Ⓡ 🐦 ♨ ♿
Large, smartly-decorated, road-
house with a 'Millers Kitchen'
restaurant, and a well-equipped
children's play area.

New England
(Birdbrook)   C1

12-2; 6-11 (12-3; 7-10.30 Sun)

Birdbrook Tavern
Boreham Place, New England
(A1017, was A604, Jcn B1054)
Tel: (01440) 788277
Bass Draught Bass,
Worthington BB **H**
🍺 🇩 ◖◗ 🍺 🏠 🍴 ♨
Roadhouse with function suite.
Beer festivals. No food
Mondays. Formerly the "Colne
Valley Arms"

Newbury Park   A4

11-11 (12-10.30 Sun)

Avenue
902 Eastern Avenue (A12)
Tel: (0181) 590 3465
S&N Courage Best Bitter **H**
🍺 Ⓡ 🍺 🍴 ⊖
Attractive, roadside pub, mainly
serving local trade. Separate
public bar and distinct restaurant area. Real Ale not always
available.

Greengate
Horns Road / Eastern Avenue
(A12)
Bass - Pub closed and converted
to a "McDonald's". Formerly the
"Farmhouse Table" & the
"Green Gate".

Newney Green C3
(Writtle)

Tiny hamlet.

11-3; 6-11 (12-3; 7-10.30 Sun)

Duck Inn
Newney Green (nr A414)
OS: TL651070
Tel: (01245) 421894
S&N Theakstons BB, Old
Peculier, Youngers IPA; **Guest
Beers H**
🍺 🇩 ◖◗ Ⓡ ♨
Remote pub/restaurant.
Expensive, though generally
good beer - with three, regular-
ly-changing guest beers. The
large garden has a pond.

Newport   B1

*Pleasant linear village, much-
relieved by the M11 motorway.*

11-11 (12-10.30 Sun)

Coach & Horses
Cambridge Road (B1383)
Tel: (01799) 540292
Whitbread Flowers Original;
Youngs Bitter; **Guest Beers H**
🍺 🇩 ◖◗ Ⓡ 🐦 ♨ ♿ 🍷
Warm, welcoming, 16th century
coaching inn, with an excellent
restaurant and bar food.
Attractive garden.

11-3; 5.30-11 (12-3; 7-10.30 Sun)

Hercules
London Road (B1383)
Tel: (01799) 542121
Bass Draught Bass,
Worthington BB **H**
🍺 🇩 ◖◗ 🍺 🏠 ♨
Large pub with small garden.
Darts and pool played.

12-3 (4 Sat); 6 (7 Sat)-11 (12-3; 7-
10.30 Sun)

White Horse
Belmont Hill / High Street
(B1383)
Tel: (01799) 540002
Greene King IPA, Abbot Ale,
seasonal beers **H**
🍺 🇩 ◖◗ 🍺 ♨ ♨
Friendly and comfortable 17th
century, former Rayments local,
with ghost! Darts, dominoes and
crib played. No evening meals
on Sundays. Limited parking.

Nine Ashes   B3

11-3 (Not Mon); 5.30-11 (11-4;
5.30-11 Sat; 12-10.30 Sun)

Wheatsheaf
King Street, High Ongar
Tel: (01277) 822220
Whitbread Flowers IPA,
Original; **Guest Beers H**
🍺 🇩 ◖◗ 🍺 ♨
Popular country pub, where
children are welcome. The land-
lord is a CAMRA member. Two
acre garden. Good quality food.
No music or fruit machines.

Noak Hill   B4

11-11 (12-10.30 Sun)

Bear
Noak Hill Road
Tel: (01708) 381935
Bass Hancocks IPA, Draught
Bass **H**
🍺 🇩 ◖◗ 🍺 ♨ ♿
Large, family pub with extensive
gardens, incorporating good
children's facilities. Plans to
extend the food range and
become more of a restaurant.

North End
(Gt Waltham)   B2

*Visit the fascinating 'Black
Chapel' near the pub.*

11-11 (12-10.30 Sun)

Butchers Arms
Dunmow Road (A130)
OS: TL663177
Tel: (01245) 237481
Ridleys IPA, ESX, Spectacular
(Summer), Witchfinder Porter
(Winter) **H**
◖◗ Ⓡ 🍴 ♨ ♿
500 year old, timber-framed,
'beamed' local, with open-plan
layout and separate dining area.
Large garden. Sunday evening
entertainment includes singers,
quizzes and karaoke. No meals
Sunday evenings.

North End (Lt Yeldham) C1

10.30-2.30; 6-11 (12-3; 7-10.30 Sun)

Stone & Faggot
North End Road, North End)
OS: TL789390
Tel: (01787) 237157
Free-house - No Real Ale.

North Fambridge D4

Popular with smugglers!

12 (11 Sat & Summer)-3; 7 (6.30 Sat, 6 Summer)-11 (12-4; 7-10.30 Sun: 12-10.30 Summer Sun)

Ferry Boat Inn
Ferry Road
Tel: (01621) 740208
Morlands Old Speckled Hen;
Wadworths 6X; **Whitbread**
Flowers IPA **H**
⑪ⅅ◖▮**R**▬▬🐾❀
Small, 15th century, beamed pub with nautical flavour, near the banks of the River Crouch. The family conservatory relieves the pressure on the dining room.

North Ockendon B5

Small country village with beautiful church.

11-3; 6-11 (12-3; 7-10.30 Sun)

Old White Horse
Ockendon Road (B186)
Tel: (01708) 853111
Guest Beers H
⑪◖⊕🚃
Excellent, traditional, friendly local. London's most easterly pub. Three guest beers - usually from the Ind Coope / Tetley range. Blowlamp collection. Shove ha'penny played. An escape from the modern world.

North Shoebury D5

11-3; 5.30-11 (12-3; 7-10.30 Sun)

Angel Inn
Parsons Corner, North Shoebury Road (A13/B1017)
Tel: (01702) 589600
Fullers London Pride; **Greene King** IPA, Abbot Ale; **Guest Beers H**
⑪◖▮**R**❀⚹
Excellent restoration of a group of grade II listed, timber-framed buildings, dating from around 1650, and comprising an old post office, wheelwrights and blacksmiths.
Now a traditional-style pub with thatched restaurant attached. Genuine flagstones and carved bar. No electronic machines or loud music.

North Stifford B5

A village of character, with chicanes in the road.

11-11 (12-10.30 Sun)

Dog & Partridge
Stifford Hill (between B186 & A13)
Tel: (01375) 379689
Ind Coope Benskins BB, Burton Ale; **Tetley** Bitter **H**
⑪ⅅ◖▮⊕❀⚹
Food-oriented pub. The garden has excellent play equipment for children.

11-11 (12-10.30 Sun)

Stifford Moat House
Stifford Clays Road (by A13/A1012)
Tel: (01375) 371451
Bass Draught Bass **H**
⑪ⅅ◖▮⊞▬▬❀⚹
Large hotel complex with bar, that is due for a refit to establish a more pub-like atmosphere. Guest beers expected.

North Weald Bassett A3

Former WW2 Fighter Station. The old airfield is still used for gliding and occasional air displays and bus rallies.

11-11 (12-10.30 Sun)

Kings Head
Ongar Road (B181)
Tel: (01992) 522204
Bass Draught Bass, Stones Bitter; **Guest Beer H**
⑪ⅅ◖▮**R**❀⚹
The building is many hundreds of years old, but the pub is very food-dominated - more of a restaurant than a pub (Toby Inn)!
It is expected to be turned into a 'Fork & Pitcher', with an even more limited drinking area, and there is a campaign locally against this.

11-3; 5.30-11 (12-3; 7-10.30 Sun)

Queens Head
87 High Road (B181, nr A414)
Tel: (01992) 522277
Ruddles County **H**
S&N Courage Directors **H**
⑪ⅅ◖▮❀
A very large single-bar pub.

Norton Heath B3

11-3; 6-11 (closed Mon: 12-3; 7-10.30 Sun)

White Horse
(nr A414)
Tel: (01277) 821258
Ruddles Best Bitter **H**
⑪ⅅ◖▮**R**❀
400 year old, up-market, coaching inn with restaurant.

Nounsley C3

11-3; 6-11 (12-3; 7-10.30 Sun)

Sportsmans Arms
Sportsmans Lane
OS: TL797105
Tel: (01245) 380410
Ind Coope Friary Meux BB;
Guest Beers H
⑪ⅅ◖▮**R**❀
Pleasant, country pub with large garden, situated in quiet village and popular with the locals. 'A la Carte' menu as well as pub grub.

Old Harlow A3

Original heart of Harlow. Modernised but retains character.

(See Harlow map for location of pubs)

11.30-3; 5-11 (11-5; 7-11 Sat: 12-3; 7-10.30 Sun)

Chequers OH1
2 Market Street (nr B183)
Tel: (01279) 429859
S&N Courage Best Bitter, Directors, John Smiths Bitter **H**
⑪ⅅ◖▮❀⚹
Popular local by shopping precinct, with strong games and sporting interests.

Churchgate Manor Hotel OH2
Churchgate Street (nr B183)
Tel: (01279) 420246
Free-house - No Real Ale.

11-11 (12-3.30; 5.30-10.30 Sun)

Crown OH3
40 Market Street (nr B183)
Tel: (01279) 427212
Greene King IPA **H**, Abbot Ale **H**, seasonal ales **H**
⑪ⅅ◖▮**R**⚹
Tastefully, enlarged and expanded in November 1996. A small (two-table) room has been set aside for eating.

11-11 (12-10.30 Sun)

Green Man Hotel OH4
2 Mulberry Green (nr B183)
Tel: (01279) 442521
Bass Draught Bass; **S&N** Courage Best Bitter, Directors **H**
⑪ⅅ◖▮**R**⊞▬▬⚹❀⚹
600 year old former coaching inn, with extensive hotel development at rear. Large and busy public bar and a small, cosy saloon with deep upholstery.

11-3; 5.30-11 (11-11 Sat: 12-10.30 Sun)

Marquis of Granby OH5
2 Fore Street / Market Street
Tel: (01279) 429442
Ind Coope Benskins BB; **Tetley** Bitter; **Guest Beer H**
⑪ⅅ◖▮⊕
16th century pub with long-standing landlord. Good range of regulars, friendly atmosphere. Limited parking.

11-3; 6-11 (12-3; 7-10.30 Sun)

Queens Head OH6
26 Churchgate Street (nr B183)
Tel: (01279) 427266
Nethergate Porters Suffolk
Bitter; **Ruddles** Best Bitter;
S&N Courage Best Bitter,
Directors **H**
🍺 🍴 🏠 🌳 ♿
Attractive, traditional low-
beamed pub, with good local
and passing trade.

11-3; 6.30-11 (11-3.30; 7-11 Sat:
12-3; 7-10.30 Sun)

White Horse OH7
160 Old Road / Wheatfields (nr
A1184)
Tel: (01279) 437385
Greene King IPA, Abbot Ale **H**
🍺 🍴 🌳 ♿ 🚂
Original old pub, now surround-
ed by modern housing develop-
ment. A friendly local only 5
minutes walk from Harlow Mill
Station.

Orsett B5

*A huge hospital in centre of vil-
lage has brought changes. There
are some attractive cottages and
an ancient village lock-up.*

11-11 (12-10.30 Sun)

Dog & Partridge
Brentwood Road (A128)
OS: TQ647847
Tel: (01375) 891377
S&N Courage Best Bitter,
Directors, John Smiths Bitter **H**
🍺 🍴 🅁 🌳 ♿
Cosy local, with restaurant at the
rear.

11-3.30; 6-11 (11-11 Sat: 12-3.30;
7-10.30 Sun)

Foxhound
18 High Road (B188)
OS: TQ643820
Tel: (01375) 891295
Crouch Vale Woodham IPA;
Morlands Old Speckled Hen;
S&N Courage Best Bitter,
Directors, Websters Yorkshire
Bitter **H**
🍺 🍴 🅁 🌳 🚃
Popular with locals and visitors
alike, a natural meeting place.
"Warm" and comfortable
saloon and more basic public
bar. Fox's Den Restaurant
attached is popular with the
locals.

11-11 (12-10.30 Sun)

Kings Arms
Stifford Clays Road, Baker Street
(B188)
OS: TQ633814
Tel: (01375) 891219
Greene King IPA; **Ind Coope**
Burton Ale; **Tetley** Bitter **H**
🍺 🍴
Plush pub consisting of several
areas in an open-plan style, with
a recently completed extension.
Seems to attract a younger
crowd than the other village
pubs.

11-11 (12-10.30 Sun)

Orsett Cock
Stanford Road (A1013, by
A13/A128 interchange)
Tel: (01375) 891259
S&N Courage Best Bitter **H**
🍺 🍷 🚗
Large roadhouse near round-
about. Live music most
evenings, popular with young-
sters.

11-11 (12-10.30 Sun)

Orsett Hall
Prince Charles Avenue
Tel: (01375) 891402
Free-house - No Real Ale.

11-3; 6-11 (11-11 Sat: 12-10.30
Sun)

Whitmore Arms
Rectory Road (B188)
Tel: (01375) 891259
Greene King IPA, Abbot Ale **H**
🍺 🍷 🍴 🌳
Comfortable local.

Orsett Heath B5

11-11 (12-10.30 Sun)

Fox
176 Heath Road (nr A1013)
OS: TQ639800
Tel: (01375) 841129
Crouch Vale Best Bitter;
S&N Websters Green Label;
Guest Beer H
🍺 🍷 🍴 ♿
Plush and recently-renovated
saloon with a more basic public
bar. Attracts a mixed and some-
times lively crowd. Evening
meals on Fridays and Saturdays.

11-11 (12-10.30 Sun)

Greyhound
106 Heath Road (nr A1013)
Tel: (01375) 375436
Bass Hancocks HB **H**
🍴
Locals pub which caters for all
ages. Friendly atmosphere with
helpful landlord and staff. The
smaller public bar is home to the
darts team.

Paglesham D4

*Remote and isolated hamlet,
near the River Roach, opposite
Potton Island. Good country
walks.*

11.30-3; 6.30-11 (12-4.30; 7-10.30
Sun)

Plough & Sail
East End
Tel: (01702) 258242
Marstons Pedigree; **Whitbread**
Boddingtons Bitter, Flowers
IPA; **Guest Beer** (occasional) **H**
🍺 🍷 🌳
16th century, weather-boarded,
former mill, with cosy, low-
beamed interior. Displays of
brassware, miniatures and
bric-a-brac.
Food-oriented and quiet with
connecting bars, and two real
fires. No games. Aviary in the
garden.

11.30-3; 6.30-11 (12-3; 6.30-10.30
Sun)

Punchbowl
Church End
Tel: (01702) 258376
Adnams Bitter; **Morlands** Old
Speckled Hen; **Guest Beers H**
🍺 🍷 🌳
16th century, weather-boarded
rural pub. Formerly a sail-mak-
ers and bakers until the 18th
century. Intimate, low-beamed,
food-oriented and quiet.
Ornamental fire places and
brassware. Set menu includes
specials board, fresh-fish and
Sunday roasts. Book for children's meals.

Panfield C2

12-3; 7-11 (10.30 Sun)

Bell Inn
37 Kynaston Road (nr B1053)
OS: TL735252
Tel: (01376) 324641
Ridleys IPA **H**
🍺 🍷 🌳
Cosy 16th century, two-bar village local. Camping by arrangement in field at the rear. Darts,
pool and football teams. No
food Tuesdays.

Parkeston F2

11-11 (12-10.30 Sun)

Captain Fryatt
65 Garland Road (off A136)
Tel: (01255) 503535
Ind Coope Friary Meux BB;
Tetley Bitter **H**
🍺 🍷 🅁 🌳 🛏 🍴 🐕 🌳
🚃
Time - and the main road - has
passed it by! Town-pub 'feel'.
Formerly the "Garland Hotel".

Paslow Wood Common B3

12-3; 6-11 (12-3; 7-10.30 Sun)

Black Horse
Nine Ashes Road
OS: TL588017
Tel: (01277) 821915
Free-house - No Real Ale - all beers reported to be on top pressure!

Pattiswick D2

11-3; 6.30-11 (12-3; 7-10.30 Sun)

Compasses
Compasses Road
OS: TL820247
Tel: (01376) 561322
Greene King IPA, Abbot Ale;
Marstons Pedigree H
𝕀𝔻 ◑ 🅁 🅑 ❀
Extended pub in rural setting, with a busy restaurant trade, popular with walkers. Occasional guest beers.

Pebmarsh D2

12-2; 7 (5 Fri)-11 (12-3;7-10.30 Sun)

Kings Head
The Street (1½ miles East of A131)
OS: TL851335
Tel: (01787) 269306
Greene King IPA; **Guest Beers** H
𝕀𝔻 ◑ 🅁 🅔 ⟝ 🐾 ❀
Village local, with an oak-beamed interior dating from 1470. Three constantly-changing guest beers - a Real Ale paradise. October beer festival. Skittles and table football played.

Peldon E3

11-2.30; 5.30-11 (12-3; 7-10.30 Sun)

Peldon Rose
Mersea Road (B1025)
OS: TM006159
Tel: (01206) 735248
Whitbread Boddingtons Bitter, Flowers IPA, Original; **Guest Beer** (occasional) H
𝕀𝔻 ◑ 🅁 🍴 ⟝ 🐾 ❀
Original old building at front, conservatory at rear, in delightful gardens. No gaming machines or music here. Real fires. Good cross-section of home-cooked food. Restaurant open Friday and Saturday evenings only. B&B - three rooms.

11-11 (12-10.30 Sun)

Plough
Lower Road
OS: TL990164
Tel: (01206) 735370
Bass Draught Bass; **Greene King** IPA; **Morlands** Old Speckled Hen H
𝕀𝔻 ◑ 🅁 🅔 ❀ ♿
Weather-boarded village local with real fires and a resident ghost upstairs! No food Sunday evening.

Pentlow D1

Pretty village with round-tow-ered church and thatched cottages.

12-2.30; 7 (5 Fri)-11 (12-4; 7-10.30 Sun)

Pinkuah Arms
Pinkuah Lane (nr B1064)
OS: TL816448
Tel: (01787) 280857
Greene King IPA H
𝕀𝔻 ❀
Well-run family pub - the most northerly in Essex.

Pilgrims Hatch B4

12-11 (10.30 Sun)

Black Horse
402 Ongar Road (A128)
Tel: (01277) 372337
Bass Hancocks HB, Draught Bass; **Guest Beer** H
𝕀𝔻 ◑ ◐
Early Tudor house, originally converted from two cottages. Beer rather cold and served through 'sparklers' - ask for them to be removed! Children welcome in the food area. 'Event-free' pub.

10.30-11 (12-10.30 Sun)

Rose & Crown
390 Ongar Road (A128)
Tel: (01277) 372322
S&N Courage Best Bitter, Directors, Theakstons BB; **Guest Beer** (Winter) H
𝕀𝔻 ◑ 🅁 🅔 ⟝ 🍴
Listed, traditional, timbered building with separate restaurant. The former 'Pub 80' "Stocks" area is thankfully long gone!

Pitsea C5

Shown as 'Piceseia' in the Domesday Book, it has now been absorbed into its larger neighbour.

(See Basildon map for the location of the pubs).

11-11 (12-10.30 Sun)

Cromwell Manor P1
Wat Tyler Lane (nr A13/A132)
Tel: (01268) 555553 / Fax: (01268) 583868
Morlands Old Speckled Hen; **S&N** Courage Best Bitter, Directors H
𝕀𝔻 ◑ 🅁 ⟝ ❀ ♿ ⇌
Restored manor house, with function room and restaurant. Handy for Pitsea Station. Food all day on Sundays.

11-11 (12-10.30 Sun)

Great Chalvedon Hall P2
Rectory Road, Tyfields (B1011)
Tel: (01268) 553193
Whitbread - No real Ale.

Pitsea Leisure Centre P3
Northlands Pavement (nr B1464)
Free - Bar closed, the building has been renamed the 'Pitsea Welcome Centre'.

11-11 (12-10.30 Sun)

Railway P4
The Broadway (B1464)
OS: TQ737881
Tel: (01268) 552497
Ind Coope 'House' Bitter H
𝕀𝔻 ◐ ⟝ 🚃 ⇌
Large, Tudor-style pub. Part was formerly known as "Trax".

Pleshey C3

Attractive award winning village built almost wholly within ancient castle earthworks.

11-3; 6-11 (12-3; 7-10.30 Sun)

Leather Bottle
The Street
Tel: (01245) 237291
Ridleys IPA H, ESX, Witchfinder Porter (Winter) G
𝕀𝔻 ◑ 🅔 ❀
Village local, with an excellent, unspoilt public bar, and a small lounge. An aviary, full of interesting birds is in the garden area.

12-3; 7-11 (11-11 Sat: 12-10.30 Sun)

White Horse
The Street
Tel: (01245) 237281
Guest Beers H
Guest Cider (occasional) G
𝕀𝔻 ◑ 🅁 ❀
Pleasant, old timber-framed building, opened out into a single room, but split into distinct areas. Two or three varying guest beers from the small bar. Strong food-based trade, with an extensive menu.

95

Point Clear (St Osyth) E3

11-3; 7-11 (12 Fri/Sat: 12-10.30 Sun)

Ferry Boat Inn
Western Promenade, Clear Bay Park
Tel: (01255) 820366
Free (Bourne Leisure Group) - No Real Ale.

Rosie O'Grady's Jubilee Bar
Clear Bay Park
Tel: (01255) 821511
Free-house - now a club for residents/members only.

Potter Street (Harlow) A3

Engulfed by Harlow New Town. (See Harlow map for location of pubs)

11-11 (12-10.30 Sun)

Gatekeeper PS1
Old London Road (nr A414)
Tel: (01279) 424414
Wadworths 6X; **Whitbread** Boddingtons Bitter, Flowers Original H
◑ ◐ ◑ R ❀ ♿
Large, new Beefeater pub/restaurant built on the site of the former "Sun & Whalebone". Rather expensive. Ask for the 'sparkler' to be removed when ordering.

11-11 (12-3; 7-10.30 Sun)

Red Lion PS2
109 Potter Street / Red Lion Lane (nr A414)
Tel: (01279) 416132
Allied Domecq - No Real Ale.

11-3; 7-11 (12-3; 7-10.30 Sun)

White Horse PS3
155 Potter Street (nr A414)
Tel:
Hardys Dorchester Bitter; **Guest Beer** (Occasional) H
◑ ◐ ◑ ❀ ♿
Largish pub, where three rooms have been knocked into one. Long-established landlord. Beers are taken from the Carlsberg-Tetley range, and change every few weeks.

Prittlewell D5

Original settlement of Southend with ancient church.

12-3; 5-11 (12-11 Fri/Sat: 12-3; 7-10.30 Sun)

Bell
Prince Avenue (A127) / Rochford Road
Tel: (01702) 351331
Allied Domecq - No Real Ale. A sad loss - under previous management it sold some excellent beers.

11-11 (12-10.30 Sun)

Golden Lion
287/289 Victoria Avenue (A127)
Tel: (01702) 347737
Marstons Pedigree; **Ind Coope** Burton Ale; **Guest Beer** H
◑ ◐ ◑ ❤ ⛟ ❀ ⇌
Warm, friendly traditional pub with a function room for 100. Food all day. Thursday quizzes.

11-11 (12-10.30 Sun)

Nelson Hotel
North Road (nr A13 & A127)
Tel: (01702) 332687
Greene King IPA H
◑ ◐ ⛁
Large, back-street local with two distinct bars. Pool and darts played in the Public bar. Marquee in the garden all year round - heated in the Winter! Loud music. No food at weekends. Limited parking.

11-11 (12-10.30 Sun)

Railway Tavern
108 East Street (200yds off A127, and opposite Prittlewell Station)
Tel: (01702) 616214
S&N - No Real Ale.

Reids
3 Victoria Avenue (A127/B1015)
Inntrepreneur - expected to re-open soon after a long period of closure. Formerly the "Blue Boar".

11.30-3; 5-11 (11.30-11 Thu/Fri: 11-3 (4 match days); 7-11 Sat: 12-4; 7-10.30 Sun)

Spread Eagle
267 Victoria Avenue (A127)
Tel: (01702) 220061
Bass Hancocks HB; **Fullers** London Pride; **Guest Beers** H
◑ ◐ ◑ ❤ ⇌ ⛟ ⇌
High-ceilinged, Edwardian-style alehouse, close to Southend United FC and railway station. Excellent beer quality and a good variety of guest beers - but at a price! Pool, dominoes, darts, cards. Friday evening Folk Club.

11-11 (12-10.30 Sun)

Strawberry Field
Thanet Grange, Princes Avenue (A127/B1013)
Tel: (01702) 341175
Marstons Pedigree; **Whitbread** Boddingtons Bitter, Flowers Original H
◑ ◐ ◑ R ❤
New 'Brewers Fayre' pub-restaurant with adjacent hotel. Near Tesco's.

Purfleet B5

Somewhat under-pubbed - compared to nearby Aveley. The area near the hotel is attractive and shows the existence of a former spa.

11-11 (12-10.30 Sun)

Royal Hotel
London Road / High Street (A1090)
Tel: (01708) 865432
Whitbread Boddingtons Bitter, Flowers Original H
◑ ◐ ◑ R ⛁ ❤ ❤ ⛟ ❀
♿ ⇌
More character than most 'Beefeaters', with downstairs (locals) bar, an upstairs bar for diners and a riverside terrace. Good river views.

Purleigh D4

George Washington's ancestor was rector here. See memorial in the interesting old church. Local vineyard!

11-3; 6-11

Bell
The Street (nr B1010)
OS: TL842020
Tel: (01621) 828348
Adnams Bitter; **Greene King** IPA; **Ind Coope** Benskins BB; **Guest Beer** H
◑ ◐ ◑ ❤ ⌂
Spacious and comfortable 16th century pub, commanding the high ground in the village, with super views over Blackwater estuary. A wealth of exposed beams and a large inglenook. No food Tuesday evenings.

Quendon B2

Fine tile-canopied fountain, near main road. Quendon Hall nearby has an octagonal Dove Cote which is larger than most houses.

Quendon Arms
Cambridge Road (B1383)
Free-house - Pub closed.

Radley Green B3

12-2; 7 (Not Tue in Winter, 6 Sat)-11 (12-4; 7-10.30 Sun)

Cuckoo
Radley Green (500yds North of the A414, between Norton Heath and Writtle)
OS: TL622054
Tel: (01245) 248356
Ridleys Mild (Summer), IPA, ESX, Witchfinder Porter (Winter), seasonal ales H
◑ ◐ ◑ ❀
Secluded, quiet and friendly, one-bar country local, with a large caravan/camping area. Formerly the "Thatchers Arms".

Radwinter B1

An attractive village.

11.30-3(3.30 if busy); 6.30-11 (12-4;7-10.30 Sun)

Plough
Sampford Road (B1053/B1054)
OS: TL612375
Tel: (01799) 599222
Fullers London Pride; **Greene King** IPA; **Hook Norton** Old Hooky; **Shepherd Neame** Spitfire; **Woodfordes** Wherry; **Guest Beers** H

⬤❶◗R🅁⬛🍴⬛❀↯

Traditional country pub - grade II listed, with fine gardens, and a patio covered by 'Clematis Montana' that is reputedly over 100 years old.
A la Carte menu, with some home-made specialities. Self-contained Bed and Breakfast (2 ES rooms). No pool tables or juke boxes - conversation dominates!
Usually four or five beers on at a time - including IPA and an 'Ale of the Month'. The landlord is a CAMRA member.

Rainham B5

The old village centre with its fine Norman church and the adjacent 18th century Rainham Hall still retains some character.

10-11 (12-10.30 Sun)

Albion
2 Rainham Road (Dovers Corner, A125/A1306)
Tel: (01708) 552445
Ruddles County H

⬤❶◗R⬛⬛❀↯

Large, much-altered pub which retains its public bar and a function room. Over 21s only.

12-11 (9 Sun)

Angel Inn
31 Broadway (B1335)
Tel: (01708) 522829
Free-house - No Real Ale.

11-3; 5-11 (11-11 Sat: 12-3; 7-10.30 Sun)

Bell
Broadway (B1335)
Tel: (01708) 520037
Adnams Bitter; **Greene King** Abbot Ale; **Ind Coope** Burton Ale; **Morlands** Old Speckled Hen; **Tetley** Bitter H

⬤❶◗R❀↯

Cosy, popular local.

Berwick Manor
Berwick Pond Road
OS: TQ545833
Free-house - Night-club only.

Cauliflower
58-66 Upminster Road South (nr A1306)
Free-house - Pub closed and converted to an Indian restaurant.

11-11 (12-3; 7-10.30 Sun)

Phoenix
Broadway (B1335)
Tel: (01708) 553700
S&N Courage Best Bitter, Directors, John Smiths Bitter; **Guest Beer** H

⬤❶🍴❀↯

Spacious, well-furnished family pub. Landlord sometimes plays the organ in the saloon bar.

12-11 (10.30 Sun)

Saxon Horn
Upminster Road North / Lambs Lane (nr A1306)
Tel: (01708) 520853
Bass - No Real Ale.

Ramsden Bellhouse C4

11.30-11 (12-10.30 Sun)

Fox & Hounds
Church Road
OS: TL718948
Tel: (01268) 710286
Crouch Vale SAS; **Tetley** Bitter; **Whitbread** Flowers IPA; **Guest Beers** H

⬤❶◗R❀

Comfortable, friendly, 1930s local, catering for all ages. Large, pleasant garden with play area and pets corner. Carvery on Sundays, also Summer Sunday barbecues.
Occasional live music - piano, etc. Home of the local cricket and football teams.

Ramsden Heath C4

11.30-11 (12-10.30 Sun)

Nags Head
Heath Road
Tel: (01268) 710191
Ridleys IPA, ESX, Rumpus H

⬤❶◗❀🍺

A typical, modernised and 'improved' village pub. Recently acquired by Ridleys. Try the Indian curry menu.

11-3; 6-11 (12-4; 7-10.30 Sun)

White Horse
Heath Road / Church Road / Downham Road
OS: TL713959
Tel: (01268) 710297
S&N Courage Directors, John Smiths Bitter, Websters Yorkshire Bitter H

⬤❶◗R⬛⬛➤❀↯

Large, comfortable and very popular, though rather expensive! Quiz night on Tuesdays, 60s disco on Thursdays and (non-deafening) hit music on Sundays.
Speciality fish night Fridays. Large garden. No Smoking area.

Ramsey F2

11-3; 5.30-11 (12-10.30 Sun)

Castle Inn
The Street (nr B1352 / A120)
Tel: (01255) 880203
Whitbread Best Bitter, Boddingtons Bitter; **Guest Beers** H

⬤❶◗R❀

17th century pub with a nautical feel, even though it's inland. Two guest beers. Camping at rear of pub for 10 tents.

Ranks Green (Fairstead) C3

A hamlet on the 'Essex Way' long distance footpath.

Pretty Lady
Ranks Green (1½ miles East of A131)
OS: TL748180
Ridleys - Pub sadly closed in 1991.

Rawreth C4

11-11 (12-10.30 Sun)

Carpenters Arms
London Road / Chelmsford Road (A129, nr A130)
Tel: (01268) 785437
Greene King IPA; **S&N** Courage Directors, John Smiths Bitter H

⬤❶◗R❀

Comfortable roadside tavern, interesting 'A la Carte' menu.

11.30-2.30 (Sat only); 6.30-11 (12-3; 7-10.30 Sun)

Chichester Hotel
Old London Road (off A129)
OS: TQ779926
Tel: (01268) 561234
Whitbread Flowers Original H

⬤❶◗R🍴⬛❀🅖

More of a banqueting centre than a pub. Extensive, with a quiet atmosphere. Real Ale in the 'Stable Bar'.

Rayleigh C4

A former market town, with a fine old church and a well-preserved windmill.

11-11 (12-10.30 Sun)

Crown
84 High Street (A129)
Tel: (01268) 742340
Greene King IPA; **S&N** Courage Directors, Theakstons BB H

⬤❶◗🅖↯

18th century coaching inn, with an 'old-fashioned' interior that has been preserved throughout recent refurbishment. Bar Billiards, pool and darts played. Formerly "Ye Olde Crown".

10-11 (12-10.30 Sun)

Half Moon
5 High Street (A129)
Tel: (01268) 742209
Greene King IPA; **Tetley** Bitter;
Guest Beers H
◖◗ ⌨ 🛏 ♿ ⇄
Enlarged, one-bar pub, near to the church. The old restaurant area has been reclaimed for drinkers. Cheap food specials, except Sundays. Discos on Thursday and Sunday evenings. Quiz nights on Thursdays.

11 (10 Fri/Sat)-11 (12-4; 7-10.30 Sun)

Old White Horse
39-41 High Street (A129)
Tel: (01268) 749041
Bass Draught Bass; **Fullers** London Pride; **Greene King** IPA; **Guest Beers H**
◖◗ ✿ ⇄
Small, one-bar, family-run, traditional, locals pub, with good value food.

Palms 'Trading Post'
19 High Street (A129)
Free-house - Bar closed, nightclub only.

11-11 (12-10.30 Sun)

Paul Pry Tavern
14 High Road (A129)
Tel: (01268) 742859
S&N Courage Directors,
Theakstons BB **H**
◗ ✿ ♿ ⇄
Popular pub, refurbished in 'olde worlde' style. Named after a figure in an 1823 play by John Poole. Children's menu. Large outside patio area, and playground for children.

11-11 (12-10.30 Sun)

Rayleigh Lodge
70 The Chase (nr A1015)
Tel: (01268) 742149
S&N Courage Directors,
Theakstons BB **H**
◖◗ ◗ ® ✿
Historic building, with Henry VIII connections. Good garden, set back from the road. Popular carvery restaurant.

10-11 (12-10.30 Sun)

Spread Eagle
93 High Street (A129)
Tel: (01268) 775717
Greene King IPA; **Marstons** Pedigree; **Tetley** Bitter;
Guest Beers H
◖◗ ◗ ⊞ ✿ ⇄
Friendly, two-bar local, with varying guest beers from the 'Tapsters Choice' range. Crib night on the last Monday of the month. Limited parking.

11-11 (12-10.30 Sun)

Travellers Joy
(Hungry Horse)
Downhall Road/London Road (A129)
Tel: (01268) 784545
Greene King Martha Greene's, IPA, Abbot Ale; **Guest Beers H**
◖◗ ◗ ⊩ 🛏 ♿ ⇄
Edge of town centre pub, near to the railway station. Good value food. Formerly "Peers".

10-11 (12-10.30 Sun)

Weir
Rayleigh Weir (A127/A129)
Tel: (01268) 774179
Marstons Pedigree; **Tetley** Bitter; **Youngs** Bitter **H**
◖◗ ◗ ® ⊞ 🖘 ⌨
"Big Steak" family pub/restaurant, with a single large bar.

Rayne   C2

Large village on Stane Street - an old Roman road. Almost a suburb of Braintree with period isinglass factory. Bypassed.

11-11 (12-10.30 Sun)

Cock
47 The Street (old A120)
Tel: (01376) 320474
Ridleys IPA **H**
◖◗ ⊞ ✿
Compact, traditional two-bar pub, in which the bars have been partly 'knocked-through' so that the football on large screen TV spills into both bars. Large variety of pizzas. Sunday lunches. Dominoes played.

11-3; 5-11 (11-11 Fri/Sat: 12-10.30 Sun)

Swan
1 The Street (old A120)
Tel: (01376) 322662
Ind Coope Ansells BB;
Guest Beer H
🍺 D ◗ R ⊞ ⊫ ⊛ 🍴
16th century pub, with a variety
of drinking areas. In addition to
the main bar and public bar,
there is a snug a clubroom and a
30 cover restaurant. Evening
meals Friday and Saturday only.
The large garden has petanque
in summer, and is ideal for
children.

11-3; 7-11 (12-4; 7-10.30 Sun)

Welsh Princess
21 The Street (old A120)
Tel: (01376) 345822
Adnams Bitter; **Greene King**
IPA; **Guest Beer H**
🍺 ◗ 🍴 🍴
Caters for all ages and has a varied clientele. Two Sunday football teams, two darts teams and
occasional live music.

Redbridge   A4

11-11 (12-10.30 Sun)

Red House
Redbridge Lane East (nr
A12/A406/M11 interchange)
Tel: (0181) 550 6451
Adnams Bitter; **Whitbread**
Boddingtons Bitter, Flowers
Original; **Guest Beer H**
🍺 D ◗ R 🚗 ⊱ ⊛ ⊖
Large, multi-level 'Beefeater'
Steak House with miniature
waterfall and coloured lights.
Rather pricey. New 'Travelodge'
accommodation adjoining.
Opposite the Tube Station.

Rettendon   C4

*Collection of houses spread out
along the Chelmsford Road.*

11-2.30; 7-11 (12-4; 7-10.30 Sun)

Bell
Main Road, Rettendon Common
(A130)
Tel: (01245) 400616
Ruddles Best Bitter; **S&N**
Courage Directors, Websters
Yorkshire Bitter **H**
🍺 D ◗ R ⊫ ⊱ ⊛
Very attractive roadhouse with
family area. Restaurant closed
Sunday and Monday evenings -
hot meals available in the bar.

11-11 (12-10.30 Sun)

Plough & Sail
Southend Road, Rettendon
Common (A130)
OS: TQ755999
Tel: (01245) 400276
Marstons Pedigree; **Whitbread**
Boddingtons Bitter, Flowers
IPA; **Guest Beers H**
🍺 D ◗ R ⊱ ⊛ ⬧
The pub has been converted to a
'Brewers Fayre', with a food-
dominated theme and preferen-
tial prices for children. Braille
menus available, children's
parties catered for.
Large garden and mini-lake,
children's playground, covered
patio and weekend Bar-B-Q's.

11-3; 6.30 (6 Sat)-11 (12-10.30
Sun)

Wheatsheaf
Main Road, Rettendon Common
(A130)
Tel: (01245) 400264
Ridleys IPA, ESX, Witchfinder
Porter (Winter), Rumpus **H**
🍺 D ◗ D ⊞ ⊛
Pleasant family pub, with
additional new bar in the garden
at weekends, and live music in
the marquee.
Some might find the pink Morris
Minor, helicopter and milk float
all 'advertising' the pub rather
distasteful.

Rickling Green A2

*The highest recorded cricket
score in England was made here
in 1882. The village retains a
cricketing tradition.*

12-3; 6-11 (12-3; 6.30-10.30 Sun)

Cricketers' Arms
(½ mile West of B1383)
OS: TL511298
Tel: (01799) 543210
Whitbread Flowers IPA; **Guest
Beers G**
🍺 D ◗ R ⊞ 🚗 ⊱ ⊛
Enlarged pub in idyllic situation,
overlooking the village cricket
green. Excellent food.
Unusual gravity dispense, for
the varying range of Real Ales.
Always a bitter and a strong ale,
usually a dark beer as well.

Ridgewell   C1

11-3; 6-11 (12-10.30 Sun)

King's Head
Chapel Road (A1017, was A604)
OS: TL737410
Tel: (01440) 785303
Greene King IPA, Abbot Ale
(Winter) **H**
🍺 D ◗ D R ⊞ ⊛
15th century 'olde-worlde' pub
with cosy bars. Popular with
families.

11-3; 6-11 (12-3; 7-10.30 Sun)

White Horse Inn
Mill Road (A1017, was A604)
Tel: (01440) 785532
Adnams Bitter; **Nethergate**
IPA; **Guest Beers H**
Guest Cider G
🍺 D ◗ R ⊫ ⊛
Attractive, low-ceilinged, 17th
century pub, where the locally-
brewed Nethergate beer is a
speciality. Try your hand at
arm-wrestling here! Walkers and
cyclists welcomed.

Rivenhall End   D3

11-11 (12-10.30 Sun)

Fox
London Road (A12 - Eastbound)
Tel: (01376) 513147
Greene King IPA **H**
🍺 D ◗ D ⊞ ⊛
Refurbished 20s/30s roadhouse,
with food, TV and pool.

11-11 (12-10.30 Sun)

Rivenhall Motor Inn
London Road (A12 - Westbound)
Tel: (01376) 516969
Bass Draught Bass **H**
🍺 D ◗ R 🚗 ⊫ ⊱ ⊛
Pleasant bar in smart motel,
with its own sports/health club.

Rochford   D4

*Relatively unspoilt town close to
Southend airport. Stambridge
mills are impressive. Tuesday
market.*

11-3; 5 (6 Sat)-11 (12-3; 7-10.30
Sun)

Anne Boleyn
93/95 Southend Road
Tel: (01702) 545116
Greene King IPA, Abbot Ale **H**
🍺 D ◗ R ⊞ ⊫ 🚗
Impressive-looking, comfortably
furnished, 1930s ex-Charrington
house with emphasis on food.

Butlers Pantry & Pub
Southend Airport
Eastwoodbury Crescent
Free-house - Bar closed. Airport
terminal buildings may be
resited and extended.

12-2.30 (3 Sat/Sun); 7-11 (10.30
Sun)

Cherry Tree
1 Stambridge Road
Tel: (01702) 544426
S&N Courage Directors;
Morlands Old Speckled Hen;
Whitbread Flowers IPA **H**
🍺 D ◗ R ⊞ ⊛ ⊛ 🚆
Spacious, 'beamed' country
pub, around 300-400 years old.
Traditional home-cooked food -
fish a speciality. Sparklers used,
but are removed on request.

Golden Lion
35 North Street
Tel: (01702) 545487
Fuller London Pride; **Greene King** Abbot Ale; **S&N** Theakstons Old Peculier; **Guest Beers H**
Farmers Tipple Cider **H**
◖◗ ◖ 🍴 ⇌
Small, basic 300 year old ex-tailors shop. A 'no frills' drinkers pub, with a constantly-changing range of cask ales. Pub games. Slightly extended bar area and new patio.
CAMRA SE Essex Branch 'Pub of the Year' several times.

11-3.30; 6-11 (12-3; 7-10.30 Sun)
Horse & Groom
1 Southend Road
Tel: (01702) 544318
Bass Toby Cask, Draught Bass; **Ridleys** IPA; **Guest Beers H**
◖◗ ◖ ┗ 🏵 ⇌
Pleasant, comfortable, one-bar pub, with two distinct drinking areas, on the edge of town. Regular guest beers - especially from Ridleys. Beer variable. Sunday night quizzes. Beware 'Cidermaster' Cider on fake handpump.

11-11 (12-10.30 Sun)
Kings Head Hotel
11 West Street
Tel: (01702) 530286
Shepherd Neame Masterbrew, Spitfire **H**
◖◗ ◖ ⊞ ⇌
Originally a coaching inn, it is rumoured that Henry VIII stayed here. Situated in the market square, where weekly cattle market took place.
One of the few pubs in the town with separate bars. Acquired by Shepherd Neame (of Faversham) in 1997 - only their third pub in Essex.

11-3; 6-11 (12-3; 7-10.30 Sun)
Marlborough Head
71 West Street
Tel: (01702) 531036
Adnams Bitter; **Marstons** Pedigree; **Tetley** Bitter **H**
◖◗ ◖◗ (Not Sun)
⊞ 🏵 ⚹ ⇌
Popular, traditional, low-beamed, 500 year old pub, near the station. Occasional speciality live music. A selection of daily papers available for customers to read. The best chips in town at lunchtimes!
Parking available in public car park nearby.

10-11 (12-10.30 Sun)
Milestone
Union Lane
Tel: (01702) 544229
Greene King IPA, Abbot Ale; **Guest Beer H**
◖◗ ◗ ◖ 🏵 ⇌
Converted to a pub in recent years and tucked away in Union Lane, it has a real milestone outside. Thai restaurant upstairs. Handy for the station.

11-11 (12-5; 7-10.30 Sun)
New Ship Inn
7 East Street
Tel: (01702) 544244
Bass Worthington BB, Draught Bass; **Guest Beer H**
◖◗ ◖ 🏵 ⚹ ⇌
Nice, with a nautical flavour, and older than the "Old Ship"! Live music.

11-11 (12-10.30 Sun)
Old Ship
12-14 North Street
Tel: (01702) 544210
Ind Coope 'House Bitter', Burton Ale; **Marstons** Pedigree; **Morlands** Old Speckled Hen; **Guest Beers H**
◖◗ ◗ ◖ ┗ 🏵 ⇌
Traditional, 15th century, market-town public house, spacious and comfortable with olde worlde atmosphere. Excellent value food available Monday to Friday. Fine stained-glass windows.

10.30-4; 6-11 (10.30-11 Sat: 12-4.30; 7-10.30 Sun)
Rose & Crown
42 North Street
Tel: (01702) 530112
Ridleys Mild; **S&N** Courage Directors; **Guest Beers H**
◖◗ ◖ ⊞ ⇌
Large, 1930s style, corner pub, with a plush saloon bar, busy public bar and an unspoilt Gents. No food weekends.

10-11 (12-10.30 Sun)
White Horse
66 North Street
Tel: (01702) 544249
Bass Draught Bass **H**
◖◗ ◗ ⊞ 🏵 ⇌
'Working-class' pub with occasional live music at weekends.

Romford   A4
Popular shopping centre with lively thrice-weekly market. Romford Brewery - which had been keg only for some years - has now been demolished.

The former beer desert area of South Street, between the station and the shopping centre, has gained four 'superpubs' in as many years, virtually next door to each other.

11-3; 5.15-11 (11-11 Fri/Sat: 12-10.30 Sun)
Amalia's / Inner Secrets   1
48 High Street (nr A118 & A125)
Tel: (01708) 741584
Free-house - No Real Ale. Formerly the "Woolpack".

12-3; 6-11 (12-11 Sat: 12-10.30 Sun)
Asylum 66   2
166 South Street (nr A125)
Tel: (01708) 731974
Free-house - No Real Ale. Formerly the "Iced Tea Bar".

11-11 (12-10.30 Sun)
Big Hand Mo's   3
Rush Green Road (A124)
Tel: (01708) 740249
S&N - No Real Ale. Formerly the "Rush Green".

10-11 (12-10.30 Sun)
Bull   4
76 Market Place (nr A118)
Tel: (01708) 740476
Adnams Bitter; **Tetley** Bitter; **Youngs** Bitter; **Guest Beer H**
◖◗ ◗ ◖◗ ⊞ ┗ 🏵 ⚹ ⇌
Market local with baby-changing facilities and variable beer. Real Ale not always available. Pool played.

9-11 (Thu-Sat only)
Cellar Bar   5
27 North Street (nr A118 & A125)
Tel: (01708) 725566
Free-house - No Real Ale. Formerly "Charmers Wine Bar".

12-1am (7.30-10.30 Sun)
Color's   6
26 The Liberty, off Mercury Gardens (nr A118)
Tel: (01708) 769415
Bass - No Real Ale. Previously "Liberty's", the "Birdcage" and the "King's Head".

10-11 (or later)
Connex Cafe Bar   7
72/74 South Street (nr A125)
Tel: (01708) 728139
Free-house - No Real Ale. Formerly the "Global Netcafe".

11-11 (12-10.30 Sun)
Crown   8
260 London Road (A118) / Spring Gardens
Tel: (01708) 723935
Ind Coope 'House' Bitter; **Tetley** Bitter **H**
◖◗ ◗ ┗ ⚐ 🍴
Near dog track - refurbished in mock Victorian style. Beer variable.

Dolphin Bar   9
Dolphin Sports Centre, 2 Main Road (A118) / Mercury Gardens
Free-house - Bar and centre closed due to lack of funds. Site expected to be redeveloped.

12-3.30; 5-11 (11-11 Sat: 12-10.30 Sun)
Durham Arms   10
101 Brentwood Road (nr A125)
Tel: (01708) 748601
Ind Coope 'House' Bitter, **Tetley** Bitter **H**
◖◗ ◗ ◖ ┗ 🏵
Clean, comfortable pub with occasional live music. Parking difficult.

ROMFORD

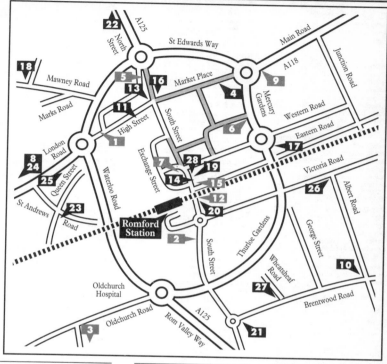

11-11 (12-10.30 Sun)

Ford & Firkin   **11**
15 High Street (nr A118 & A125)
Tel: (01708) 742923
Ford & Firkin River Ale, Ford
Ale, Flash Flood Bitter,
Dogbolter **H**
🍺 🍴 ◖ ◗ ⇌
New 'Firkin' brewery established
in January 1998, in the former
Romford Brewery Company's
old brewery tap. Supplies most
of the other Essex 'Firkins'.
Beware "Addlestone's" Cider on
fake handpump.
Snacks available until 6.30pm.
Formerly "Clutterbucks Ale
House", "Harts" and the "Bitter
End".

11-11 (closed Sun)

Freddie Whales Bar   *12*
141 South Street (nr A125)
Tel: (01708) 730534
Free-house - No Real Ale.
Formerly "Temptations".

11-11.30 (12-10.30 Sun)

Golden Lion Tavern   **13**
2 High Street (nr A125/A118)
Tel: (01708) 740081
S&N Courage Directors; John
Smiths Bitter, Theakstons BB,
XB, Old Peculier; **Guest Beer H**
Bulmers Cider **H**
🍺 🍴 ◖ ◗ **R** ⬛ ⇌
Nicely refurbished, much-
improved, but expensive town
centre pub. Various foreign
bottled beers. Parking difficult.

10-11 (12-10.30 sun)

Hogshead   **14**
113/117 South Street (nr A125)
Tel: (01708) 731846
Greene King Abbot Ale;
Wadworths 6X; **Whitbread**
Boddingtons Bitter, Flowers
IPA, Original, Abroad Cooper;
Guest Beers H/G
🍺 ◖ ◗ ♿ ⇌
New 'Hogshead' opened in
1996, in a former shop unit.
Typical decor, with an island bar
and intrusive 'music'. 'Draught'
and bottled Belgian beers also
available.

6-12 (12.30 Fri/Sat, 10.30 Sun)

Jaks   *15*
131 South Street (nr A125)
Tel:
Rank Entertainment - New bar
built in former commercial
premises - No Real Ale.

10 (6am Fri/Sat, 8am Wed)-11
(12-3; 7-10.30 Sun)

Lamb   **16**
5 Market Place (nr A118)
Tel: (01708) 741729
Tetley Bitter; **Youngs** Bitter;
Guest Beer **H**
🍺 ◖ ◗ 🍴 ⇌
Market local, with early break-
fasts on market days. Parking
can be a problem on market days.

11-11 (12-10.30 Sun)

Liberty Bell   **17**
Mercury Gardens / Western
Road (by A125, nr A118)
Tel: (01708) 760570
Wadworths 6X; **Whitbread**
Boddingtons Bitter,
Flowers Original **H**
🍺 🍴 ◖ ◗ **R** 🛏 🐕 🅿 ♿ ⇌
New 'Brewers Fayre' pub/restau-
rant that opened in December
1995. 'Travelodge' attached.

12-11 (10.30 Sun)
Mawney Arms 18
44 Mawney Road (nr A12)
Tel: (01708) 741077
Greene King IPA; Ind Coope
Burton Ale; **Tetley** Bitter **H**
◑ ⅅ ◑ ℝ ⊞ ⊫ ✳
Large and comfortable 'Big
Steak' pub, with regularly-
changing guest beer.

11-11 (12-10.30 Sun)
Moon & Stars 19
99-103 South Street (nr A125)
Tel: (01708) 730117
Fullers London Pride; **Greene
King** IPA; **S&N** Courage
Directors, Theakstons BB;
Guest Beers H
Westons Cider **H**
◑ ⅅ ◑ ⅆ ⅁ ⊟ ⅄ ⇌
Large 1994 'Wetherspoon' con-
version of former 'Pizza Hut'
restaurant, and the first of the
South Street 'superpubs'. Good
range of well-kept guest beers.
Toilets (except disabled)
upstairs.

10-11 (12-10.30 Sun)
Morland Arms 20
143 South Street (nr A125)
Tel: (01708) 722029
Morlands Old Speckled Hen;
Tetley Bitter; **Youngs**
Special; **Guest Beer H**
◑ ⅆ ⊟ ⅆ ⇌
Almost opposite the railway &
bus stations. Renovated some
years ago, in traditional style,
but with large screen TV and
background music. Parking difficult, although there is a car park
at the rear. Beer variable.
Beware 'Addlestones' Cider
believed to be on CO2.

11-3; 5-11
Old Oak 21
279 South Street / Brentwood
Road (nr A125)
Tel: (01708) 740364
S&N Courage Best Bitter **H**
◑ ⅅ ⊟ ⇌
Busy, friendly locals pub.

11-11 (12-10.30 Sun)
Parkside 22
290 North Street (A125, nr A12)
Tel: (01708) 750236
Ind Coope 'House' Bitter **H**
◑ (Not weekends) ⊟
Large town pub with lots of TVs
and one large screen showing
MTV or sport. 'L'-shaped pool
table.

11-11 (12-10.30 Sun)
Prince Albert 23
32 St Andrews Road (nr A118)
Tel: (01708) 766501
Ridleys IPA; **Whitbread**
Boddingtons Bitter **H**
◑ ⅅ ✳
Genuine back-street local.

11-11 (12-10.30 Sun)
Slaters Arms 24
164 London Road (A118)
Tel: (01708) 741347
S&N John Smiths Bitter; **Guest
Beer H**
⊞ ⊟ ⅆ
Bizarre decor - a mixture of
various refurbishments!?

11-11 (12-10.30 Sun)
Sun 25
45/47 London Road (A118)
Tel: (01708) 743423
S&N Courage Directors,
Theakstons BB, Websters
Yorkshire Bitter **H**
◑ ⅅ ◑ ⊟ ⅆ
Spacious and comfortable pub
with young clientele, isolated
from the town centre by the ring
road. Limited parking.

11-11 (12-10.30 Sun)
Victoria 26
122 Victoria Road (nr A125)
Tel: (01708) 747061
Bass Toby Cask; **Morlands** Old
Speckled Hen; **Wadworths** 6X;
Guest Beer H
◑ ⅅ ◑ ◑ ✳ ⇌
Pleasant local on the edge of
town, near ring-road.

12-11 (10.30 Sun)
Wheatsheaf 27
45 Wheatsheaf Road /
Brentwood Road (nr A125)
Tel: (01708) 760002
Ind Coope 'House' Bitter;
Tetley Bitter **H**
◑ ⅅ ⊞ ⇌
Landlord would not assist with
survey!

10-11 (12-10.30 Sun)
Yates's Wine Lodge 28
87/89 South Street / Western
Road (nr A125)
Tel:
Whitbread Boddingtons Bitter **H**
◑ ⅆ ⊟ ⇌
New street-corner, Yates's pub
on two levels, that opened in
November 1997. Disappointingly
limited 'range' of Real Ales!

Roundbush
(Purleigh) D4

11-3 (flexible); 6-11 (12-3 (flexi-
ble); 7-10.30 Sun)
Round Bush
Round Bush Road
OS: TL858019
Tel: (01621) 828354
Greene King IPA, Abbot Ale;
Guest Beers G
◑ ⅅ ◑ ◑ ⊞ ⊟ ✳
Traditional, friendly beer house,
in a pleasant rural setting - clas-
sic country pub. Lots of agricul-
tural artefacts on walls. Evening
meals and snacks Thursday to
Saturday only.
Probably the only "Roundbush"
in the country.

Rowhedge E2
Riverside village with boat yard.

11-2.30; 6.30-11 (12-3; 7-10.30
Sun)
Anchor Inn
High Street
Tel: (01206) 728382
Bass Draught Bass **H**
◑ ⅅ ◑ ℝ ⊞ ✳
Pleasant, pub with a nautical
theme and curiosities. The ter-
race is on the bank of the River
Colne, the home to many swans.
Limited parking.

11-3; 5.30-11 (11-11 Fri/Sat:
12-10.30 Sun)
Freemasons Arms
Church Street
Tel: (01206) 728477
Greene King IPA; **Ind Coope**
Burton Ale; **Whitbread**
Flowers IPA **H**
⊞ ⊟ ⅀ ✳
Friendly, two-bar locals pub,
with a good darts following.

12-3 (4 Sat); 7-11 (12-4; 7-10.30
Sun)
Ye Olde Albion
High Street
Tel: (01206) 728972
Ridleys IPA; **Guest Beer H**
◑ ⅅ ◑
Single, split-level bar with nauti-
cal theme, overlooking the River
Colne. Limited parking.

Roxwell B3

12-3; 5-11 (12-11 Sat: 12-4; 7-
10.30 Sun)
Chequers
The Street
Tel: (01245) 248240
Greene King IPA; **Wells**
Bombardier **H**
◑ ⅅ ◑ ◑ ✳
Cosy, family-owned, one-bar vil-
lage pub.

11.30-3; 6-11 (12-3; 7-10.30 Sun)
Hare & Hounds
Bishops Stortford Road (A1060)
OS: TL659083
Tel: (01245) 248214
Ind Coope Burton Ale;
Whitbread Flowers IPA **H**
◑ ⅅ ◑ ℝ ⊟ ⅀ ✳
Modernised, roadside, country
pub, catering for families, one
mile east of village. Beware
cider on fake handpump!

Roydon A3

11-2.30 (3 Sat); 5.30 (6 Sat)-11
(12-3; 7-10.30 Sun)
Crusader
42 High Street (B181)
Tel: (01279) 792161
McMullens Original AK,
Country, Gladstone; **S&N**
Courage Directors; **H**
◑ ⅅ ◑ ◑ ⊟ ⇌
Spacious pub. Ask for the
'sparkler' to be removed when
ordering.

New Inn

11-2.30; 6-11 (12-3; 7-10.30 Sun)

90 High Street (B181)
Tel: (01279) 792225
Bass Draught Bass; **Ind Coope**
Burton Ale; **Tetley** Bitter **H**
◐ ◗ ◖ ◗ **R** (Weekends)
🔥 ➤ ≈

Friendly 15th century local, with
occasional live music.

11-2.30; 5.30-11 (12-3; 7-10.30
Sun)

White Hart

43 High Street (B181)
Tel: (01279) 792118
Marstons Bitter, Pedigree,
seasonal beers **H**

◐ ◗ ◖ ◗ **R** 🔥 ▦ ≈

Very friendly and pleasant, 15th
century coaching inn. A former
free-house now acquired by
Marstons, featuring the 'Head
Brewers Choice' of seasonal
ales. Strong food theme. Live
music Saturday evenings.

11-2.30; 6-11 (12-3; 7-10.30 Sun)

White Horse

2 High Street (B181)
Tel: (01279) 793131
S&N Courage Best Bitter,
Directors **H**

◐ ◗ ◖ ≈

Old, 'beamed' local, known as
the 'Top House'. Evening meals
Wednesday to Saturday only.

Roydon Hamlet A3

11-3; 6-11 (12-3; 7-10.30 Sun)

Green Man

Tylers Road (nr B181)
Tel: (01279) 793591
Ind Coope Benskins BB,
Burton Ale; **Tetley** Bitter;
Whitbread Flowers IPA **H**

◐ ◗ ◖ ◗ ❀

Small pub with emphasis on
food. under threat of closure.

Rudley Green (Purleigh) D4

12-3; 7-11 (12-5; 7-10.30 Sun)

Queens Head

Chelmsford Road (B1010)
OS: TL834029
Tel: (01621) 828229
Whitbread Flowers IPA,
Original **H**

◐ ◗ ◖ ◗ ❀

Nice old pub - cool in summer.
Friendly and roomy. Evening
meals and snacks Saturday and
Sunday only.
Monthly 'Scalextric' races.

Runwell C4

12-3; 5-11 (12-11 Thu-Sat: 12-4;
7-10.30 Sun)

Quart Pot

Runwell Road (A132)
Tel: (01268) 732399
Bass Draught Bass; **Fullers**
London Pride **H**

◐ ◗ ◖ ◗ ⊞ ❀

Old pub with two contrasting
bars, that are bigger than they
look from outside. Petanque and
darts played, regular quiz nights.
Home of local pigeon-fanciers
club. Large secluded garden
with duckpond. Stop press may
lose its public bar and become
another boring "Eatery"

11-3; 6-11 (12-10.30 Sun)

Thomas Kemble

Runwell Road (A132)
Tel: (01268) 769671
Bass (Toby Inn) - Real Ale only
available occasionally.

Saffron Walden B1

*An architectural delight with
interesting shops, a large common and magnificent church.
Audley End House open to public is nearby. A 'Wetherspoon' is
expected to be opened in the
High Street.*

12-2.30; 6-11 (12-10.30 Sun)

Axe   1

60 Ashdon Road
Tel: (01799) 522235
Greene King IPA, Abbot Ale **H**

◐ ◗ ◖ ◗ **R** ⊞ ❀

Popular town local, with nice
friendly atmosphere. The decor
is interesting, and there are
displays of framed cigarette
cards, first day covers and
English banknotes.
Good pub food available
Monday to Saturday lunchtimes
and Wednesday to Saturday
evenings. Formerly the "Axe &
Compasses".

11-3; 6-11 (11-11 Sat: 12-10.30
Sun)

Crocus   2

40 Pleasant Valley / Rowntree
Way
Tel: (01799) 527668
Greene King IPA, Abbot Ale,
seasonal beers **H**

◐ ◗ ◖ ◗ ❀ ⚄

Large pub, popular with the
younger set. Meals (special roast
dinners) on Wednesdays only.
Petanque played.

10.30-11 (12-10.30 Sun)

Cross Keys Hotel   3

32 High Street (B184)
Tel: (01799) 522207
Ind Coope Benskins BB,
Burton Ale; **Tetley** Bitter;
Guest beers H

◐ ◗ ◖ ◗ ⊞ ⛵ 🔥 ❀ ⚄

Upmarket 15th century
timbered, street-corner pub with
limited parking to rear. Pool and
darts played.

11-2.30; 6-11 (12-3; 7-10.30 Sun)

Duke of York   4

96 High Street (B1052)
Tel: (01799) 523011
Greene King IPA; **Whitbread**
Flowers Original **H**

◐ ◗

Small and popular with cosy
interior.

11-3; 6-11 (12-10.30 Sun)

Eight Bells   5

18 Bridge Street (B184)
Tel: (01799) 522790/526237
Adnams Bitter; **Ind Coope**
Friary Meux BB, Burton Ale;
Tetley Bitter **H**
Addlestones Cider **H**

◐ ◗ ◖ ◗ **R** ⊞ 🔥 ⛷ ❀

16th century timber-framed inn,
noted for its food and Tudor
barn restaurant (Egon Ronay &
Les Routiers). Two outdoor
drinking areas. Excellent facilities for families. Beware low
beams in the gents.

11-3; 6-11 (11-11 Fri/Sat: 12-10.30
Sun)

Gate   6

74 Thaxted Road (B184)
Tel: (01799) 522321
Greene King IPA, Abbot Ale,
Seasonal Ales **H**

◐ ◗ ◖ ◗ (Not Sat/Sun)

⊞ 🔥 ⛷ ❀

Floodlit Petanque court with two
teams, three football teams,
quizzes and darts played. The
Meeting / Function room is also
used as a family room and for
pool. The Garden has swings for
children.
The fake handpump for
'Scrumpy Jack' Cider has now
been removed.

11-11 (12-10.30 Sun)

Kings Arms   7

Market Hill
Tel: (01799) 522768
Greene King IPA; **Marstons**
Pedigree **H**

◐ ◗ ◖ ◗ ⊞ 🔥 ⛷ ❀

Known as 'Smiling Jacks'. No
machines, coal fire, original
off-sales and counter. Parking
difficult.

10-11 (12-10.30 Sun)

Old English Gentleman   8

Gold Street (nr B184/B1052)
Tel: (01799) 523595
Fullers London Pride; **Greene
King** IPA; **Wadworths** 6X;
Whitbread Flowers Original **H**

◐ ◗ ◖ ◗ **R** ⛷ ▦ ⚄

Noisy town local with patio at
rear. Parking difficult.

Queen Elizabeth   9

2 East Street (B184)
Tel: (01799) 523832
Morlands Old Speckled Hen;
Whitbread Boddingtons Bitter **H**
Street-corner local with discos,
photos and pop memorabilia.
Parking difficult.

SAFFRON WALDEN

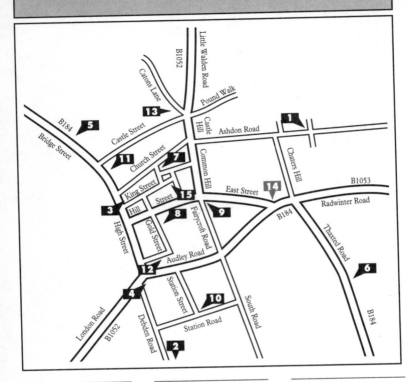

11-3; 6-11 (12-3; 7-10.30 Sun)

Railway Arms   **10**
Station Road (nr B184)
Tel: (01799) 522208
Ind Coope Burton Ale;
Tetley Bitter, Imperial **H**
⊕ ⅅ ◖ ❀ ⅋
Plain, but comfortable and
friendly. Still retaining original
off-sales counter. Long-serving
landlord. Meals Thursday and
Friday only.

11-11 (12-10.30 Sun)

Saffron Hotel   **11**
8-12 High Street (B184)
Tel: (01799) 522676
Adnams Bitter; **Greene King**
IPA; **Marstons** Pedigree **H**
⊕ ⅅ ◖ ⊞ ⅋ ⎎ ➤ ❀
Haunted, 16th century timber-
framed building with comfortable interior. Framed aircraft
photo in bar. Excellent, varied
menu. Limited parking.

11-11 (12-10.30 Sun)

Sun   **12**
59 Gold Street (nr B1052) off
High Street
Tel: (01799) 506035
Ridleys IPA, ESX/Rumpus **H**
⊕ ⅅ ◖ ⎎ ❀
Small, pleasant pub with pargetted facade and snug at rear.
Close to the town centre (near
the war memorial) - yet retaining
its local feel. Separate games
room and cellar bar - that is
available for private functions
and meetings. Ridleys northern
outpost!

11-3; 6-11 (11-11 Fri/Sat: 12-10.30
Sun)

Victory   **13**
1 Little Walden Road (by B1052)
Tel: (01799) 522234
Greene King IPA, Abbot Ale **H**
⊕ ⅅ ◖
Cosmopolitan town pub with
characterful landlord. Beware
flying ducks in the lounge!
Unusual brass pump handles.
Retains original off-sales
counter. No food Sundays and
Mondays.

Waggon & Horses   **14**
41 East Street (B184)
Bass - Pub closed after the death
of the licensee.

10-11 (12-10.30 Sun)

White Horse   **15**
4 Market Square / Market Street
(nr B184)
Tel: (01799) 506288
Adnams Broadside; **S&N**
Courage Best Bitter, Directors **H**
⊕ ⅅ ◖
Large, busy grade 2 listed build-
ing, supposedly haunted.

Salcott-cum-Virley   **D3**

Sun
The Street
OS: TL950137
Free-house - Very sadly closed
and now a private house.

Sandon C3

Rare old oak tree on village green.

12-3; 6-11 (12-3; 7-10.30 Sun)

Crown
The Green, Graces Cross Road (nr A414)
Tel: (01245) 472219
Fullers London Pride; **Bass** Hancocks HB; **Guest Beer H**

Characterful 16th century pub, the centre of village life. No juke box or other music, radio in the public bar only, pool and darts played.

Sawbridgeworth A3

A town with many pubs of character - all except this one are 'over the border' in Hertfordshire.

12-11 (12-4; 7-10.30 Sun)

Railway Inn
Station Road
Tel: (01279) 724317
Morlands Old Speckled Hen; **S&N** Courage Best Bitter; **Guest Beer** (Occasional) **H**

Lively pub - liked by the younger set. Right on Hertfordshire/Essex border, by the railway station.

Seven Kings A4

11-11 (12-10.30 Sun)

Ashgrove
271 Green Lane (A1083)
Tel: (0181) 599 4181
Bass Worthington BB; **Fullers** London Pride **H**

Comfortable local with toby jugs etched onto the windows.

Cuckoo's Nest (Kings)
700 High Road (A118)
Free-house (Wheatley's) - Pub closed and demolished.

11-11 (12-10.30 Sun)

Joker
1 Cameron Road (nr A118)
Tel: (0181) 590 3063
Bass Draught Bass; **S&N** Websters Green Label **H**

Refurbished in typical 'Magic Pub' style. Still lively, and with a strong Irish following. A variety of sporting pictures adorn the walls. Close to Seven Kings station.

Sewards End B1

Green Dragon
4 Walden Road (B1053)
Free-house - Sadly closed and demolished. New houses now built on the site.

Sewardstone A4

Linear village uniquely in Essex and 'E4' London postal district.

11-11 (12-10.30 Sun)

Fox & Hounds
Sewardstone Road (A112)
Tel: (0181) 529 1164
Morlands Old Speckled Hen; **S&N** Websters Green Label **H**

Cavernous pub, with friendly landlord. Barbecues on Summer evenings. Occasional 'theme' evenings. Pool table. Near campsite.

11-2.30 (3.30 Sat); 5 (7 Sat)-11.30 (12-3; 7-10.30 Sun)

Plough
Sewardstone Road (A112) / Mott Street
Tel: (01992) 711097
McMullens Original AK, Country, Gladstone **H**

Bar billiards and pool tables. Limited parking.

11.30-3; 6-11 (12-3; 7-10.30 Sun)

Royal Oak (Venners)
Sewardstone Road (A112)
Tel: (0181) 529 1178
S&N Courage Directors **H**

Quiz nights alternate Thursdays.

Shalford C2

On River Pant, with trout farm.

Fox
Church End (nr B1053)
OS: TL721279
Ridleys - Pub closed and converted to residential use.

"The Crown", Sheering

12-3; 6.30-11 (12-3.30; 7-10.30 Sun)

George Inn
Braintree Road (B1053)
Tel: (01371) 850207
Adnams Broadside; **Greene King** IPA; **Guest Beer H**
◑ ◐ ◑ ◐ ※ ⌂

Plenty for interior designers to look at, in this 500 year old 'beamed' pub, that has been dressed-up in country farm-house style. Even the toilets are decorated with furnishings. Huge old fireplace in the bar area. Interesting variety of dishes.

Sheering   A3

11.30-3; 6-11 (12-10.30 Sun)

Cock
The Street (B183)
Tel: (01279) 734229
Ind Coope Benskins BB; **Guest Beers H**
◑ ◐ ◑ ◐ ※

Tastefully decorated large single bar, with real fire. Two guest beers - usually from Essex. No food Sunday evening.

11-3.30; 5-11 (11-11 Fri/Sat: 12-4; 7-10.30 Sun)

Crown Inn
The Street (B183)
Tel: (01279) 734203
Adnams Bitter; **S&N** Courage Best Bitter H
◑ ◐ ◑ ◐ R ※

Bright, cosy and cheerful village local. Fish from Billingsgate market.

Queen's Head
The Street (B183)
McMullens - Pub closed.

Shelley   B3

Village on northern outskirts of Chipping Ongar.

Bowling Inn
Fyfield Road (B184)
Free-house - Pub closed and rebuilt as "Smith's Bistro". Formerly the "Red Cow".

Shenfield   B4

Eastern suburb of Brentwood. The old village has wooden-steepled church.

(See Brentwood map for location of pubs).

11-3; 5.30-11 (11-11: 12-10.30 Sun)

Eagle & Child   S1
13 Shenfield Road (A1023, nr A129)
Tel: (01277) 210155
Greene King IPA; **Mighty Oak** Burntwood; **S&N** Courage Best Bitter H
◑ ◐ ◑ ◐ R ⊞ ⌂ ※ ⇌

Large mock-Tudor pub with dark wood-panelled walls and lots of USA and UK street signs. Pool played. Background music. Carvery/Restaurant doubles as meeting room if required.

10 (10.30 Sat)-2.30; 6 (7.30 Sat)-11

Hollands Wine Bar   S2
234 Hutton Road (A129)
Tel: (01277) 210261
Free-house - No real ale.

12-2.30; 6-11 (12-3; 7-10.30 Sun)

Rose   S3
138 Chelmsford Road (A1023)
Tel: (01277) 210321
Ind Coope Benskins Best Bitter, Burton Ale; **Tetley** Bitter H
◑ ◐ ◑ ◐ ⌂

Attractive, listed building with beams, brasses and a patio. A quiet pub with no music or games, just conversation. No meals Sunday evenings.

10-2.30; 5.30-11 (11-11 Sat)

Ye Olde Green Dragon   S4
112 Chelmsford Road (A1023/A129)
Tel: (01277) 210086
Ind Coope Benskins BB; **Tetley** Bitter H
◑ ◐ ◑ ◐ ⌂ ⇌

16th century pub, which used to sell a good range of guest beers, now a 'lager pub'. Pool room. Sunday lunches, but no snacks Sunday evenings.

Shoeburyness   D5

11-11 (12-10.30 Sun)

Captain Mannerings
Campfield Road (nr A13)
Tel: (01702) 297575
Marstons Pedigree; **Tetley** Bitter H
◑ ◐ ◑ ◐ R ⌛ ※ ⇌

Pleasant pub on the site of old army hospital, recently refurbished as a 'Big Steak'. Nice interior on the theme of the Shoebury Garrison. Children catered for.

11-11 (12-10.30 Sun)

Parsons' Barn
Frobisher Way, North Shoebury (nr A13)
Tel: (01702) 297373
Greene King IPA; **S&N** Theakstons BB H
◑ ◐ ◑ ◐ ⌛ ※ &

Large, spacious, open-plan, pre-served barn, by 'Asda'. Display of farm implements. Ask for 'sparkler' to be removed when ordering.

11-11 (1am Sat: 12-10.30 Sun)

Shoe & Cobbler
84 Ness Road (A13/B1016)
Tel: (01702) 292762
Inntrepreneur - No Real Ale. Formerly the "Warehouse" and the "Duke of Cambridge".

10-3; 5-11 (11-11 Fri/Sat: 12-3; 7-10.30 Sun)

Shoeburyness Hotel
1 High Street
Tel: (01702) 292005
Bass Hancocks HB, M&B Brew XI H
◑ ◐ ◑ ◐ ⊞ ※ ⇌

Traditional, 1930s type pub with separate games room. Friendly atmosphere with old-style piano player some evenings.

11-11 (12-10.30 Sun)

Shorehouse
Ness Road / Waterford Road (B1016)
Tel: (01702) 292892
Marstons Pedigree; **Morlands** Old Speckled Hen; **Wadworths** 6X; **Whitbread** Flowers Original H
◑ ◐ ◑ ◐ R ⊞ ⌂ ☞

Family-friendly, re-built pub with large 'Brewers Fayre' restaurant, and 'Charlie Chalk Factory' for children. Would benefit from the addition of an adults room! Ask for the 'sparkler' to be removed when ordering your beer.

12-3; 7-11 (11-11 Fri/Sat: 12-10.30 Sun)

Sportsman
100 Constable Way
Tel: (01702) 290924
S&N John Smiths Bitter H
⊞

Modern estate pub with two bars, that reopened as a pub after a spell as a private club. Formerly the "Osprey".

Sible Hedingham   C1

Large attractive village with fine buildings and church.

Bell Inn
46 Swan Street (A1017, was A604)
Greene King - Pub closed.

12-11 (10.30 Sun)

Sugar Loaves
175 Swan Street (A1017, was A604)
Tel: (01787) 462720
Adnams Bitter, Broadside H
◑ ◐ ◑ ◐ R ⊞ ⌂ ※

Restored, 15th century, oak-beamed inn with two bars.

11-11 (12-10.30 Sun)
Swan
Swan Street (A1017, was A604)
Tel: (01787) 461351
Greene King IPA; **Guest Beers H**
◑ ◐ ◑ ❀
Large, lively, friendly and comfortably-furnished bar and TV/games room. Popular with younger drinkers in early evenings. Occasional live music.

12-3; 7-11 (10.30 Sun)
White Horse
39-41 Church Street
OS: TL776343
Tel: (01787) 460742
Greene King IPA, Abbot Ale **H**
◑ ◐ ◑ **R** ⊞ ⇔ ❀
Well-maintained, 15th century pub in substantial grounds, brim-full of character. Super collection of chamber pots. Camping by arrangement. No food on Mondays.

11-11 (12-10.30 Sun)
White Lion
6 Church Street
Tel: (01787) 462534
Greene King IPA, Abbot Ale
(Winter) **H**
◑ ◐ **R** ⊨ ❀ ⅍
One-bar 'Grays' pub with live music at weekends. Popular with the younger clientele.

Silver End   D2

11-11 (12-10.30 Sun)
Silver End Hotel
Broadway
Tel: (01376) 583161
Greene King IPA **H**
◑ ◐ ◑ **R** ⊞ ⊨ ❀ ⅍
Interesting, friendly and unusually-styled, time-warp hotel in centre of village. Originally part of the Crittal Windows empire. Keen landlord. A-la Carte available.

11-3; 5-11 (11-11 Fri/Sat: 12-10.30 Sun)
Western Arms
Western Road
Tel: (01376) 583336
Greene King IPA, Abbot Ale, seasonal beers **H**
◑ ◐ ◑ ⊞ ⇔ ❀
Good family pub with separate room for pool and darts. Beer garden has swings and slides for children. Comfortable lounge - ideal for meals. Live duos Friday and Saturday evenings.

Socketts Heath B5

12-11 (10.30 Sun)
Oak
35 Lodge Lane (A1013)
Tel: (01375) 372589
Bass Hancocks HB **H**
◑ ◐ ◑ ⊞ ⇔ ❀ ⅍
Large pub with large-screen entertainment and live music on Saturdays.

South Benfleet C5

Still retains some village character.

11-11 (12-10.30 Sun)
Anchor
1 Essex Way (B1014) / High Road (B1006)
Tel: (01268) 756500
Morlands Old Speckled Hen;
Ruddles Best Bitter, County;
S&N Courage Directors,
Theakstons BB; **Guest Beer H**
◑ ◐ ◑ **R** ⊞ ⊨ ⇔ ❀ ⅍
⇌
Heavily-beamed, listed building dating from 1380, with 'Coach House' function room at rear.

12-11 (10.30 Sun)
Benfleet Tavern
Richmond Avenue / High Road (B1006)
Tel: (01268) 882031
Bass Hancocks HB, Draught Bass; **Fullers** London Pride **H**
◑ ◐ ⊞ ❀ ⅍
Despite the modern exterior, there is an olde-worlde charm inside. Formerly the "Appleton Arms", but has now lost its nominal link with local history.

12-11 (10.30 Sun)
Half Crown
27 High Street (B1014)
Tel: (01268) 792027
Bass Hancocks HB, Draught Bass; **Fullers** London Pride;
Harveys Sussex Bitter; **Guest Beers H**
◑ ◐ ◑ ❀ ⇌
Open-plan, 'beamed' tavern, near Benfleet Station. Bright and lively, with good value food and regular beer festivals. No food Friday to Sunday evenings.

11-11 (12-10.30 Sun)
Hoy & Helmet
24-32 High Street (B1014)
Tel: (01268) 792307
Greene King IPA; **S&N** Courage Directors, Theakstons BB **H**
◑ ◐ ◑ ❀ ⇌
Ancient, picturesque inn, where numerous rooms have been joined to form a multi-level, many-beamed interior. Food available in the evenings until 8pm (7pm at weekends). Separate pool room.

11-11 (12-10.30 Sun)
Lighthouse (Pickled Newt)
203 London Road (A13)
Tel: (01268) 755756
Greene King Martha Greene's, IPA; **S&N** Courage Best Bitter **H**
◑ ◐ ◑ ⇔
Pleasant, 'pubby' interior, inspite of 'box-like' external appearance. Adorned with fishing memorabilia. Formerly "Sam Lord's".

12-11 (10.30 Sun)
Tarpot
437 London Road (A13) / High Road (B1006)
Tel: (01268) 793258
Bass Draught Bass **H**
◑ ◐ ◑ **R** ❀
By famous road junction, look out for 'Real' Tarpot over an entrance, and the mock-up Grocers 'shop' inside. Now a 'Harvester'.

South
Fambridge   D4

Yachting centre on River Crouch, first sea plane trials held here.

11-3; 6-11 (10.30 Sun)
Anchor Hotel
Fambridge Road
Tel: (01702) 203535
Greene King Abbot Ale;
Nethergate Porters Suffolk Bitter; **Guest Beers H**
◑ ◐ ◑ **R** ❀
A fine drinking establishment, with a nautical feel, and a homely atmosphere, in small village. Two or three guest beers from independent breweries. Good food. Children's area. Darts and pool played upstairs.

South
Hanningfield   C4

11-3; 6-11 (12 Thu-Sat: 12-3; 7-10.30 Sun)
Old Windmill
South Hanningfield Road
OS: TQ741975
Tel: (01268) 710762
S&N Courage Directors,
Theakstons BB, XB **H**
◑ ◐ ◑ **R** ⊨ ❀ ⅍
Very attractive, well-appointed, popular and spacious. Restaurant closed Sunday evenings. Rivals the reservoir as a birdwatchers paradise.

South
Hornchurch   B5

Modern estates built on and about the wartime fighter station.

11-11 (12-10.30 Sun)
Cherry Tree
119 Rainham Road (A125)
Tel: (01708) 552082
S&N John Smiths Bitter;
Theakstons BB **H**
◑ ◐ ◑ **R** ⊨ ❀
A 'Country Carvery' with one bar open to non-diners.

11-11 (12-10.30 Sun)
Good Intent
South End Road
Tel: (01708) 554644
S&N Courage Best Bitter, John Smiths Bitter, Theakstons BB **H**
◑ ◐ ◑ ⊨
Large, well-furnished one-bar pub.

107

12-11 (12-3; 7-10.30 Sun)

Welcome Hand
Simpson Road / Sowrey Avenue (nr A125)
Tel: (01708) 524225
Youngs Bitter **H**

Two-bar pub.

South Ockendon B5

Has a fine old church, Grange Waters Country Park and Thurrock's oldest pub, but is dominated by post-war urban sprawl.

11-11 (12-10.30 Sun)

Archer
Garron Lane (nr B1335)
Tel: (01708) 853087
S&N - No Real Ale.

11-11 (12-10.30 Sun)

Jack O'Lantern
Daiglen Drive
Tel: (01708) 852389
Bass - No Real Ale.

11-11 (12-10.30 Sun)

Knight of Aveley
Darenth Lane / Derry Avenue
Tel: (01708) 841522
Whitbread - No Real Ale.

12-3; 5-11 (12-11 Sat: 12-10.30 Sun)

Prince Of Wales
1 West Road (nr B186)
Tel: (01708) 851194
Morlands Old Speckled Hen **H**

Restaurant planned.

11.30-11 (12-10.30 Sun)

Royal Oak
The Green (nr B186)
Tel: (01708) 853363
S&N John Smiths Bitter, Theakstons BB, XB, Old Peculier **H**

Picturesque pub, situated on green. Food-oriented, 'sparklers' removed on request.

11-11 (12-10.30 Sun)

Troubadour
Broxburn Drive / Cawdor Avenue
Tel: (01708) 851167
Allied - No Real Ale.

11-11 (12-10.30 Sun)

Village Inn
92 South Road (B186)
Tel: (01708) 852328
Bass - No Real Ale. Formerly the "Plough".

South Weald B4

Charming hill-top village, with a fine church and the Weald Country Park, that is accessible from several points.

11-11 (12-10.30 Sun)

Chequers Tavern
Chequers Road/Coxtie Green Road
OS: TQ551951
Tel: (01277) 372415
Greene King IPA **H**

Refurbished country pub with large garden.

11-11 (12-10.30 Sun)

Tower Arms
Weald Road (opposite church)
OS: TQ572938
Tel: (01277) 210266
Greene King IPA; **S&N** Courage Best Bitter, Theakstons BB, XB, Old Peculier **H**

Friendly and cosy traditional pub. Petanque & Ring the Bull played - a real gem! No evening snacks on Sunday. Situated opposite 14th century church and handy for Weald Country Park. Fairly expensive.

South Woodham Ferrers D4

Adult 'Legoland' New Town with traffic-free centre.

12-3; 6-11 (12-11 Sat: 12-10.30 Sun)

Curlew
80 Gandalf's Ride (off Inchbonnie road)
Tel: (01245) 321371
Shepherd Neame Masterbrew Bitter, Porter, Spitfire Ale, Bishop's Finger; **Guest Beer H**

Modern, one-bar community pub.

11-11 (12-10.30 Sun)

Ferrers Arms
50 Hullbridge Road (nr B1012)
Tel: (01245) 320262
Greene King IPA; **Guest Beer** (Occasional) **H**

Adjacent to the railway Station, this two-bar pub has been sadly neglected in recent years.

11-11 (12-10.30 Sun)

Oakland Hotel
2-6 Reeves Way/Merchant Street (nr B1012)
Tel: (01245) 320773
S&N Courage Directors; **Wadworths** 6X **H**

More of a night-club than a pub these days - tends to be busy at night.

11-11 (12-10.30 Sun)

Shaw Farm
Old Wickford Road (nr B1012)
Tel: (01245) 320916
S&N Courage Directors, Theakstons BB **H**

Converted 16th century farm-house is now the restaurant. The bar has been added on in 'ye olde barn style'. Huge, well-equipped garden with play area for kids.

11-11 (12-10.30 Sun)

Sweethearts
16 Queen Elizabeth II Square
Tel: (01245) 328004
Free-house - No Real Ale. Formerly the "Tavern in the town" and "Rumours".

11-11 (12-10.30 Sun)

Town Crier
Chandlers Way (nr B1012)
Tel: (01245) 329774
Adnams Bitter; **Ind Coope** Burton Ale; **Tetley** Bitter **H**

Modern, domed 'Big Steak' pub, by ASDA. Busy and noisy, with recorded and live music. Popular with families during the day - the haunt of teenagers at night.

12-11 (10.30 Sun)

Whalebone
Old Wickford Road (nr B1012)
Tel: (01245) 320231
Marstons Pedigree; **S&N** John Smiths Bitter; **Guest** Beers **H**

One of the older pubs in town, now opened out inside and deceptively spacious. Good beer range includes guest beers from Crouch Vale and Ridleys. Sports and games such as cricket, football, darts and crib played.

Southchurch D5

Boots & Laces
123 Eastern Avenue (A1159)
Tel: (01702) 462111
Free-house (Southend United FC) - No Real Ale.

11-11 (12-10.30 Sun)

Invisible Man
266 Eastern Ave / 415 Hamstel Road (By A1159)
Tel: (01702) 467414
Ex Grand Met - No Real Ale (despite prominent signs outside!). Formerly the "Rusty Bucket".

11-11 (12-10.30 Sun)

White Horse
Southchurch Boulevard (A13)
Tel: (01702) 465790
S&N Courage Directors, Theakstons XB, Websters Yorkshire Bitter **H**

Vast, two-bar pub with live music Thursdays and Sundays.

Southend-on-Sea D5

The most populous town in Essex with beautiful gardens, fine houses, the Golden Mile, the world's longest pier - over 1¼ miles with its own railway. An expensive town to drink in.

10.30-4; 5.30-12 (2am Fri/Sat: 12-4; 7-10.30 Sun)

Bakers Bar 1
15-17 Alexandra Street
Tel: (01702) 390403
Free-house - No Real Ale. A sad loss of a former 'Good Beer Guide' basement bar. Hours subject to change - due to a recent court decision.

11-11 (12-10.30 Sun)

Britannia 2
6 Eastern Esplanade (B1016)
Tel: (01702) 467091
Ruddles County; **S&N** Websters Yorkshire Bitter **H**
◖◖❀⅄
Small, pleasant, timbered pub, with occasional entertainment on Sundays.

11-11 (12-10.30 Sun)

Castle Hotel 3
92 Eastern Esplanade (B1016)
Tel: (01702) 467152
S&N Courage Best Bitter, Theakstons XB, Old Peculier **H**
◖◗⒭🍺
Much-altered with upstairs restaurant. Fish and Chip pub, have a drink, while you're waiting for your take-away! Beware 'Westons Cider' on fake handpump!

11-2am (12-10.30 Sun)

Chicago Rock Cafe 4
2-6 Warrior Square (nr A1160)
Tel: (01702) 619191
Free-house (Luminar Leisure) - No Real Ale.

11-12 (6-11 Winter: 12-10.30 Sun)

Chinnerys 5
21-22 Marine Parade (nr A1160 & B1016)
Tel: (01702) 467305
Bass Draught Bass; **Fullers** London Pride; **Guest Beer H**
◖◗◖⒟⎸📠⅄⤅
Comfortable, refurbished, 'trendy' seafront pub, with disco attached. Live rock music venue with Real Ale in the music bar. Parking difficult. Formerly the "Ivy House", renamed after the licensee, and it's a Scottish - rather than Irish - name.

5.30-11 (7-10.30 Sun: closed lunchtimes)

Clarence Yard 6
23-29 Clarence Street
Tel: (01702) 713182
Adnams Bitter; **Guest Beers H**
⤅
Small bar - converted from a shop. The entrance incorporates an enclosed courtyard, furnished with beer 'barrels' used as tables and chairs. The remainder of the bar has wooden tables and chairs.

12-11 (10.30 Sun)

Cliff Hotel 7
48 Hamlet Road / Park Street
Tel: (01702) 341593
Ind Coope 'House' Bitter **H**
⎸📠
A pleasant, corner pub with beautiful, ornate mirrors and a tiled picture of a milkmaid in an old doorway, that indicates the building's previous use as a dairy.

11-11 (Closed Sun)

Cork & Cheese 8
10 Talza Way, Lower Ground Floor, Victoria Plaza (nr A13/A127)
Tel: (01702) 616914
Tolly Cobbold 'House Beer';
Guest Beers H
Real Cider G
◖◗◖⒭⎸📠⅄❀⤅
Deceptively-spacious, town centre free-house, at the base of the shopping centre precinct, with satellite TV. Always a large selection of guest beers available. Disco on Fri & Sat nights. CAMRA SE Essex Branch 'Pub of the Year' 1997/98.

10-11 (12-10.30 Sun)

Cornucopia 9
39a Marine Parade (nr A1160 & B1016)
Tel: (01702) 460583
Guest Beers H
◖🍺
Possibly the smallest bar in Essex. Local flavour. Now a free-house, with two changing guest beers. Games room upstairs, with pool and darts. Parking can be difficult.

10-8 (12-5 Sun)

Daisy Root Tavern 10
Southend Central Railway Stn, Clifftown Road
Tel:
Free-house - No Real Ale. Formerly the "Clifftown Buffet".

11-11 (12-10.30 Sun)

Esplanade 11
Western Esplanade
Tel: (01702) 346658
Whitbread - Pub temporarily closed for conversion to a 'Brewers Fayre' pub/restaurant, with 'Charlie Chalks' children's play area.
An expansive seafront pub, with fine views of the Thames estuary. Limited parking in summer.

11-11 (12-10.30 Sun)

Falcon Hotel 12
45 Marine Parade (nr A1160 & B1016)
Tel: (01702) 466302
Ridleys IPA, ESX, seasonal ales **H**
📠📠
Ridleys' south-eastern outpost, situated on Southend seafront.

11-11 (12 Fri/Sat: 12-10.30 Sun)

Fish & Firkin 13
53 Alexandra Street
Tel: (01702) 345934
Firkin Fish T'Ale, Whale Ale, Dogbolter **H**
◖⒟◖◗�⅄⎸❀⤅
Lively pub, converted to typical 'Firkin' theme with bare floorboards, etc. When converted, the pub was one of the few brewing 'Firkin' - and you could view it from the garden. However, the beers now come from another 'Firkin' brewery. Formerly the "Alexandra (Top Alex)".

Foresters Arms 14
65 Marine Parade (nr A1160 & B1016)
Tel: (01702) 467927
Inntrepreneur - No Real Ale.

11-11 (12-10.30 Sun)

Guildford 15
95-97 Sutton Road / Guildford Road (nr A13)
Tel: (01702) 610305
Whitbread - No Real Ale.

11 (9 Sat)-11 (12-10.30 Sun)

Hogshead 16
6-8 Southchurch Road (nr A13/A127)
Tel: (01702) 619517
Whitbread Boddingtons Bitter, Flowers IPA, Original; **Guest Beers H/G**
◖⒟◖◗⒭❀⅄
A shop conversion into a typical 'Hogshead'. Up to 12 beers on at a time, some on Gravity. Swannecks with tight sparklers on all the handpumps.
Ask for the sparklers to be removed for any beer except the 'Boddingtons'. No smoking area. Parking difficult.

Hope Hotel 17
34 Marine Parade (nr A1160/B1016)
Tel: (01702) 467413
Free-house - No Real Ale.

10-11 (12-10.30 Sun)

Il Vicolino 18
20 Alexandra Street
Tel: (01702) 390326
Free-house - No Real Ale.

Inane Cafe 19
19 Alexandra Street / Market Place
Tel: (01702) 332889
Free-house - No Real Ale, but may try it.

SOUTHEND-ON-SEA

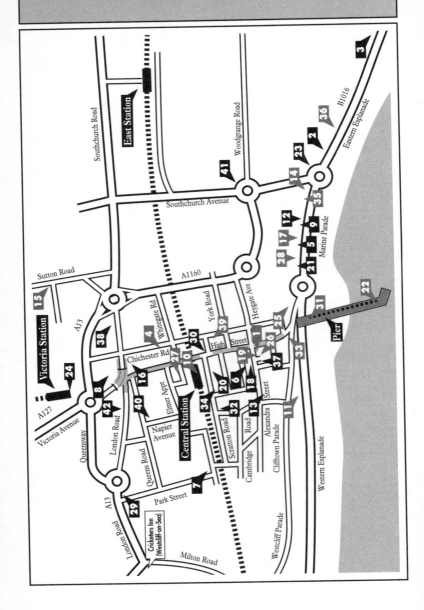

10-11 (12-10.30 Sun)

Last Post **20**
5 Weston Road & 8-10 Clifftown
Road
Tel: (01702) 431682
S&N Courage Directors,
Theakstons BB, XB;
Guest Beers H
◁ D ◀ ▶ R & ⚥ ⊓ ≷
Huge 'Wetherspoon' conversion
of a former Post Office, with
daily and monthly specials.

10-11 (12-10.30 Sun)

Liberty Belle **21**
10-12 Marine Parade (nr
A1160/B1016)
Tel: (01702) 466936
S&N Courage Best Bitter,
Directors; **Guest Beers H**
Guest Cider H
◁ ◀ ⌂ ⛵ ❄ & ≷
Friendly seafront pub with pool,
darts and chess. Snooker room.
Good value, regular guest beers
- see chalkboards for details.
Disabled toilets planned. Look
out for the 'flasher'!

11-Dusk (Not Sun eve)

McGinty's Cafe Bar *22*
Pier Head, Southend Pier
Tel: (01702) 469405
Free-house - No Real Ale.
Subject to the hours of the pier,
for which there is an entrance
fee. Formerly the "Jolly
Fisherman".

11-11 (12-10.30 Sun)

Minerva **23**
1 Eastern Esplanade
(B1016/A1160)
Tel: (01702) 467632
Guest Beer H
▙
One-bar pub - a recent convert
to Real Ale.

10 (12 Sun)-10

Monk & Fisherman **24**
Victoria Station, Victoria Circus
(by A127/A13)
Tel: (01702) 600042
Whitbread Flowers IPA **H**
◁ D ◀ ▶ ≷
Pleasant bar at the end of the
line. Food available until 8pm.
Limited parking.

10-11 (12-10.30 Sun)

Motels *25*
Pier Hill
Tel: (01702) 612000
Free-house - No Real Ale.
Formerly "DJ's" & "Luke's Bar".

11-11 (12-10.30 Sun)

O'Donoghue's *26*
8-11 Market Place
Tel: (01702) 394700
Free-house - No Real Ale.

11-11 (12-10.30 Sun)

O'Neill's *27*
Luker Road, rear of 119 High
Street
Tel: (01702) 335164
Bass (O'Neill's) - No Real Ale.
Formerly the "Dickens".

10-11 (12-10.30 Sun)

Papillon *28*
14-15 Marine Parade (nr
A1160/B1016)
Tel: (01702) 468084
Bass - No Real Ale.

11-11 (12-10.30 Sun)

Park Tavern **29**
124 London Road (A13) / Park
Street
Tel: (01702) 335226
S&N Theakstons XB **H**
◁ D ◀ ▶ ⊞ ▙ 🚗
Traditional local with quizzes on
Thursdays, darts on Mondays
and Wednesdays, and pool on
Tuesdays.

11-3; 6 (7 Sat)-11 (closed Sun)

Pipe of Port Wine Bar **30**
84 High Street (nr A1160)
Tel: (01702) 614606
Crouch Vale Best Bitter **G**
◁ D ◀ ▶ ≷
Cellar wine-bar, with cask ale
behind the counter and sawdust
on the floor.

Quarter Deck Bar *31*
Southend Pier, Pier Hill
(Above bowling alley)
Tel: (01702) 463081
Free-house - Bar closed and
demolished after a major fire.

11-11 (12-10.30 Sun)

Railway Hotel **32**
Clifftown Road
Tel: (01702) 343194
Bass Hancocks HB; **Fullers**
London Pride; **Guest Beers H**
◁ ◀ ▙ ≷
Victorian-style pub close to
Central Station. Food 12-7 Mon -
Fri. Quiz Sundays, disco Fridays.
Parking difficult.

Royal Hotel *33*
1 High Street (Top of Pier Hill)
Free-house - Hotel closed.

11-11 (2am in cellar bar)

Saks *34*
24-25 Clifftown Road
Tel: (01702) 332179
S&N - No Real Ale.

11-11 (12-10.30 Sun)

Ship **35**
64 Marine Parade (nr
A1160/B1016)
Tel: (01702) 603945
Shepherd Neame Masterbrew,
Spitfire **H**
Young persons disco / live music
pub. Real Ale available in
Summer only.

11-11 (2am Thu-Sat: 12-10.30
Sun)

Smithy's / Brocketts *36*
33 Eastern Esplanade (B1016)
Tel: (01702) 466574
Free-house - No Real Ale.
Formerly "Stocks".

12-12 (1am Sat: 12-10.30 Sun)

Sun Rooms **37**
20-21 Market Place
Tel:: (01702) 436661
Guest Beers H
◀ ▙ ❄ ≷
Young persons bar, with psy-
chedelic decor! Pricey, but
changing range of up to three
Real Ales on offer. Foreign bottled beers and Real Cider available.
Regular live music in the
upstairs bar.

11-11 (12-10.30 Sun)

Sutton Arms **38**
79 Southchurch Road (nr A13)
Tel: (01702) 611023
S&N Courage Directors **H**
◁ D ◀ ▶ ❄
Friendly, regulars pub with good
value food all day. Karaoke on
Thursdays, discos Fridays and
Saturdays. Pinball machine.
Formerly "Debonairs".

11-12 (12-10.30 Sun)

TGF Churchills *39*
Tylers Avenue (nr A1160)
Tel: (01702) 617866
Free-house - No Real Ale (hand-
pump disused). Formerly
"Hickory's" & the "Turtle Bay".

11-11 (12-10.30 Sun)

Town House **40**
23 Queens Road / Elmer Ave (nr
A13)
Tel: (01702) 342846
Marstons Pedigree; **Whitbread**
Boddingtons Bitter, Flowers
Original **H**
◁ D ◀ ▶ ≷
Trendy Whitbread pub with
music, which seems to cater
mainly for the 'lager' trade now.
A great shame, as it was once
Southend's main Real Ale free-
house. Formerly the
"Aristocrat".

11-11 (12-10.30 Sun)

Woodgrange **41**
62 Southchurch Avenue (A1160)
Tel: (01702) 460133
Shepherd Neame Masterbrew,
Spitfire, seasonal beers **H**
Trendy youngsters pub with
loud music. Formerly
"Cromwell's".

11-11 (12-10.30 Sun)

Yates's Wine Lodge **42**
London Road (nr A13)
Tel:
Whitbread Boddingtons Bitter **H**
◁ D ◀ ▶ ≷
New Yates's opened in 1998, as
part of a new cinema complex.
Disappointing beer range.

Southminster D4

11-3; 5-11 (11-11 Fri/Sat: 12-10.30 Sun)

Kings Head
2 High Street (B1020/B1021)
Tel: (01621) 772216
Morlands Old Speckled Hen;
S&N Courage Best Bitter, John
Smiths Bitter **H**

⊂⊃ ◑ ⊞ ⍢ ⌊ ⊟ ⇌

A town centre pub in a village!
Home-cooked food. Three letting rooms.

11-11 (12-10.30 Sun)

Queens Head
36 Queen Street (B1020)
Tel: (01621) 772315
Greene King IPA **H**

⊂⊃ ⊏ ⍝ ⍢ ⊛ ⌺

Special price deals on food and
beer. Happy hours.

Rose & Crown
High Street (B1020)
Inntrepreneur - Pub closed.

12-3; 5.30-11 (12-3; 7-10.30 Sun)

Rose Inn
Burnham Road (B1021)
Tel: (01621) 772915
Greene King IPA, Abbot Ale;
Guest Beers G
Theobalds Cider (Summer) **G**

⊂⊃ ◑ ⊞ ⊛

Small, friendly and comfortable
Grays village pub - halfway to
Burnham. Occasional Greene
King XX Mild.
Interesting range of malt
whiskies. Darts played. Well
worth seeking out.

12-2.30; 6 (5.30 Thu/Fri)-11 (12-11
Sat: 12-4; 7-10.30 Sun)

Station Arms
39 Station Road (nr
B1020/B1021)
Tel: (01621) 772225
Crouch Vale Best Bitter;
Fullers London Pride; **Ridleys**
IPA; **Guest Beers H**
Guest Cider G

⊂⊃ ◑ Ⓡ ⊏ ⍝ ⊛ ⇌

Small, friendly, weather-boarded
pub with regular guest beers
and Real ciders. Beer festivals at
the Spring and August Bank holidays and during the
Southminster Flower Show -
2nd weekend in July.
Good value home-cooked food
in the restaurant or bar, available Thursday to Saturday
evenings and Sunday lunchtime
in winter. East Anglian Regional
Pub of the Year 1997/98.

11-11 (12-10.30 Sun)

White Horse Hotel
20 North Street (B1021)
Tel: (01621) 772712
Greene King IPA; **S&N** Courage
Best Bitter **H**

⊂⊃ ◑ ⊞ ⍢ ⇌

Basic community local, with five
letting rooms. Music some
Fridays and Saturdays.

Springfield C3

*Still a village despite the
encroachment of Chelmsford.*

11-11 (12-2.30; 7-10.30 Sun)

Endeavour
351 Springfield Road (B1137)
OS: TL724078
Tel: (01245) 257717
Greene King XX Mild, IPA,
Abbot Ale; **Shepherd Neame**
Spitfire; **Guest Beer H**

⊂⊃ ◑ ⊞ ⊏

Friendly, three-roomed, suburban Grays pub with rural atmosphere. Well-kept, very
reasonably priced beer. Real fire
and an interesting pub sign.
A mobile phone-free zone,
offenders donate to charity.
Limited parking.

11-11 (12-10.30 Sun)

Plough
306 Springfield Road (B1137)
OS: TL725078
Tel: (01245) 353375
Bass Hancocks HB, Draught
Bass **H**

⊂⊃ ◑ ⊛

Refurbished pub in pseudo-tra-
ditional style, with emphasis on
food.

11-11 (12-10.30 Sun)

Springfield Arms
Crocus Way, Pump Lane
Tel: (01245) 461020
Whitbread - No Real Ale.
Formerly "Trainers".

"The Endeavour", Springfield

11-3; 6-11 (11-11 Sat: 12-10.30 Sun)

Tulip
Arbour Lane / Church Lane
OS: TL716080
Tel: (01245) 283219
Greene King IPA; **Shepherd Neame** Masterbrew; **Guest Beers H**
🍺 🍴 🍷 ⚫ ♿
Popular two-bar Grays local, with varied clientele, particularly busy in the evening. Has benefited from Grays more flexible Guest beer policy.

11-11 (12-10.30 Sun)

Two Saxons
64 Bodmin Road / Tavistock Road)
OS: TL720083
Tel: (01245) 494159
S&N Websters Yorkshire Bitter **H**
🍺 🍷 ⚫
Typical, modern estate pub, with comfortable and friendly lounge bar. Good value food.

11-11 (12-10.30 Sun)

White Hart
Colchester Road (by A130)
OS: TL736088
Tel: (01245) 736088
Ind Coope Benskins BB, Burton Ale; **Tetley** Bitter **H**
🍺 🍷 ⚫ R 🦮 ⚫ ♿
Large out-of-town pub, fairly devoid of genuine pub atmosphere.
Recently converted to a 'Big Steak', with its typical food-oriented style, and incorporating a 'Wacky Warehouse' - so expect lots of children.

St Lawrence   D4

Riverside settlement dominated by caravans and speedboats. Fine views of estuary.

12-3 (4 Sat); 7-11 (10.30 Sun)

St Lawrence Inn
8 Main Road
OS: TL955055
Tel: (01621) 779388
Adnams Bitter; **Fullers** London Pride (Summer); **Ridleys** IPA **H**
🍺 🍷 ⚫ R 🦮 ⚫
Pleasant free-house with bar made to resemble an Essex barge, and access to the river. Caters for adjacent caravan park. Children's playground, barbecue area.
Live music on Saturdays (Easter to November). Darts, pool and ten-pin bowling alley.

12.30-3.30; 7.30-11 (11 (12-4; 7-10.30 Sun: 12-4; 7-11 Mon-Sat in Summer)

Stone Inn
Main Road (The Stone)
OS: TL952062
Tel: (01621) 779215
Greene King IPA; **Guest Beers H**
🍺 🍷 ⚫
Riverside pub with fine views, live entertainment in Summer. Limited parking.

St Osyth   E3

Village near the coast, with 12th century priory and incorporating an impressive 15th century gatehouse. Water-skiing on the lake.

Buccaneer Wine Bar
23 Spring Road
Free-house - Pub closed and converted to an Indian Restaurant.

11-3.30 (or later); 7-11 (12-3; 7-10.30 Sun)

Kings Arms
10 Colchester Road (nr B1027)
Tel: (01255) 821156
Greene King IPA; **S&N** Courage Directors; **Guest Beer H**
🍺 🍷 ⚫ 🦮 ⚫
Typical, old village pub, with very good beer garden. Children's Certificate. May open all day in Summer.

11-11 (12-3; 7-10.30 Sun)

Lake View Bar
64 Mill Street (Lakeside)
Tel: (01255) 820941
Free-house - No Real Ale.

12-3; 7-11 (12-4; 7-10.30 Sun)

Matchbox Inn
71 Mill Street
Tel: (01255) 820318
Adnams Bitter; **Guest Beers H**
🍺 🍷 ⚫ R 🦮 ⚫
Friendly village pub with photos of old Essex life. Mini beer festivals. Essex 'Pub of the Year 1995'. Formerly the "White Hart".

10-3.30; 5.30-11 (11-11 Sat: 12-10.30 Sun)

Red Lion
8 Clacton Road
Tel: (01255) 820256
Ind Coope Benskins BB; **Wadworths** 6X **H**
🍺 🍷 ⚫ R 🦮 🍴 🦮 ⚫
Friendly village local, by the village crossroads. Features 'apocryphal' tunnels from the cellars to various romantic places - the beach, priory, etc. Special 'Good Value' meals are a regular feature.

St Osyth Beach   E3

'Mobile Homesville'

11-11 (later on Fri/Sat: 12-10.30 Sun)

Goodlife Inn
Whyers Hall, Beach Road
Tel: (01255) 821456
Free-house - No Real Ale.

11-11 (12-10.30 Sun). Open March to October only.

Sailor Boy
Beach Road
Tel: (01255) 821062
Greene King IPA, Abbot Ale **H**
🦮 ⚫
Seasonal pub by the beach and caravan area.

Seagull/Haven Lounge Bar
Beach Road
Free-house - Pub closed and converted to a club.

St Osyth Heath E3

11-3; 7-11 (12-10.30 Sun)

Beehive Inn
Heath Road
OS: TM139185
Tel: (01255) 830396
Adnams Bitter; **Greene King** IPA; **Tetley** Bitter **H**
🍺 🍷 ⚫ R 🦮 ⚫ ♿
Rebuilt pub near the crossroads, difficult to find, but well-worth the effort. A welcome addition to the 'Good Beer Guide'.

Stambourne   C1

Charming remote village.

Red Lion
Church Road (2 miles West of A1017, was A604)
OS: TL721387
Free-house - Pub closed and delicensed.

Stambridge   D4

12-2; 7-11 (10.30 Sun)

Royal Oak
Stambridge Road
OS: TQ899918
Tel: (01702) 258259
Morlands Old Speckled Hen; **Ruddles** Best Bitter; **S&N** Websters Yorkshire Bitter **H**
🍺 🍷 ⚫ R 🍴 ⚫ ♿
350 year old, upmarket, country pub - very busy for home-cooked traditional meals.

Stanford Rivers   B4

11-3; 7-11 (12-10.30 Sun)

Drill House
Mutton Row, Toot Hill Road (near Greensted, 1½ miles off A113)
OS: TL532025
Tel: (01277) 362298
Ridleys IPA; **Guest Beers H**
🍺 🍷 ⚫ ♿
Guest beers include Crouch Vale. Pub is hard to find - but well-worth the effort, and is near the former 'Blake Hall' railway station.

11-3; 6-11 (11-11; 12-10.30 Sun)

White Bear
149 London Road (by A113)
Tel: (01277) 362185
Greene King IPA, Abbot Ale;
Guest Beers H
◖◗◖▶ℝ▐▬ ✿
Cosy, old-style country pub with
large garden. Two guest beers -
often from small breweries. Beer
variable. Restaurant open week-
ends only. Floodlit petanque,
darts.
Motorcycle club meet
Wednesday evenings, car clubs
for Lotus, Porsche, Triumph
Roadster, Land Rover and AJS &
Matchless also meet here regu-
larly.

11-11 (12-10.30 Sun)

Woodman
155 London Road (A113)
Tel: (01277) 362019
Mighty Oak Burntwood Bitter;
Nethergate Bitter; **Shepherd
Neame** Spitfire; **Woodfordes**
Wherry; **Guest Beers H**
◖◗◖▶ ✿
Cosy, country pub with low-
beamed ceilings, two open fire-
places and a very pleasant
garden, and occasional beer fes-
tivals. Excellent home-cooked
meals. Beer range may change.
CAMRA (SW Essex branch)
'Pub-of-the-Year' 1998.
Stop press - now owned by
Shepherd Neame

Stanford-le-Hope   C5

*A dormitory town with a 12th
century church, near the petro-
chemical industrial area of the
River Thames.*

*Named after a place with a ford,
where ships used to anchor
while waiting for wind and tide
on the Thames.*

11-11 (12-10.30 Sun)

Catcracker
The Sorrells (nr A1014)
Tel: (01375) 674275
S&N Theakstons BB, XB **H**
◖◗◖▶ ✿
Refurbished pub. Formerly
"Sports".

12-3 (4 Sat); 6-11 (12-3; 7-10.30
Sun)

Inn On The Green
The Green
Tel: (01375) 674254
Greene King IPA, Abbot Ale **H**
◖◖▬ ≈
400-year old converted doctor's
house, now a lively town pub
attracting a mixed crowd of
locals and youngsters. Home of
a local rugby club.
Can be busy in the evenings,
may open all day on occasions.
No food weekends. Formerly the
"Village Inn".

11-11 (12-10.30 Sun)

Kings Head
39 King Street (nr A1014)
Tel: (01375) 673046
Guest Beer H
◖◖ℝ▐▬ ✿ ❤ ≈
Weekly-changing guest beer,
often from small independent
breweries. Many promotions
available - always something
happening.

12-11 (10.30 Sun)

Railway Tavern
1 King Street
Tel: (01375) 640337
Ind Coope 'House' Bitter **H**
◖◗◖▶ ◗ ✿
Plush corner local with Victorian
decor. Parking available on-
street and in local car parks.

12-3; 7-11 (12-10.30 Sun)

Rainbows End
Billet Lane
Tel: (01375) 672159
Free-house - Real Ale may be
available occasionally. Formerly
the "Billet".

11-11 (12-10.30 Sun)

Rising Sun
Church Hill (nr A1014)
Tel: (01375) 671911
Marstons Pedigree; **S&N**
Courage Best Bitter,
Directors; **Guest Beer H**
◖◗◖▶ ◗ ✿ ≈
Intimate local in the shadow of a
900 year old church. Children's
play area. Sports on TV. Guest
beer includes 'Mighty Oak'.

11-11 (12-10.30 Sun)

St Clere's Hall
London Road (A1013)
Tel: (01375) 673007
Whitbread Flowers IPA **H**
◖◗◖ ◗ ✿
Golf Club bar that is also open to
the public. Real Ale not always
available.

Stansted   B2

*The area around and including
the Airport complex.*

11-3; 6-11 (12-10.30 Sun)

Bury Lodge Hotel
Bury Lodge Lane, near the old
airport terminal.
Tel: (01279) 817056
Greene King IPA; **Guest
Beer H**
◖◗◖▶ℝ ⌂ ▬ ✿
Warm, cosy & friendly
bar/restaurant - a much better
place to meet than the imper-
sonal airport bar.

Butlers
New Terminal, Stansted Airport
Tel: (01279) 662046
Free-house (THF) - No Real Ale.

Hilton National
Round Coppice Road, Stansted
Airport
Tel: (01279) 680800
Free-house - No Real Ale.
Formerly the "Quin's (Harlequin
Hotel)".

Pavilion Bar
Stansted Airport (Original
Terminal)
Free-house - Bar closed.

Stansted Mountfitchet   A2

*Large hilly village with some
very pleasing architecture in the
old quarter. The windmill is
open 1st Sunday each month
and bank holidays.
Reconstructed Norman castle.
Drinkers paradise.*

11.30-3; 6-11 (12-3; 7-10.30 Sun)

Cock
Silver Street (B1383)
Tel: (01279) 812964
Greene King IPA, Abbot Ale,
seasonal beers **H**
◖◗◖▶ ✿ ≈
Pleasant, comfortable roadside
inn, with single, open bar. Very
food-oriented in the evening.

10-2.30; 5.30-11 (12-3; 7-10.30
Sun)

Dog & Duck
58 Lower Street (B1351)
Tel: (01279) 812047
Greene King IPA, Rayments
Special, Abbot Ale **H**
◖◖◗ ✿ ≈
Excellent, popular village local
with good atmosphere and pool
tables. Meals and snacks not
served on Sunday. Featured in
the 'Good Beer Guide' for many
years, until 1998. Close to station.

12-3.30 (not Mon/Tue); 5-11 (12-
4; 7.30-11 Sat: 12-4; 7-10.30 Sun)

Feathers
21 Cambridge Road (B1383)
Tel: (01279) 813374
Whitbread Flowers IPA **H**
◗ ✿ ≈
Large village pub, not a CAMRA
flagship. Beer variable. Formerly
the "Bell & Feathers".

11-11 (12-3; 7-10.30 Sun)

Kings Arms Hotel
Station Road (B1051)
Tel: (01279) 812948
Wadworths 6X; **Whitbread**
Flowers IPA **H**
◖◗◖▶ ◗ ⌂ ✿ ≈
Large friendly pub, close to the
railway station. No food
Saturday evenings. Limited
parking.

11-11 (12-10.30 Sun)
Old Bell Hotel
Pines Hill (B1383)
Tel: (01279) 816555
Adnams Bitter, Broadside **H**
◐ D ◀ ▶ **R** ⊟ ☙
Friendly, comfortable, low-beamed old hotel bar, with character, real fires and good food. New accommodation block.

11-3; 5.30 (7 Sat)-11 (12-3; 7-10.30 Sun)
Queen's Head
3 Lower Street (B1051)
Tel: (01279) 812458
Bass Draught Bass; **Wadworths** 6X; **Whitbread** Flowers IPA; **Guest Beer H**
◐ ◀ ⊞ ☙ ⇌
Comfortable, traditional, 17th century village local, with bar billiards, darts and shove ha'penny. Brass and agricultural implements adorn the walls. Limited parking.

11-3; 5.30-11 (12-3; 7-10.30 Sun)
Rose & Crown
31 Bentfield Green (nr B1383)
OS: TL507255
Tel: (01279) 812107
Adnams Bitter; **Hardys** Pope's Traditional **H**
◐ D ◀ ▶ ▙ ☙
Friendly pub, overlooking the green, in a quiet backwater of Stansted, with pump outside. Games room. No dogs or children.

12-11 (10.30 Sun)
Three Colts
86 Cambridge Road (B1383)
Tel: (01279) 812960
Greene King IPA **H**
◐ D ☙
Extensive pub, trying to attract the younger trade with Sky TV and music.

Stanway   D2

Harvester
London Road (B1408, nr A1124)
Tel:
New Harvester under construction, due to open August 1998.

11-3; 6.30-11 (11-11 Sat: 12-10.30 Sun)
Live & Let Live
12 Millers Lane (nr A1124, was A604)
OS: TL956247
Tel: (01206) 574071
Greene King IPA; **Ruddles** Best Bitter **H**
◐ ⊞ ☙
Popular and friendly local, with an emphasis on games. Live music (duo) on alternate Friday evenings. Darts, pool and juke box.

11-3; 5-11 (12-3; 7-10.30 Sun)
Swan
283/285 London Road (B1408)
Tel: (01279) 210252
Greene King IPA, Abbot Ale, seasonal beer **H**
◐ D ◀ ▶ **R** ☙
Modern pub/restaurant, with bar billiards.

11-11 (12-10.30)
White Hart
342 London Road (B1408)
Tel: (01206) 213411
Whitbread Boddingtons Bitter, Flowers Original; **Guest Beers H**
◐ D ◀ ▶ **R** ☙ ♿
Typical 'Brewers Fayre' pub/restaurant.

Stapleford Abbotts   A4

12-3; 6.30-11 (10.30 Sun)
Rabbits
Stapleford Road (B175)
OS: TL501966
Tel: (01708) 688203
Adnams Bitter; **Greene King** IPA; **Ind Coope** Benskins BB **H**
◐ D ◀ ☙
Country pub with real fires in winter. Large garden catering for children. Beer variable.

11-2.30 (3 Sat); 6-11 (12-3; 7-10.30 Sun)
Royal Oak
Oak Hill (B175)
Tel: (01708) 741861
Ridleys Rumpus; **Whitbread** Boddingtons Bitter, Flowers IPA **H**
◐ D ◀ ▶ **R** ⛵ ☙ ♿ (Bar)
Large food-oriented pub, with speciality fish restaurant. Bar food only on Mondays.

Stapleford Tawney   A4

12-3; 7 (6 Summer)-11 (12-10.30 Sun)
Moletrap
Tawney Common, Theydon Mount
OS: TL500014
Tel: (01992) 522394
Guest Beers H
◐ D ◀ ▶ ☙
Small, friendly, low-beamed, old-fashioned, ale house, in idyllic location. Popular with all ages, it is mainly a farming community pub. Once owned by the inventor of a type of moletrap. Recently enlarged, but retains its character. Three to four guest beers. No taped music. Evening meals at weekends. Difficult to find - but well-worth the effort. Local CAMRA branch 'Pub of the Year' 1997.

Stebbing   C2

Compact old village.

Kings Head
High Street
Tel: (01371) 856289
Free-house - Pub closed

11-3; 5.30-11 (11-11 Sat: 12-10.30 Sun)
White Hart
High Street (2 miles North of A120)
Tel: (01371) 856383
Adnams Bitter; **Greene King** IPA; **Guest Beer H**
◐ D ◀ ▶ ☙
15th century, split-level, village pub, catering for all. Numerous framed cigarette cards, poes, TV, and and old 'GR' postbox. Pool played.

Steeple   D4

12-3; 7 (6 Sat)-11 (12-3; 7-10.30 Sun)
Star
The Street
Tel: (01621) 772646
Adnams Bitter; **Guest Beers H**
◐ D ◀ ▶ **R** ▙ ⛵ ☙ ♿
Comfortable free-house with caravan/camping facilities at the rear.

12-3.30; 7-11 (12-3; 7-10.30 Sun)
Sun & Anchor
The Street
OS: TL937029
Tel: (01621) 772700
Greene King IPA, Abbot Ale **G**
◐ D ◀ ▶ ⛵ ☙ ♿
(ramps to bar)
Friendly, community-minded Grays local, built in 1938. Separate games room with darts, pool and fruit machines. Large field hosts the village fete and boot sales. CCC registered, pets welcome.

Steeple Bumpstead   C1

Village with ancient Moot Hall. A Memorial in the church records ex-resident Heroine-Nurse Edith Cavell.

11.30-3 (2 Mon/Tue); 6-11 (11-11 Sat: 12-3; 7-10.30 Sun)
Fox & Hounds
3 Chapel Street (B1054/B1057)
Tel: (01440) 730281
Greene King IPA; **Whitbread** Flowers IPA **H**
◐ D ◀ ▶ **R** ⊞ ▙ ☙
Small cosy pub. No food Mondays, and Sunday evenings.

11.30-3; 6.30-11 (11.30-11 Fri/Sat:
12-10.30 Sun)

Red Lion
8 Church Street (B1054/B1057)
Tel: (01440) 730515
Greene King IPA, Abbot Ale **H**
◑ D ◐ 🍴 🛏 ✿
Friendly village local.
Accommodation by prior
booking only.

Stifford Clays   B5

11-11 (12-10.30 Sun)

Acorn
1 Crammavill Street / Fairway
Tel: (01375) 373908
S&N Courage Directors **H**
◑ D 🍴 🛏 ♿ ✿
Very large function room (200
capacity). Large screen enter-
tainment and live entertainment.

Stisted   C2

*Once a feudal village. Almost
every house built in the Onley
family style.*

11-3; 6-11 (12-3; 7-10.30 Sun)

Dolphin
Coggeshall Road (A120)
Tel: (01376) 321143
Ridleys XX Mild, IPA, ESX **G**
◑ D ◐ 🍴
Attractive, unspoilt, 15th century
family pub, with roaring log fires
in winter. Charming, many-
beamed interior. Casks on stil-
lage behind bar. Swings and
aviary in garden. No meals
Tuesday evenings. Limited
parking.

11-3; 7-11 (12-3; 7-10.30 Sun)

Onley Arms
The Street
OS: TL800248
Tel: (01376) 325204
Ridleys IPA, ESX, Witchfinder
Porter (Winter) **H**
◑ D ◐ **R** ✿ ♿
Friendly 19th century, gabled
local. Petanque (boules) played.
Fish 'n' chips and curries are a
speciality.

Stock   C4

*Picturesque village keenly
guarded against desecrating
developers. Difficult to approach
via the Hanningfields, in view of
maze of country roads.*

11-3.30; 6-11 (12-4; 7-10.30 Sun)

Bakers Arms
Common Road (nr B1007)
Tel: (01277) 840423
Greene King IPA; **Ruddles** Best
Bitter; **S&N** Courage Directors,
Websters Yorkshire Bitter **H**
◑ D ◐ **R** 🛏 ✿
Excellent pub catering for all.
Restaurant available as a meet-
ing room early in the week.
Weekend barbecues - subject to
the weather.

11.30-3; 5.30-11 (11-11 Sat: 12-
10.30 Sun)

Bear
16 The Square (by B1007)
Tel: (01277) 840232
Adnams Bitter; **Marstons**
Pedigree; **Morlands** Old
Speckled Hen **H**
◑ D ◐ **R** 🍴 🛏 ✿
Excellent old pub, with pleasant
garden. Many years ago a man
known as 'Old Spider', had the
strange habit of crawling up the
chimney in one bar and down
the chimney in the next.
One day he went missing, and
was never seen again. It is said
that he still haunts the pub!

11-3; 6-11 (12-3; 7-10.30 Sun)

Cock Inn
High Street (B1007)
Tel: (01277) 840258
Ruddles Best Bitter; **S&N**
Courage Directors, Websters
Yorkshire Bitter **H**
◑ D ◐ ✿ ♿
A fine, tastefully-refurbished, old
pub, with live music on Fridays
and DJ on Sundays. Children's
Certificate held. Barbecues
Sat/Sun eves in summer.

10-11 (12-10.30 Sun)

Hoop
21 High Street (B1007)
Tel: (01277) 841137
Adnams Bitter; **Guest Beers H/G**
Real Cider / Perry G
◑ D ◐ ✿
Very popular, small, timber-
framed pub, whose landlord is
justifiably proud of his range of
unusual beers, normally 6 to 8
available. Bar-B-Q's in summer.
Well-known for its May beer festival in the garden. Home-made
food available.

11-3; 5-11 (11-11 Sat: 12-10.30
Sun)

Old King's Head
Stock Road (B1007)
Tel: (01277) 841175
Greene King IPA; **Morlands** Old
Speckled Hen; **S&N** Courage
Directors; **Guest Beer H**
◑ D ◐ **R** 🛏 ✿
Old roadhouse inn with covered
barbecue area. Once known as
'The pub with a car on the roof' -
the vehicle was removed when
the toilet block was rebuilt with a
pitched roof.

Stondon
Massey   B4

11-2.30 (3 Fri); 5-11 (11-11 Sat:
12-10.30 Sun)

Bricklayers Arms
Ongar Road/Nine Ashes Road
OS: TL585005
Tel: (01277) 821152
Greene King IPA, Abbot Ale;
Guest Beers H
◑ D ◐ 🛏 ✿
Friendly and comfortable split-
level village pub with enclosed
garden area in front - accessible
by stile. Cricket played in
Summer. No food Monday.

Stones Green   F2

Green Swan
Clacton Road (1½ miles off
A120)
OS: TM166267
Free-house - Pub closed and
unlikely to reopen.

Stow Maries   D4

11-11 (12-10.30 Sun)

Prince Of Wales
Woodham Road (nr B1012)
OS: TQ830993
Tel: (01621) 828971
Fullers Chiswick Bitter;
Guest Beers H
Thatcher's Medium Cider **G/H**
◑ D ◐ 🛏 🍴 🛏 ✿
Superbly-restored, 18th century
roadside pub, with a working
Victorian bakery. Traditional
throughout, with real fires, and a
fine range of five or six guest
beers, including stouts and
milds.
Belgian beers on 'draught'.
Occasional beer festivals. Good
home-cooked food. Functions in
the 'barn'. Occasional live enter-
tainment. Magnificent fireworks
display in November.
Several times winner of
CAMRA's 'Jack Hillier' award for
Essex 'Pub-of-the-Year'.

Stow Bullocks
Stow Road (nr B1012)
Inntrepreneur - Pub closed and
used as a private house.

Stroud Green
(Rochford)   D4

*Busy main road between
Rochford and Hockley.*

11-11 (12-10.30 Sun)

Cock Tavern
Hall Road (B1013)
Tel: (01702) 540429
S&N Courage Directors,
Theakstons BB, XB, Old
Peculier; **Guest Beer H**
◑ D ◐ **R** 🛏 ✿
Large, upmarket, country pub
set back from road, refurbished
with comfortable seats.
Traditional, home-cooked fayre.

Sturmer C1

Where the apples come from.

11.30-3; 6-11 (12-3; 7-10.30 Sun)
Red Lion
The Street (A1017, was A604)
OS: TL695441
Tel: (01440) 702867
Greene King IPA, Abbot Ale **H**
⟨D ⟨D ⟨D R 🐾 ❀
Refurbished, roadside pub with
emphasis on food. Great for
families.

Takeley B2

*Long village bordering Hatfield
Forest.*

11-11 (12-10.30 Sun)
Four Ashes
Dunmow Road (A120) /
Parsonage Road (Brewers End)
Tel: (01279) 870228
Nethergate Websters Wonderful
Wallop; **Ruddles** Best Bitter;
S&N Theakstons BB **H**
⟨D ⟨D ⟨D 🍺 ⟨📫 ❀
Two hundred year old pub, now
part of Chas Webster's pub
chain. Breakfasts served from
8.30 am. Pizzas 'all the time' and
bar meals.
Sky Sports, pool and darts.
Three bedrooms. Occasional
Guest Beers.

11-3; 6-11 (12-3; 7-10.30 Sun)
Green Man
The Street (A120)
Tel: (01279) 870367
Ridleys IPA, ESX, Rumpus **H**
⟨D ⟨🍺 📫
Friendly pub with darts and
pool. Sunday lunch fish specials.
Casino nights, quiz nights.
Reputedly haunted.

Old Mill
The Street (A120, 1½ miles East
of M11, J8)
Tel: (01279) 870224
Free-house - Pub temporarily
closed.

Tendring F2

11-3; 6-11 (12-8.30 Sun, 10.30
Summer Sun)
Cherry Tree Inn
Crow Lane
OS: TM152240
Tel: (01255) 830340
Adnams Bitter; **Greene King**
IPA, Abbot Ale; **Guest Beer H**
⟨D ⟨D ⟨D R ❀
Nice, 17th century, country pub,
with a pleasant mock-tudor inte-
rior. Food is a major feature -
especially at weekends.
Blackboard menus.

Tendring Heath F2

11.30-2.45; 7-11 (12-3; 7-10.30
Sun)
Tendring Tavern
Heath Road (B1035)
Tel: (01255) 870262
Greene King IPA; **Whitbread**
Flowers Original **H**
⟨D ⟨D ⟨D R 🐎 🐾 ❀
Wicker basket-bedecked ceiling.
Unusual meals available includ-
ing a Thai menu. Formerly the
"Live & Let Live".

Terling C3

*Pretty village with deep ford,
and a windmill which once featured in the Will Hay film 'Oh!
Mr Porter'*

11-2.30; 6-11
Rayleigh Arms
Owl's Hill
OS: TL771151
Tel: (01245) 233228
S&N Courage Best Bitter,
Directors; **Guest Beer H**
⌐ ❀ ♿
Victorian village pub comfort-
ably modernised, and known
locally as 'The Monkey', see the
coat of arms displayed. Folk
music on the first Friday of the
month, monthly R&B in the
function room.

Thaxted B2

*An architectural gem. The steep
High Street, the medieval Guild
Hall, windmill, Almshouses, and
above all the Church of
Cathedral proportions make this
a place not to be missed.*

7-11 (Thu-Sat only) (12-4 Sun)
Cuckoo Wine Bar
36 Town Street (B184)
Tel: (01371) 830482
Greene King IPA **H**
⟨D R
Friendly wine bar with Real Ale -
good food a speciality. Limited
parking.

12-2; 7-11
Four Seasons Hotel
Walden Road (B184/B1051)
Tel: (01371) 830129
Free-house - No Real Ale.

12-3; 6-11 (12-3; 7-10.30 Sun)
Rose & Crown Inn
31 Mill End (by B184)
Tel: (01371) 831152
Ridleys IPA; **Guest Beers H**
⟨D ⟨D ⟨D R 🍺 📫 ❀
Excellent home-cooked food -
book for Sunday lunch, and
three guest beers. Supposedly
haunted.

11-11 (12-10.30 Sun, closes 4-7
Winter)
Star
Mill End (B184)
Tel: (01371) 830368
Adnams Mild (occasional),
Bitter, Extra, Broadside **H**
⟨D ⟨D ⟨D 🍺 ❀
Popular local, with exposed
beams and vast brick fireplaces.
Keen followers of darts and
pool. Good value food.

11-11 (12-10.30 Sun)
Swan Hotel
Bull Ring (B184)
Tel: (01371) 830321
Greene King IPA, Abbot Ale;
Guest Beers H
⟨D ⟨D ⟨D R 🛏 🍴 ❀
Improved, but unspoilt 14th cen-
tury inn, with a wealth of beams
and friendly service.

Theydon Bois A4

*Attractive village with green on
the edge of Epping Forest.*

11-11 (12-3; 7-10.30 Sun)
Bull
Station Approach/Coppice Row
(by B172)
Tel: (01992) 812145
Adnams Bitter; **Ind Coope**
Burton Ale; **Tetley Bitter H**
⟨D ⟨D ⟨D R 🍴 🐾 ❀ ⊖
Huge 'Bull' sign. Handy for
London underground station.
Quiz and theme nights, live
entertainment. Beware sparklers
used.

11-3 (4 Sat); 5.30 (6 Sat)-11 (12-3;
7-10.30 Sun)
Queen Victoria
Coppice Row (B172)
Tel: (01992) 812392
McMullens Original AK,
Country, Gladstone **H**
⟨D ⟨D ⟨D R 🍺 🍴 🐾 ❀ ⊖
Comfortable and popular 3-bar
local. Beware tight sparklers on
the beers.

11-3; 6.30-11 (12-3; 7-10.30 Sun)
Railway Arms
Station Approach (nr B172)
Tel: (01992) 812268
Greene King IPA;
Whitbread Flowers IPA, Original,
Fuggles IPA **H**
⟨D ⟨D ⟨D 🍴 🐾 ❀ ⊖
Small locals' pub.

11.30-3; 6-11 (12-3; 7-10.30 Sun)
Sixteen-String Jack
Coppice Row (B172)
Tel: (01992) 813182
McMullens Original AK,
Country, Gladstone **H**
⟨D ⟨D ⟨D 🍺 📫
Named after local highwayman,
John Rann, executed 1774 who
wore 16 silk strings in his
breeches. Quiz nights, theme
food nights, but no food
Sundays or Monday evenings.

"The Carpenters Arms", Thornwood Common

Thornwood Common A3

Early ribbon development on old London to Norwich main road.

11-3; 6-11 (11-11 Sat: 12-10.30 Sun)

Blacksmiths Arms
Woodside (nr B1393)
Tel: (01992) 574357
Ind Coope Burton Ale; **Tetley** Bitter; **Guest Beer** H
🍺 🛏 ◗ ▋ Ⓡ 🐾 &
Large roadside pub, converted to the 'Big Steak' theme.

11-3; 6-11 (11-11 Fri/Sat: 12-10.30 Sun)

Carpenters Arms
Carpenters Arms Lane / High Road (B1393)
Tel: (01992) 574208
Adnams Broadside; **Crouch Vale** Best Bitter, SAS; **McMullens** Original AK; **Guest Beers** H
Real Cider G
🍺 🛏 ◗ 🚭 🐾 🌳
Excellent, restored, wood-pan-elled village local, with three bars and a new patio at the front.
Now a family-run free-house, with traditional pub games and up to four Guest Beers.
Occasional beer festivals.
Regular Celtic music nights, food nights, crib and darts nights. No food Sundays.
CAMRA Essex 'Pub of the Year' 1998.

Thorpe Bay D5

Quiet part of seafront.

11-11 (12-10.30 Sun)

Halfway House
213 Eastern Esplanade (B1016)
Tel: (01702) 588645
S&N Theakstons BB, XB H
🍺 🛏 ◗ ▋ Ⓡ 🚭 ▐ &
Seafront pub with a large restaurant. Popular with younger drinkers in the evenings.

Thorpe-Le-Soken F2

11-11 (12-10.30 Sun)

Bell Hotel
High Street (B1033)
Tel: (01255) 861394
Greene King IPA; **Tetley** Bitter, Imperial H
🍺 ◗ ▋ Ⓡ 🚭 🛏 ▐ 🐾 &
Excellent, multi-level, 15th century pub/hotel. The public bar is not obvious. Occasional live music. The Car park is across the road.

Bonker's Bar
Station Road (by B1414)
Free-house - Pub closed.
Formerly the "King Edward VII".

11-11 (12-10.30 Sun)

Crown
High Street (B1033)
Tel: (01255) 861296
S&N Courage Directors, Trumans IPA H
🍺 🛏 ◗ ▋ Ⓡ 🚭 🐾 🌳
Friendly, family pub built in a large 'L' - shape. Separate children's room.

11-3; 7-11 (12-3; 7-10.30 Sun)

Olive Branch
High Street (B1033)
Tel: (01255) 861199
Greene King IPA, Abbot Ale; **Guest Beer** H
🍺 🛏 ◗ ▋ Ⓡ 🚭
Large, new glass windows over-look the High Street, and there is a modern continental 'feel' to the bar. Interesting artwork, and young clientele.
Describes itself as a Bistro/Brasserie. Formerly the "Maids Head".

11.30-2.30; 6.30-11 (not Mon: 12-3; 7-10.30 Sun)

Rose & Crown Inn
High Street (B1033)
Tel: (01255) 861525
Adnams Bitter H
🍺 🛏 ◗ ▋ Ⓡ
Half restaurant, half pub, with a plush, red velveteen interior.

Thorrington E3

11-3; 6.30-11 (12-4; 7-10.30 Sun)

Red Lion
Clacton Road (B1027)
Tel: (01206) 250664
S&N Courage Directors, Trumans IPA H
🍺 🛏 ◗ 🚭 ▐ 🐾 🚂
17th century inn with long-standing landlord. Comfortable lounge bar with huge open fire. Public bar has darts.
Very busy food trade, with large, good-value menu and daily spe-cials. Campsite nearby.

11-11 (12-10.30 Sun)

Silver Springs Motel
Tenpenny Hill (B1027)
Tel: (01206) 250366
Free-house - No Real Ale.

Threshers Bush A3

11.30-2.30; 7-11 (12-10.30 Sun)

John Barleycorn
Threshers Bush
OS: TL503093
Tel: (01279) 422675
Adnams Bitter; **Morlands** Old
Speckled Hen; **S&N** Courage
Best Bitter **H**
◑ ✿ ♿
Isolated, picturesque, olde-
worlde country pub designed for
tourists, with famous gardens.

Thundersley C4

*On high ground overlooking the
Thames. The charabancs found
Bread & Cheese Hill a tough
climb.*

11-11 (12-10.30 Sun)

Bread & Cheese
520 London Road (A13)
Tel: (01268) 792262
S&N - No Real Ale.

11-11 (12-3; 7-10.30 Sun)

Cutley Lynch
21-25 Hart Road
Tel: (01268) 751312
Guest Beers H
◑ ◖
Looks like a wine bar, but turns
out to be a small, friendly,
enthusiastically-run locals pub.
The beer range varies, but usual-
ly includes Crouch Vale or
Ridleys beers. Pool and darts,
Sky TV.

11-3; 5-11 (11-11 Fri/Sat: 12-10.30
Sun)

White Hart
Hart Road
Tel: (01268) 756245
Bass Hancocks HB, Draught
Bass; **Guest Beers H**
◑ ◑ ◖ ◗ (Not Sun) ✿
Old pub with resident ghost -
according to the 'history' board
in the bar. The lower end of the
pub has been extended and chil-
dren are welcome in that area.
Occasional quizzes. Beware keg
cider on fake handpump!

11-11 (12-10.30 Sun)

Woodman's
Rayleigh Road (A129)
Tel: (01268) 775799
Ind Coope 'House' Bitter;
Tetley Bitter; **Guest Beer H**
◑ ✿
Spacious, single bar, mod-
ernised with brass and stained
glass. Large screen TV and occa-
sional live music. Sunday roast
lunch. Beware 'Addlestones'
Cider on handpump!

11-11 (12-10.30 Sun)

Zach Willsher
170-180 Church Road (nr A13)
Tel: (01268) 751781
S&N John Smiths Bitter,
Theakstons XB; **Guest
Beers H**
◑ ◑ ◖ ⊞ ✿
Large estate pub with pleasant
garden. Enduringly popular with
the younger set. Guest beers
from the S&N range. Satellite
TV.

Tilbury B5

*Docks-dominated district, where
Queen Elizabeth 1 reviewed the
fleet in 1588, before it met the
Spanish Armada. The 17th cen-
tury Tilbury Fort is now a
National Monument. Tilbury
Riverside station has closed and
the Gravesend Ferry is now
served by minibus from Tilbury
Town.*

11-3; 7-11 (11-11 Fri/Sat: 12-10.30
Sun)

Anchor
Civic Square (nr A126)
Tel: (01375) 842439
Free-house - No Real Ale.

11-11 (12-10.30 Sun)

Porters Free-house
174 Dock Road (nr A1089)
Tel: (01375) 846132
Free-house - No Real Ale.
Formerly "Buffs Bar & Bistro"

Ship
140 Dock Road (nr A1089)
Bass - Pub closed and converted
to a post office.

12-11 (10.30 Sun)

Worlds End
Fort Road (nr A1089)
Tel: (01375) 840827
Morlands Old Speckled Hen;
Whitbread Flowers IPA; **Guest
Beer H**
◑ ◑ ◖ ◗ ♿ 🛏
Extensively-restored as a free-
house in 1998, following serious
fire damage. Low ceiling in one
of the bar areas. Located by the
entrance to Tilbury Fort. Rather
pricey.

"The Cap & Feathers", Tillingham

Tillingham   E4

Attractive and remote marshland village on Dengie peninsular.

11.30-3; 6-11 (12-4; 7-10.30 Sun)
Cap & Feathers
8 South Street (B1021)
OS: TL993036
Tel: (01621) 779212
Crouch Vale Best Dark Ale, Woodham IPA, Best Bitter, Millennium Gold, SAS, Willie Warmer (Winter); **Guest Beers H**
Thatchers Medium Cider **G**
◖◗ ◖◗ Ⓡ ⇔ ⊫ ⇆ ❀ 🖾
Unspoilt, 15th century pub with a superb atmosphere - reputedly haunted. Crouch Vale's only tied house, not all the beers are necessarily 'on' at the same time. Bar Billiards, Devil Amongst the Tailors and Shove Ha'penny played. Excellent food. CAMRA's 'National Pub of the Year' 1990.

11.30-3; 6-11 (11.30-11 Sat: 12-10.30 Sun)
Fox & Hounds
12 The Square (By B1021)
Tel: (01621) 779416
Greene King IPA; **Guest Beer H**
◖◗ ◖◗ Ⓡ 🚍
Homely, spick and span, quietish 19th century pub facing the village green, with a warm, gentle atmosphere. Pool table.

Swan Hotel
29 North Street (B1021)
Whitbread - Pub closed and delicensed.

Tiptree   D3

Busy village in fruit growing area. Famous for its Wilkins Jam Factory and windmill.

12-11 (12-4; 7-10.30 Sun)
Anchor
9 Station Road (nr B1022)
Tel: (01621) 815248
Ruddles Best Bitter; **S&N** Websters Yorkshire Bitter **H**
◖◗ ◖ ⊞ ❀
Set well-back from the road, with children's play area. Pool table.

11-4; 7-11 (12-4; 7-10.30 Sun)
Kings Arms
Kelvedon Road (B1023)
Tel: (01621) 815393
Greene King, Martha Greene's Brewery Bitter, IPA **H.**
◖◗ ◖◗ ❀
A large 'Hungry Horse' with good facilities for Families

Maypole
Messing Road / Oak Road (B1022)
Allied - Pub closed and converted to a restaurant.

11-3; 6-11 (12-10.30 Sun)
New Times
85/87 Maldon Road (B1022)
Tel: (01621) 817002
Greene King IPA, Abbot Ale;
Shepherd Neame Masterbrew **H**
◖◗ ◖◗ Ⓡ ❀
Large, 1974-built pub, with separate restaurant/carvery.

11-11 (12-10.30 Sun)
Oak
40 Oak Road (nr B1022)
Tel: (01621) 815579
Greene King IPA **H**
❀ ♿
Renovated pub in residential road. Pool table.

11-11 (12-10.30 Sun)
Ship
152 Maldon Road (B1022)
Tel: (01621) 815437
Greene King IPA; **Ruddles** Best Bitter; **Whitbread** Flowers IPA **H**
◖◗ ◖◗ Ⓡ ⊞ ⊫ ❀
Old pub on main road with cosy low-beamed lounge and good reputation for food. New conservatory.

Tollesbury   D3

Ancient port which once had a pier and a railway station, now a haunt of wildfowlers. The huge weather-boarded buildings, standing on stone blocks by the river are for drying sails.

11-11 (12-10.30 Sun)
Hope Inn
16 High Street (by B1023)
Tel: (01621) 869238
Greene King IPA **H**
◖◗ ◖◗ ⊞ ⇔
Built in 1928. Porthole in saloon bar door. Food served in lounge, but no food Mondays or Tuesdays.

11-3; 6-11 (Sat 11-11: 12-10.30 Sun)
Kings Head
1 The Square, High Street (B1023)
Tel: (01621) 869203
Greene King IPA; **Guest Beer H**
◖◗ ◖◗ ⊞ 🚍
Attractive pub with separate eating area in the lounge bar. Traditional games in the public bar. Occasional live music.

Tolleshunt D'Arcy   D3

12-2.30; 5.30-11 (12-4; 7-10.30 Sun)
Plough Inn
Oxley Hill, Oxley Green (B1023)
Tel: (01621) 815341
S&N Courage Best Bitter;
Guest Beers H
◖◗ ◖◗ Ⓡ ❀
Plush and comfortable country pub, with separate a-la-carte restaurant. A mile north-west of village.

12-3; 6-11 (11-11 Fri/Sat: 12-10.30 Sun)
Queens Head
15 North Street (B1026)
OS: TL930120
Tel: (01621) 860262
Greene King IPA, Abbot Ale **H**
◖◗ ◖◗ ⊞ ❀
Traditional village pub - the public bar is a gem, unchanged by time. The lounge is comfortable with a wealth of beams and a notable fireplace.

11-3; 6-11 (12-3; 7-10.30 Sun)
Red Lion
9 South Street (B1026) / Tollesbury Road (B1023)
OS: TL930118
Tel: (01621) 860238
Adnams Bitter; **Ridleys** IPA, ESX **H**
⊞ ⊫ ❀
Wonderfully haphazard and cluttered pub, with a one-eyed cat, and an amazing range of wines. The only free-house in the village.

12-3; 7-11 (12-4; 7-10.30 Sun)
Thatcher's Arms
1 North Street (B1026)
OS: TL931121
Tel: (01621) 860655
Whitbread Boddingtons Bitter, Flowers IPA **H**
◖◗ ◖◗ Ⓡ ❀
Welcoming, 400-year old village pub, with one 'I'-shaped bar, catering for the younger clientele. Children's play area and barbecues in the garden. Reputed to have a ghost. Longer hours in Summer.

Tolleshunt Knights   D3

Rose & Crown
25/35 D'Arcy Road (B1023)
OS: TL908149
Tel: (01621) 815282
Greene King IPA; **S&N** Courage Best Bitter, Directors **H**
◖◗ ◖◗ Ⓡ ⊞ ❀
Two-bar, country pub, with restaurant at rear. Special rates for meals for senior citizens. Occasional events.

Tolleshunt Major   D3

Centre of fruit growing and packaging industry.

11-3; 6-11 (12-3; 7-10.30 Sun)
Bell
Beckingham Street
OS: TL899113
Tel: (01621) 860329
Greene King IPA; **Guest Beer H**
◖◗ ◖◗ ⊞ ❀
Pleasant and cosy village pub, set back off the road, with large natural pond in new garden. Eating area in lounge bar.

Toot Hill A4

11-3; 6-11 (12-3; 7-10.30 Sun)

Green Man
OS: TL515025
Tel: (01992) 522255
Crouch Vale Woodham IPA;
Guest Beers H

◑ D ◐ ● R 🕸 & Ns

Excellent, 19th century, country pub, with fine views from garden. Two guest beers from small independent breweries. Notable food, served from the two restaurants - one in the main building, the other in the barn - across the yard. Busy at weekends.

Toppesfield C1

Compact village with square.

Crawley Arms
1 The Street (2 miles West of A1017, was A604)
OS: TL739375
Free-house - Pub closed.
Formerly the "Chestnut".

11-2.30; 7-11 (12-3; 7-10.30 Sun)

Green Man
3 Church Lane (2 miles West of A1017, was A604)
OS: TL739374
Tel: (01787) 237418
Greene King IPA **H**

◑ D ◐ ● R 🍺 ┗ 🕸

Excellent roomy local, in small village - that is not easy to find, but well-worth the effort. Food Friday/Saturday evenings only. Restaurant seats eighteen. Darts, dominoes, pool, quizzes and piano played.

Tylers Green B3
(North Weald)

On the fringe of North Weald.

11-11 (12-10.30 Sun)

Talbot
275 High Road (A414)
Tel: (01992) 523966
Whitbread Boddingtons Bitter,
Flowers Original; **Guest
Beers H**

◑ D ◐ ● R 🕸 &

Typical 'Beefeater' with good beer and predictable decor. A locals pub in the evening. Two guest beers.

Ugley B2

Some charming houses despite the name.

12-2.30; 6-11 (12-3; 7-10.30 Sun)

Chequers
Cambridge Road (B1383)
OS: TL512288
Tel: (01799) 540387
Greene King IPA; **Guest Beer E**

◑ D ◐ ● ┗ 🕸

Pleasant and friendly old roadside pub, restored mainly as a restaurant. Welcoming log fires, beer garden. Unusually, the beers are dispensed by electric pumps - the handpumps are dummies. Limited parking.

Upminster B5

Attractive suburban town at the end of the District Line. Its past is remembered in a beautifully preserved smock windmill, and a tithe barn.

12-11 (10.30 Sun)

**Bridge House
(Pickled Newt)**
Upminster Road, Upminster Bridge (A124)
Tel: (01708) 442657
Greene King Martha Greene's, IPA, Abbot Ale **H**

◑ D ◐ ● R 🍺 🚋 🔄

A Greene King 'Pickled Newt' by the River Ingrebourne. Recently converted from a 'Hungry Horse' and repainted in a tasteless shade of purple. Chess/chequers tables.

11-11 (12-10.30 Sun)

Essex Yeoman
70 Station Road (by BR/LT Station, nr A124/B187).
Tel: (01708) 229289
S&N Courage Directors, Theakstons BB, Websters Yorkshire Bitter **H**

◑ D ◐ ● ≷ 🔄

Recently-refurbished pub with quiz nights, TV and pool. Limited parking.

11-11 (12-10.30 Sun)

Huntsman & Hounds
2 Ockendon Road, Corbets Tey (B1421)
Tel: (01708) 220429
Guest Beer H

◑ D ◐ ● R 🍺 ┗ 🚋 🕸

Extended 'Big Steak' pub with conservatory restaurant. Sadly-depleted beer range. Pool and darts. Quiz night some Wednesdays. Children's play area in garden.

11-11 (12-10.30 Sun)

Masons Arms
311 St Mary's Lane (B187)
Tel: (01708) 220358
Tetley Bitter; **Guest Beer H**

◑ D ◐ ● 🕸 ≷ 🔄

A much-improved local, spoilt by a 'Mr Qs' conversion. Now dominated by video games, TVs and pool. Beware 'Addlestones' Cider behind dummy handpump is under CO_2 pressure.

12-11 (10.30 Sun)

Optimist Tavern
Hacton Lane / Little Gaynes Lane (nr A124 & B1421, ½ mile)
Tel: (01708) 220342
Bass Draught Bass; **Morlands** Old Speckled Hen **H**

◑ ● 🍺 🕸

Greatly-altered local, with pastel shades and water-colour prints, on the fringe of the countryside. The old public bar retains some of its original styling. Occasional live music and quizzes. Over 21's only.

12-11 (10.30 Sun)

White Hart
Hacton Lane, Hacton Corner (1½ miles South of A124)
OS: TQ547851
Tel: (01708) 220252
Fullers London Pride; **Greene King** IPA **H**

◑ D ◐ ●

Popular country pub with good-value food from the 'Sizzling Steaks' menu. Sofas in alcove at the end of the bar. Beware keg 'Cidermaster' on handpump.

Upshire A4

Pleasant village on Northern fringe of Epping Forest with some fine weather-boarded cottages.

11-11 (12-10.30 Sun)

Good Intent
Crown Hill, Copthill Green
Tel: (01992) 712066 & 769855 (Restaurant)
McMullens Original AK; **Tetley** Bitter **H**

◑ D ◐ ● R 🕸 &

Pub with popular restaurant, serving good quality food. Restaurant closed Sunday and Monday evenings. Friendly, Italian owner. Limited parking.

Horseshoes
Horseshoe Hill
OS: TL415011
Tel: (01992) 712745
McMullens Original AK, Gladstone **H**

◑ ● 🕸

Friendly, family local, dating from the late 1800s, in the middle of Epping Forest. The landlord has been in residence since 1969! Food available weekday lunchtimes only.

WALTHAM ABBEY

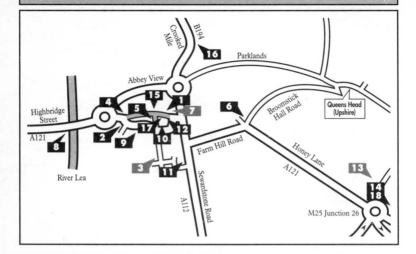

11-11 (12-10.30 Sun)
Queen's Head
60 Paternoster Hill
Tel: (01992) 718611
McMullens Original AK, Country, Gladstone **H**
◑ ◐ ● ❙ ⌂ ❀ ♿
Three darts teams, Sunday evening quizzes, Thursday and Saturday discos. Satellite TV in the public bar.

Vange   C5
At the southern edge of Basildon, a mile from Basildon Zoo.

(See Basildon map for the location of the pubs).

12-11 (May close 4-6 Mon-Thu if quiet; 12-3; 7-10.30 Sun)
Barge Inn   V1
High Road (B1464)
OS: TQ725896
Tel: (01268) 552212
Ruddles Best Bitter; **Guest Beer H**
◑ ❙ ⌖ ❀ ♿
The pub has been in the same family since 1937, and is one of the few remaining tenancies left in the old 'national brewers' estates. The landlady is being pressurised to take on a lease. Externally redecorated, but run-down interior.

11-11 (12-10.30 Sun)
Commodore   V2
Timberlog Lane
OS: TQ723888
Tel: (01268) 553204
S&N Courage Trumans IPA, Directors **H**
◑ ◐ ● ❙ ⌂ ▬
Soulless, new-town pub. External vandalism and the effects of competition from other pubs add to the gloom. Beware 'Scrumpy Jack' cider on fake handpump!

11-11 (12-10.30 Sun)
Five Bells   V3
Bells Hill Road (by A176/A13)
OS: TQ709865
Tel: (01268) 553162
Fuller London Pride **H**
◑ ◐ ● **R** ❀
Largely isolated by the construction of a flyunder on the adjacent A13. This former 'Toby Inn' has now been converted to a 'Harvester'.

12-11 (10.30 Sun)
Power House   V4
469 Clay Hill Road
OS: TQ723883
Tel: (01268) 555842
Inntrepreneur - No Real Ale. Formerly the "Bull".

12-3; 6-11 (12-11 Sat: 12-10.30 Sun)
Winged Horse   V5
Luncies Road, Barstaple East
Tel: (01268) 558169
Ind Coope 'House' Bitter, **Tetley** Bitter **H**
⌂ ▬
Family local with friendly staff and customers. Limited parking.

Wallasea Island   D4
Marshy island rising to a height of 14 feet opposite Burnham-on-Crouch. Riverside walks and yachting.

11-3; 6-11 (11-11 Holiday weekends: 12-10.30 Sun)
Creeksea Ferry Inn
Off Creeksea Road
Tel: (01702) 258722
Free-house - No Real Ale (despite the sign outside!).

Wardroom Hotel
Wallasea Yacht Marina
OS: TQ937951
Tel: (01702) 258431 / 258676
Free-house - Pub closed, but may reopen.

Waltham Abbey   A4
Parts of the abbey date from the 11th century. King Harold (1066) was buried here.

11-3; 5.30-11 (11-11 Sat: 12-10.30 Sun)
Angel   1
48 Sun Street (nr A112)
Tel: (01992) 718671
McMullens Original AK, Country, Gladstone **H**
◑ ◐ ● ❙ ⌂ ❀ ♿
A pub unchanged through passage of time. Cribbage played, monthly karaoke and occasional live music. Beware 'sparklers'. Parking difficult.

Coach & Horses 2
1 Green Yard (nr A121)
Tel: (01992) 715781
Whitbread Boddingtons Bitter **H**
Parking difficult.

Compasses 3
77 Sewardstone Street
Tel: (01992) 711083
Free-house - No Real Ale.

10-3; 6-11 (10-11 Sat: 12-10.30
Sun)
Crown 4
4 Romeland (nr A121)
Tel: (01992) 701481
McMullens Original AK,
Country, Gladstone **H**
ⓓ🄳 🄴 🄳 ❀
Friendly town local with
enthusiastic landlord. Live piano
Saturday nights. Limited
parking.

11 (10.30 Tue/Sat)-11 (12-10.30
Sun)
Green Dragon 5
21 Market Square (nr A121 &
A112)
Tel: (01992) 711205
S&N Courage Directors; **Tetley**
Bitter **H**
🄳 🄴 🄴 ❀
The oldest pub in Waltham
Abbey - over 400 years. Live
bands occasionally in
Winter/Spring. Over 21s only.

11.30-3; 6-11 (11.30-11 Sat: 12-
10.30 Sun)
Green Man 6
Farm Hill Lane (A121)
Tel: (01992) 713159
Ind Coope Burton Ale; **Tetley**
Bitter **H**
ⓓ🄳 🄴 🅁 🄴 🚃
Busy, family pub with locals bar,
and large 'Big Steak' restaurant
at rear. Quiz nights and occa-
sional discos.

11-11 (12-10.30 Sun)
New Inn 7
58 Sun Street (A112) / Crooked
Mile
Tel: (01992) 712939
Allied Domecq - No Real Ale.

11-11 (12-10.30 Sun)
Old English Gentleman 8
85 High Bridge Street (A121)
Tel: (01992) 712714
Bass Draught Bass; **McMullens**
Original AK, Country **H**
🄳 🄴 🄴 ❀ 🄳
Popular local on bridge along-
side the River Lea Navigation.

10-11 (12-10.30 Sun)
Old Spotted Cow 9
Fountain Place (nr Market
Square)
Tel: (01992) 711345
McMullens Original AK,
Gladstone **H**
ⓓ🄳 🄴 🄳 🄴 ❀
Old-fashioned local, cribbage
played.

10.30-11 (12-10.30 Sun)
Queen's Arms 10
13 Market Square (nr A121)
Tel: (01992) 717454
Morlands Old Speckled Hen;
S&N Courage Best Bitter,
Directors **H**
❀ 🄳
Small, friendly, no-frills, drinkers
pub by town centre.
Bar billiards.

12-3; 6-11 (11-11 Sat: 12-10.30
Sun)
Sultan 11
Sewardstone Road (A112)
Tel: (01992) 712720
Bass Draught Bass; **Whitbread**
Boddingtons Bitter; **Guest
Beers H**
ⓓ🄳 🄴 🅁 🄴 🔜 ❀ 🄳
Roadside family pub.

11-11 (12-10.30 Sun)
Sun Inn 12
21 Sun Street (nr A112)
Tel: (01992) 712720
S&N Courage Directors; **Tetley**
Bitter **H**
ⓓ🄳 🄴 🅁 🄴 🔜 ❀
Old timbered, beamed pub, with
aircraft pictures in the bar, and
beer jugs on ceiling.
Occasional discos/live
music/parties. Over 21s only.

Swallow Hotel 13
Old Shire Lane, off Honey Lane
(A121/M25 Jcn 26)
Tel: (01992) 717170
Vaux - No Real Ale.

11-11 (12-10.30 Sun)
Volunteer 14
Honey Lane (A121, nr M25 Jcn
26)
Tel: (01992) 713705
McMullens Original AK,
Country, Gladstone **H**
ⓓ🄳 🄴 🄳 ❀
Popular pub on the edge of
Epping Forest, noted for its tradi-
tional Chinese and English
menus.
Very busy Summer evenings
and weekends. Parking difficult.

11 (10 Tue)-3; 5-11 (10-11 Sat:
12-10.30 Sun)
Welsh Harp 15
Market Square (nr A121/A112)
Tel: (01992) 711113
McMullens Original AK,
Country, Gladstone **H**
ⓓ🄳 🄴 🚃
Picturesque 16th century arche-
typal English pub near the
Abbey.

11-3; 6-11 (12-3; 7-10.30 Sun)
Wheatsheaf 16
146 Crooked Mile (B194)
Tel: (01992) 711266
McMullens Original AK,
Gladstone **H**
ⓓ🄳 🄴 🄳 ❀
Friendly pub with large garden.
Families welcome. No meal
Sun/Mon evenings.

11-3; 6-11 (10-11 Tue/Fri/Sat: 12-
10.30 Sun)
White Lion 17
11 Sun Street (nr A112)
Tel: (01992) 718673
McMullens Original AK,
Country, Gladstone **H**
ⓓ🄳 🄴 🄳 ❀ 🄳
A single public bar, with occa-
sional live music. Sky Sports
and darts. Beware 'sparklers'.

11-11 (12-10.30 Sun)
Woodbine 18
Honey Lane (A121, nr M25 Jcn
26)
Tel: (01992) 713050
Adnams Bitter; **Tetley** Bitter **H**
ⓓ🄳 🄴 🄳 ❀
Popular, well-renovated pub
near Epping Forest, with
'Conservatory' patio. No meals
Sunday evenings.

Walton-on-the Naze F3

10-11 Summer (11.30-3; 7-11
Winter: 12-10.30 Sun)
Bath House
Princes Esplanade
Tel: (01255) 675848
Free-house - No Real Ale.

Jarvo's Wine Bar
11 Old Pier Street
Free-house - Bar closed.

JJ's Too Wine Bar
14 Newgate Street
Free-house - Bar closed.

(Closed out of season)
Naze Mariner
East Parade
Tel:
Free-house - No Real Ale.

11-11 (may close evenings out of
season: 12-3; 7-10.30 Sun, 12-
10.30 Sun after Easter)
Pier Hotel
Promenade (nr B1034)
Tel: (01255) 675725
Adnams Bitter; **Greene King**
IPA, Abbot Ale **H**
ⓓ🄳 🄴 🄳 🥢 ❀ 🚉
Massive, three-tiered hotel on
seafront, tucked in the cliff-face,
opposite the pier. Limited
parking.

11-11 (12-10.30 Sun)
Queens Head Hotel
79 High Street
Tel: (01255) 675763
Adnams Bitter **H**
ⓓ🅁 🄳 🄴 🥢 🚉
Renovated, one-bar, seaside
pub/hotel. Limited parking.

11-4 (Summer only); 7-11 (12-3;
7-10.30 Sun)
Royal Albion
High Street
Tel: (01255) 677122
Free-house - No Real Ale.
Formerly the "King's Hotel".

11-11 (12-10.30 Sun)

Royal Marine (Barkers)
3-7 Old Pier Street (nr B1034)
Tel: (01255) 674000
Adnams Bitter; **Marstons**
Pedigree; **Guest Beers H**
◖D ◖▶ R ⊞ ⇌
Classic, mellow, Victorian pub
where the cellar is above the
bar! A meeting place of thespi-
ans and mariners accompanied
by the occasional pampered
pooch. Parking can be difficult.

Station Lounge
Walton Station, Church Road (nr
B1034)
Free-house - Pub closed and
derelict.

10-11 (12-10.30 Sun)

Victory
Suffolk Street/Newgate Street
Tel: (01255) 677857
Greene King IPA, Abbot Ale,
seasonal beers **H**
◖D ◖▶ R ⊞ ❀ ⇌
Locals town pub, with lots of
nautical paraphernalia, a good
ambience and food. Limited
parking.

10.30-3; 7-11 (1am Fri) (10.30-
1am Sat & Summer: 12-10.30
Sun)

Walton Tavern
30-32 The Parade
Tel: (01255) 676000
Ruddles County; **S&N** Websters
Yorkshire Bitter **H**
◖D ◖▶ R ⇔ ⊨ ⇌
Large, modernised seafront pub
on cliff promenade, with restau-
rant open Summer and week-
ends. Limited parking. Formerly
the "Elmo's Inn" and the
"Walton Tudor Inn".

Warley   B4

*Former home of Napoleonic bar-
racks.*

*(See Brentwood map for loca-
tion of pubs)*

11-3; 6-11 (11-11 Fri/Sat: 12-10.30
Sun)

Alexandra   W1
114 Warley Hill (B186)
Tel: (01277) 210456
Greene King IPA, Abbot Ale
(sometimes) **H**
◖D ◖▶ R ❀ ⇌
Traditional pub with good local
trade. Recently-refurbished and
extended to incorporate the old
'Jug & Bottle' into the saloon.
The former public bar is now
mainly a restaurant. Beer garden, and much improved car
parking.

12-3; 5.30-11 (12-11 Sat: 12-4; 7-
10.30 Sun)

Brave Nelson   W2
138 Woodman Road (½ mile
East of B186)
Tel: (01277) 211690
Nethergate Bitter; **S&N**
Websters Yorkshire Bitter;
Guest Beer H
◖D ◖ ⊞ ❀
A cosy, local gem, with under-
stated nautical memorabilia.
Summer barbecues and
petanque in the large, chil-
dren's playground. Quiz night
Sunday. No food Sundays. Pool
played.
A rare oasis, in the area for
Nethergate beer.

11.30-2.30; 6-11 (11.30-11 Fri:
2pm-11 Sat: 12-10.30 Sun)

Charlies Bar   W3
152 Warley Hill (B186)
Tel: (01277) 212786
Greene King IPA **H**
◖D ◖ ⅙
Sporty pub with a semi-circular
bar - run by Charlie! Darts, pool,
pinball, video games and satellite TV dominate. DJs at weekends. No food at weekends.
Formerly the "Prince Albert".

11.30-11 (12-10.30 Sun)

Cherry Tree   W4
51 Queen Street (nr B186)
Tel: (01277) 263001
Crouch Vale IPA; **Guest Beers H**
◖D ◖ ⊞ ⇔
A pleasant, friendly, unspoilt,
locals pub, with a good range of
guest beers - usually three, from
small independent breweries.
Darts, dominoes and cribbage
played. Limited parking.

11-11 (12-4; 7-10.30 Sun)

Essex Arms   W5
Warley Hill / Myrtle Road (B186)
Tel: (01277) 201164
Adnams Bitter; **Mighty Oak**
Burntwood Bitter; **Guest Beers H**
◖D ◖▶ ⊨ ⇌
Much-improved and altered fol-
lowing a lengthy period of clo-
sure. Function room with regular
live music and discos. No food
Sundays. Guest beers often
include a second 'Mighty Oak'
beer.

11.30-11 (12-10.30 Sun)

Seven Arches   W6
15 Hartswood Road
Tel: (01277) 211489
Mighty Oak Barrackwood IPA,
Burntwood Bitter, **S&N**
Courage Directors **H**
◖D ◖▶ R ❀ ⅙
The exterior is traditional, whilst
the interior resembles a trendy
winebar. Petanque, dominoes
and crib played. A pleasant setting opposite the woods. Large
garden with barbecues in summer. No food Sunday evenings.

Weeley   F2

*'Weeley' pleasant village, with
large council offices and crema-
torium.*

11-3; 6-11 (12-4; 7-10.30 Sun)

Black Boy
Thorpe Road (B1033)
Tel: (01255) 830361
Fullers London Pride; **S&N**
Trumans IPA; **Guest Beers H**
◖D ◖▶ R ❀ ⇌
Large, mellow, old roadside pub
in pleasant, small village. See-
through log fire. Family-owned,
with an interest in Real Ales.

11-11 (12-10.30 Sun)

Bowling Green
Crown Green Roundabout
(A133)
Tel: (01255) 831430
Wadworths 6X; **Whitbread**
Boddingtons Bitter, Flowers
IPA **H**
◖D ◖▶ R ⇔
Popular, 'Brewers Fayre' at the
start of the Weeley bypass.

Wayland
43 Colchester Road (B1033)
OS: TM144225
Free-house - Pub closed.

11-3; 5.30-11 (12-4; 7-10.30 Sun)

White Hart
Clacton Road/Rectory Road,
Weeley Heath (B1441)
Tel: (01255) 830384
Whitbread Flowers IPA **H**
◖D ◖▶ ❀
Small roadside pub in a 1960s
timewarp.

Wendens
Ambo   B1

*Originally   two   villages -
Wendens Magna and Wendens
Parva, that were joined in the
1660s.*

*The magnificent, 17th century,
Audley End House (N.T.) is nearby. The road to the church is the
stuff tourist guides are made of.*

11.30-2.30 (or later in Summer);
6-11 (12-3; 7-10.30 Sun)

Bell
Royston Road (B1039)
Tel: (01799) 540382
Adnams Bitter; **Ind Coope**
Ansells Mild **H**; **Guest Beers H/G**
◖D ◖▶ R ❀ ⇌
Traditional, friendly village pub -
the focal point of many local
events. Children welcome in the
restaurant (no food Monday
evenings). Large garden where
petanque is played. Open fires.

11-2.30; 5-11 (12-3; 7-10.30 Sun)

Fighting Cocks
Mutlow Hill (B1383)
Tel: (01799) 540410
Whitbread Flowers IPA **H**
◖ ◖ ❀ ⇌
Spacious, 'biker-friendly,
Edwardian roadside pub.

Wennington   B5

An area of marshes, quarries and open farmland on the Essex border.

11-11 (12-10.30 Sun)

Lennards
New Road (A1306 (old A13) at B1335 jcn)
Tel: (01708) 631294
Free-house - No Real Ale.

West Bergholt   E2

12-3; 5 (5.30 Sat)-11 (12-11 Fri: 12-10.30 Sun)

Queens Head
5 Queens Road
Tel: (01206) 240394
Greene King IPA; **Ind Coope** Ansells Bitter, Burton Ale **H**

⊂◐ ◖◗ ❀ ⅙

Country pub opposite village pond. Food not available at weekends.

11.30-3; 6-11 (11-11 Sat: 12-10.30 Sun)

Treble Tile
Colchester Road (B1508)
Tel: (01206) 241712
Greene King IPA; **Ind Coope** Friary Meux BB; **Whitbread** Flowers Original **H**

⊂◐ ◖◗ ⅌ ❀

Large, two-bar roadhouse, with tasteful pink interior. Children welcome. Limited menu, but very reasonably priced.

12-2.30 (3 Sat); 6-11 (12-3; 7-10.30 Sun)

White Hart
Nayland Road (by B1508)
Tel: (01206) 240331
Bass Hancocks HB; **Tetley** Bitter, Imperial **H**

⊂◐ ◖◗ ⅌ ❀

Large, friendly 18th century inn, with open coal fires. Large garden with children's play area. Camping available in adjacent field.
Good variety of food, from snacks to big steaks and mixed grills. Vegetarians catered for. Beware handpumped Addlestones Cider may be on CO2.

West Hanningfield   C4

A maze of country roads and attractive properties. Reservoir a birdwatchers delight.

11-3; 5-11 (11-11 Summer: 12-3; 7-10.30 Sun)

Ship
Stock Road (B1007)
OS: TL704004
Tel: (01277) 840201
Whitbread Flowers IPA, Original **H**

⊂◐ ◖◗ Ⓡ ⅃ ❀

Pleasant, friendly, 17th century, timber-framed pub between Stock and Galleywood. Two bar areas and a restaurant on a different level, fish a weekend speciality. Gardens to front and rear.

11.30-3; 6-11 (12-3; 7-10.30 Sun)

Three Compasses
Church Road
OS: TQ726997
Tel: (01245) 400447
Whitbread Boddingtons Bitter; Flowers IPA **H**

⊂◐ ⅌ ☷

Unspoilt, friendly, country cottage pub, near reservoir and with two bars.
Simple public bar, 'beamed' lounge with splendid fireplace and walls adorned with pages from very old magazines and newspapers.
All-too-rare outside gents. Petanque played at the rear. Previous publicans shown on list. Popular with fishermen.

West Horndon   B4

11-11 (12-10.30 Sun)

Railway
13 Station Road (½ mile off A128)
Tel: (01277) 811340
Ind Coope Burton Ale; **Tetley** Bitter; **Guest Beer H**

⊂◐ ◖◗ ❀ ⇌

Friendly, family pub with extensive bar food menu. Good atmosphere with children's play area. Darts and pool played.

West Mersea   E3

Mersea Island, with its good oyster beds is some 9 miles due south of Colchester and is reached by the Strood Causeway which often floods at high tide. Watch out for the ghost of the famous Roman Centurion.

11-3; 7-11 (12-3; 7-10.30 Sun)

Fountain Hotel
6 Queens Corner / East Road
Tel: (01206) 382080
Greene King IPA; **Marstons** Pedigree; **Guest Beer** (Summer) **H**

⊂◐ ◖◗ ⅌ ⍩ ⅃ ☷

Function room for up to 120 people. Quiz nights Thursdays, No food on Mondays.

11-2.30; 5.30-11 (12-3; 7-10,30 Sun)

Fox Inn
East Road
OS: TM025135
Tel: (01206) 383391
Adnams Bitter; **Greene King** IPA; **Wadworths** 6X **H**

⊂◐ ◖◗ Ⓡ ❀ ⅙

Games room including 4 pool tables. Log fire, friendly atmosphere. No food Mondays.

11-3; 6-11 (11-11 Sat: 12-10.30 Summer Sun)

Victory
92 Coast Road (½ mile off B1025)
Tel: (01206) 382907
Ind Coope 'House' Bitter; **Tetley** Bitter; **Guest Beer H**

⊂◐ ◖◗ ⅌ ❀ ⅙

Good value water-front pub by boat yards and oyster sheds. A wide range of meals and snacks available. Guest beer changes fortnightly.

12-3;5-11 (11-11 Sat: 12-10.30 Sun)

White Hart
1 High Street
Tel: (01206) 382866
Greene King IPA **H**

⊂◐ ◖◗ Ⓡ ⅃ ☷

Plush, 16th century inn with award-winning restaurant (carvery at weekends). Special food deals for OAPs, discount for three courses between 7 and 10 in the evening.

West Thurrock   B5

Industrialised former working class area, enjoying vast expansion with the adjacent 'Lakeside' development.

11-11 (12-10.30 Sun)

Fox & Goose
584 London Road (nr A126)
Tel: (01708) 866026
Greene King IPA; **Tetley** Bitter; **Guest Beers H**

⊂◐ ◖◗ Ⓡ ⅌ ⅃ ❀

Excellent and good value menu, with free meals for accompanied children. Playground in garden. Book at least three days in advance for Sunday lunch. Guest beers include a mild.

11-11 (12-10.30 Sun)

Lakeside
785 London Road (nr A126)
Tel: (01708) 866556
Free-house - No Real Ale.

11.30-11 (12-10.30 Sun)

Old Shant (Clubhouse)
432 London Road (A126)
Tel: (01375) 376093
Bass - No Real Ale.

11-3; 5-11 (12-10.30 Sun)

Rabbits
767 London Road (nr A126)
Tel: (01708) 865227/863897
Shepherd Neame Master Brew
Bitter **H**
❶ⅅ ⊞ ❀
Small, friendly local, Shepherd
Neame's first tied house in
Essex. Food weekdays only.
Juke box and background
music. Beware 'Sparklers' used!

12-11 (10.30 Sun)

Ship
470 London Road (A126)
Tel: (01708) 865304
Bass Hancocks HB; **Fullers**
London Pride; **Guest Beer H**
❶ⅅ ❶❷ ⊞ ❀
Refurbished, mid 17th century
local with live entertainment on
Saturdays and loud 'background
music'. Reasonable selection of
food, including a vegetarian
meal. No food Sunday evenings.

West Tilbury B5

*Small village around green,
unspoilt despite its proximity to
riverside industry.*

10.30-3; 5.30-11 (12-3; 7-10.30
Sun)

Kings Head
The Green
OS: TQ661780
Tel: (01375) 843081
Greene King IPA; **Guest Beer H**
❶ⅅ ❶❷ ⊞ ❀
Convivial pub on village green,
with regular guest beer, usually
from small independent breweries. 'Sparklers' removed on
request. Varied range of food at
reasonable prices.

Westcliff-on-Sea D5

The 'posher' end of Southend.

11-3; 6-11 (12-3; 7-10.30 Sun)

Cliffs Pavilion
(Admiral Bar & Maritime Bar)
Station Road / Westcliff Parade
Tel: (01702) 344553
Ind Coope Burton Ale; **Tetley**
Bitter **H**
❶ⅅ ❶❷ Ⓡ ⊞ ⊫ ❀ ⅋ ⇌
Country & Western/Rock in
'Admirals Bar', Disco/comedian
in Maritime Bar. Real Ale only in
these two bars. Children allowed
in the food bar.

11-3; 7-11 (12 Wed-Sat, Closed
Sun)

Clouseau's
151 Hamlet Court Road (nr A13)
Tel: (01702) 352727
Free-house - No Real Ale.

11.30-11 (12-10.30 Sun)

Cricketers Inn
228 London Road (A13) / Milton
Road
Tel: (01702) 343168
Greene King IPA, Abbot Ale;
Guest Beers H
Thatchers Cider **H**
❶ⅅ ❶❷ ⊞ ⛳ ⇌
Recently-refurbished. Home of
'Club Riga' music club. The
lounge doubles as a function
room, when required. Live
music Sunday evenings. Gray &
Sons South Eastern outpost.

11-11 (12-10.30 Sun)

Hamlet Court
54 Hamlet Court Road (nr A13)
Tel: (01702) 391752
Greene King Abbot Ale; **S&N**
John Smiths Bitter;
Guest Beers H
❶ⅅ ❶❷ ⅋ ⇌
Converted from an old bank,
and open for breakfast at 11am.
A one-bar pub offering table ser-
vice. Regular beer festivals.
Worth a visit!
Party nights and quiz nights
each month. Free hors d'oeu-
vres at 5.30 weekdays and
Sunday lunchtime. Parking diffi-
cult. TGF Pub - formerly
"Banks".

11-11 (12-4; 7-10.30 Sun)

Jug & Bottle
270 Station Road
Tel: (01702) 332380
Free-house - No Real Ale.
Formerly the "Moonraker".

11-11 (12-10.30 Sun)

Melrose
168 Hamlet Court Road (nr A13)
Tel: (01702) 343882
Greene King IPA; **S&N**
Theakstons BB, Old Peculier **H**
❶ⅅ ❶❷ ⊟ ⇌
Superb, small and welcoming
Victorian style local, with one
large bar. Popular for food - at
reasonable prices. Quizzes on
Thursday evenings, disco and
pop quiz on Sunday evenings.
'Sparklers' removed on request.
Parking Difficult.

12-2.30 (not Sun); 6-11 (7-10.30
Sun)

Palace Theatre Centre
430 London Road (A13)
Tel: (01702) 347816
Greene King IPA; **S&N** Courage
Directors; **Guest Beers H**
❶ ❶ ❀ ⅋
Theatre bar, with live music on
Sunday evenings and jazz on
Sunday lunchtimes. Regular
guest beers. Evening meals
available on show nights.

5.30-11 (12-12 Sat; 12-5 Sun)

Players' Retreat
Bistro & Bar
36-38 Station Road / San Remo
Parade
Tel: (01702) 391961
Free-house - No Real Ale.

11-11 (12-3; 7-10.30 Sun)

Plough
428 London Road (A13)
Tel: (01702) 220041
Bass - No Real Ale.
Formerly incorporated
"Fresco's".

12 (11 Sat)-11 (12-10.30 Sun)

Porters
367 Westborough Road
Tel: (01702) 347715
Free-house - No Real Ale.

West One (Westcliff Hotel)
18-20 Westcliff Parade
Tel: (01702) 345247
Management Service
International 'free' house - Bar
closed, now for hotel use only.

Wethersfield C2

Pretty village near U.S.A.F. base.

11 (3 Mon)-11 (12-3; 7-10.30 Sun)

Brewery Tavern
Braintree Road (B1053)
Tel: (01371) 850363
Greene King Dark Mild, IPA,
Abbot Ale **H**
Small, basic and friendly one-
bar village local, with limited
parking.

12-3; 5-11 (12-11 Fri/Sat; 12-10.30
Sun)

Dog Inn
High Street (near B1053)
Tel: (01371) 850360
Greene King IPA, Abbot Ale **H**
❶ⅅ ❶❷ Ⓡ ⊞ ⊫ ❀
Welcoming and friendly village
local. No food Tuesdays.

White Colne D2

Kings Head
19 Colchester Road (A1124, was
A604)
Free-house - Pub closed and
converted to residential use.

White Notley C3

*Quiet village with fine old
church.*

11-3; 6.30-11 (12-10.30 Sun)

Cross Keys
1 The Street
Tel: (01376) 583297
Ridleys IPA, ESX, seasonal
beers **H**
❶ ❶❷ (Fri/Sat) ⊞ ❀ ⇌
Fine 14th century village local,
formerly Chappells Brewery. No
food Tuesdays.

12-2.30; 6 (7 Sat)-11 (12-3; 7-10.30 Sun)

Plough
The Green
OS: TL773195
Tel: (01376) 321080
Ridleys IPA **H**

◖◖⬤➦⬤

Small, country pub with an emphasis on beer. On the road between White and Black Notley.
New conservatory gives a new aspect to the garden. Jug collection. Simple, but friendly.

White Roding　　B3

Also known as White Roothing.

11.30-3; 6.30-11 (11-11 Sat: 12-10.30 Sun)

Black Horse
Chelmsford Road (A1060)
Tel: (01279) 876322
Ridleys IPA, ESX **H**

◖◖◖⬤⬤

17th century building. Excellent pub food, very good value for money. No food Sunday evenings.

Whalebone
Chelmsford Road (A1060)
Benskins - Pub closed and converted to a private house.

Wicken
Bonhunt　　A1

11-2.30; 5.30-11 (12-3; 7-10.30 Sun)

Coach & Horses
Wicken Road (B1038)
Tel: (01799) 540516
Greene King IPA, Abbot Ale, seasonal beers **H**

◖◖◖⬤⬤

Delightful, thatched rural pub, with friendly service and olde-worlde atmosphere. Three bars including snug. Restaurant closed Sunday evenings.

Wickford　　C4

Unprepossessing　dormitory town.

11-11 (or later)

Bubbles
Ladygate Centre (nr A129)
Tel: (01268) 573048
Free-house - No Real Ale.
Formerly "Bazils", "Silks" & "Toffs".

Buddy's
Unit 13, 15 Willowdale Centre (nr A129)
Tel: (01268) 767638
Free-house - No Real Ale.
Formerly "Roomers" & "Blighty's Wine Bar"

Castle
2 The Broadway (nr A132)
Allied Domecq - Pub closed in January 1998, and was demolished shortly afterwards, to make way for a supermarket! - a sad loss of one of Wickford's better pubs.

11-11 (12-10.30 Sun)

Darby Digger (Harvester)
Radwinter Avenue, Cranfield Park Road
Tel: (01268) 571810
Bass Draught Bass; **Fullers** London Pride **H**

◖◖◖⬤⬤

Newish pub, named after a local ploughing machine, and recently converted to a 'Harvester'. It's now a somewhat bizarre experience, entering through a 'farm shop' into someone's idea of the interior of a range of farm buildings!
Children's certificate held.
Typical 'Harvester' menu, separate bar for drinkers.

11-3.30; 6-11 (12 Thu) (11-12 Fri/Sat: 12-3.30; 7-10.30 Sun)

Dickens
3/9 London Road (A129)
Tel: (01268) 762659
Bass - No Real Ale.

11-3; 5.30-11 (11-11 Fri/Sat: 12-10.30 Sun)

Downham Arms
130 London Road (A129) / Castledon Road
Tel: (01268) 562720
Ind Coope Burton; **Tetley** Bitter **H**

◖◖◖⬤⬤

Recently converted to a 'Big Steak', and much improved by the major refurbishment. Plush and comfortable in mock-Victoriana style.
A family pub with emphasis on food - children allowed in one bar if eating. Smart/casual dress restriction.

"The Cross Keys", White Notley

11-11 (12-10.30 Sun)

Duke
80 High Street (nr A129)
Tel: (01268) 562596
Ushers Gibbs Mew Salisbury
Best, Deacon, Bishops Tipple;
Guest Beer H

◖ ◖ ❀ ≈

Modern pub of little character.
Children allowed in the bar until
6pm. Regular quizzes, karaoke
and own football team. No
meals on Sundays.
Former 'Harmony Inn', acquired
by Gibbs Mew, then Enterprise
Inns. Limited parking.

11-11 (12-10.30 Sun)

White Swan
The Broadway/Swan Lane (nr
A132)
Tel: (01268) 762801
S&N Courage Directors;
Ridleys IPA; **Wells** Bombardier **H**

◖ ◖ ⊫ ≈

Two changing guest beers. Pool
table and darts, numerous
games machines and boisterous
clientele. Quizzes on the last
Thursday of the month, discos
on Fridays, Saturdays and
Sundays.
Still retains some of its 1980s
'Open House' theme pub decor.
Formerly "Swans".

Wickham Bishops   D3

*Large village with confusing net-
work of roads, and fine views.*

11-3; 6-11 (12-10.30 Sun)

Chequers
32 The Street
Tel: (01621) 891320
Ind Coope Burton Ale;
Whitbread Flowers IPA **H**

◖ ◗ ◖ **R** 🍴 ❀

Comfortable village pub with
extensive menu - fish a speciality. Well equipped children's play
area in garden.

11.30-3.30; 5.30-11 (11.30-11 Sat:
12-10.30 Sun)

Mitre
2 The Street
Tel: (01621) 891378
Ridleys IPA, Rumpus, seasonal
beers **H**

◖ ◗ ◖ 🍴 🍴

Traditional old village pub, fairly
recently refurbished, where the
locals congregate.

Wickham St Paul's   D1

11-3; 6-11 (11.30 Sat: 12-3;
6-10.30 Sun)

Victory Inn
The Green (nr B1058)
OS: TL831364
Tel: (01787) 269364
Adnams Bitter; **Greene King**
IPA; **Nethergate** Bitter; **Guest
Beers H**

◖ ◗ ◖ **R** 🍴 🍴 ❀

Welcoming village local, in
delightful setting, opposite village green. Landlord is a Real
Ale enthusiast.
Busy, excellent-value restaurant
and traditional public bar.

Widdington   B2

*Lovely old village, off the beaten
track. Wildlife park nearby.*

12-3; 6-11 (12-4; 7-10.30 Sun)

Fleur De Lys
High Street (East of B1383)
Tel: (01799) 540659
Adnams Bitter, Broadside;
Bass Draught Bass; **Batemans**
XB; **Ind Coope** Burton Ale;
Guest Beers H

◖ ◗ ◖ **R** ⊫ 🍴 ❀

Friendly, well-run village local
with comfortable family room.
Good choice of ales.

Widford   C3

11-3; 6-11 (12-3; 7-10.30 Sun)

Sir Evelyn Wood
56 Widford Road / Widford
Chase (nr A414)
Tel: (01245) 269239
Greene King IPA, Abbot Ale;
Shepherd Neame Masterbrew;
Guest Beers H

◖ ◗ ◖ ❀

Friendly, recently refurbished,
back-street Gray and Sons local.

11-11 (12-10.30 Sun)

White Horse
London Road (A1016, by A414)
Tel: (01245) 281803
Ind Coope Burton Ale; **Tetley**
Bitter; **Guest Beer** (occasional) **H**

◖ ◗ ◖ **R** 🍴 🍴 ✄

Cosy and comfortable 'Big
Steak' house, popular with
'business-types' at lunchtimes.
Food-oriented, and has a
good-sized no smoking area.

Willingale   B3

*Pretty village with Willingale
Doe and Spain churches in same
churchyard. Also site of large
WW2 airbase that might have
been London's 3rd airport.*

11-2.30; 7-11 (12-3 Sun, closed
Sun eve and Mon)

Maltsters Arms
Fyfield Road
Tel: (01277) 896245
Ridleys IPA **H**

◖ ◗ ◖ **R** ⊫ ❀

One-bar pub with restaurant at
rear, which is open Wed-Sat
only. Rather dreary and not very
welcoming.

Witham   D3

*Pleasant expanding country
town, once the home of Dorothy
Sayers.*

11-11 (12-10.30 Sun)

Albert   1
2 Chipping Hill / Albert Street
(B1018)
Tel: (01376) 511771
Greene King IPA; **S&N** Courage
Best; **Guest Beer H**

◖ ◖ ❀

Large, attractive, open-plan,
mock-Tudor style pub, close to
railway station. Caters mainly
for the younger set, although
well-used by commuters and for
lunchtime meals.
Well-equipped children's play
area, set back from the main
roads.

11-4.30; 6-11 (12-3; 7-10.30 Sun)

Batsford Court Hotel   2
100/102 Newland Street (B1389)
Tel: (01376) 517777
Fullers London Pride; **Greene
King** IPA **H**

◖ ◗ ◖ **R** 🍴 ⊫ ≈

Comfortable 15th century hotel
bar, with facilities for wedding
receptions, etc.

11-11 (12-10.30 Sun)

Cherry Tree   3
Cressing Road (B1018)
Tel: (01376) 513000
Bass - No Real Ale.

11-3 (4.30 Sat); 6.30-11 (12-3; 7-
10.30 Sun)

Crochet   4
128-130 Newland Street (B1389)
Tel: (01376) 511051
Greene King IPA **H**

🍴

Small, two-bar, locals pub with
limited parking. Disco every
Saturday.

11.30-3; 6-11 (12-3; 7-10.30 Sun)

Crown Inn   5
53 Guithavon Street (nr B1389)
Tel: (01376) 512242
Tetley Bitter **H**

◖ 🍴 ⊫ 🍴 ≈

Small, old-fashioned, side-street,
locals pub, with two bars. Taken
over by Sycamore Inns and
refurbished.

WITHAM

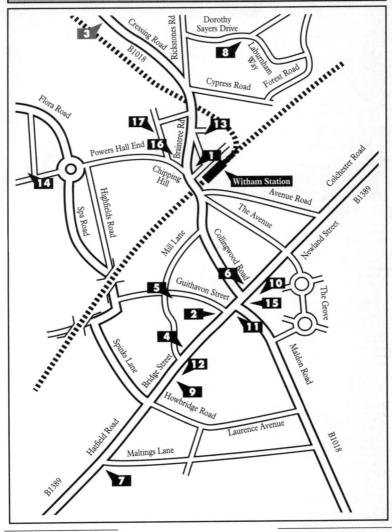

10-11 (12-3; 7-10.30 Sun)

George   **6**
36 Newland Street (B1389) /
Collingwood Rd (B1018)
Tel: (01376) 511098
Ridleys IPA, ESX **H**

◖ ◀ ◱ ▙ ⇌

Good value, welcoming, town-
centre pub with public bar and
quiet 16th century timber
framed saloon. Early opening
makes it handy for shoppers.
Limited parking.

11-11 (12-10.30 Sun)

Jack & Jenny   **7**
113 Hatfield Road (B1389) /
Maltings Lane
Tel: (01376) 512159
S&N Courage Directors, John
Smiths Bitter **H**

◖ ◀ **R** ⛱

Comfortable free-house on the
western edge of town, with separate conservatory restaurant.

"The George", Witham

12-3 (4 Fri/Sat); 6 (7 Sat)-11 (12-3; 7-10.30 Sun)

Little Elms 8
Dorothy Sayers Drive, Elm Rise
Tel: (01376) 514228
Greene King IPA, Rayments Special **H**
◧ 🏠 ❀
Spacious, two-bar, 'estate' pub with surprisingly low ceilings. Old halfpennies varnished in bar top. Snacks only available occasionally.
New landlord trying hard to reverse the previous poor reputation of the pub, and doing well.

11-2.30; 5.30 (5 Fri)-11 (11.30-4.30; 6.30-11 Sat: 12-3; 7-10.30 Sun)

Morning Star 9
13 Bridge Street (B1389)
Tel: (01376) 512129
Guest Beers H
◧ ◑ ◗ R ⊫ ⅔ ❀
Large, free-house at the edge of the town centre, with beer garden to the rear. Varying range of guest beers from Bass, S&N and Tolly Cobbold. Popular restaurant with an impressive menu.

11-11 (12-10.30 Sun)

Red Lion Ale House 10
Newland Street (B1389)
Tel: (01376) 512199
Greene King IPA; **S&N** John Smiths Bitter, Theakstons BB **H**
◧ ◑ ◗ R ⊫ ❀ ♿ ⇌
Low-beamed, former coaching inn, with darts, dominoes & cards. Strong business and shoppers trade at lunchtimes. Beware 'Sparklers' used on southern beers.

11-11 (12-10.30 Sun)

Spread Eagle Hotel 11
Newland Street (B1389)
Tel: (01376) 511097
Adnams Bitter; **Greene King** IPA; **Ind Coope** Burton Ale; **Tetley** Bitter; **Guest Beer** (Occasional) **H**
◧ ◑ ◗ R ⊟ ⊨ ⊫ ⅔ ⇌
Friendly, half-timbered, 14th century hotel. Floor slopes in plush lounge bar, the town bar has a definite public bar 'feel'. Now a 'Big Steak' pub. Beware 'Sparklers' used.

11-11 (12-10.30 Sun)

Swan 12
153 Newland Street (B1389)
Tel: (01376) 513693
Ridleys IPA, Seasonal Ales **H**
◧ ⊫ ⊫ 🍴
Single bar with two distinct areas. Bar Snacks Monday to Saturday. Limited parking at pub - but public car park nearby.

11-11 (12-10.30 Sun)

Taverner 13
Cut Throat Lane, Braintree Road (nr B1018)
Tel: (01376) 502282
Fullers London Pride; **Whitbread** Boddingtons Bitter, Flowers Original **H**
◧ ◑ ◗ R 🍴 ♿ ⇌
Typical, 'Brewers Fayre' pub/restaurant, near supermarket.

12-2.30; 6-11 (11.30-3; 5-11 Fri: 12-5; 7-11 Sat: 12-5; 7-10.30 Sun)

Victoria 14
Faulkbourne Road, Powers Hall End
OS: TL807152
Tel: (01376) 511809
Ridleys IPA, ESX/Rumpus **H**
◧ ◧ 🏠 ❀
Spacious, tastefully renovated old country house on the north-western edge of town. Well worth seeking out. Large public bar and comfortable lounge. Limited Parking.

11-11 (12-10.30 Sun)

White Hart Hotel 15
Newland Street (B1389)
Tel: (01376) 512245
Wadworths 6X; **Whitbread** Boddingtons Bitter; Flowers IPA; **Guest Beer H**
◧ ◑ ◗ R ⊟ ⊫ ❀ ♿ ⇌
Plush, 14th century hotel with a Hogshead Alehouse bar. Very popular and with emphasis on food. Limited parking.

11-3; 6-11 (11-11 Sat: 12-3; 7-10.30 Sun)

White Horse 16
2 Church Street, Chipping Hill (nr B1018)
Tel: (01376) 518155
Greene King IPA, Abbot Ale, Seasonal Ales **H**
◧ ◑ ◗ ❀ ♿ ⇌
Timber-framed pub opposite the local Blacksmiths forge, and only 200 yards from the railway station. Sadly only one bar. Bar billiards played. No food Sunday/Monday evenings. Limited parking.

11.30-11 (12-10.30 Sun)
Woolpack Inn 17
7 Church Street, Chipping Hill
(nr B1018)
Tel: (01376) 511195
Greene King IPA; **Tolly Cobbold**
'House' Beer; **Guest Beers H**
❶ 🇩 🍺 🚬
Long, low, 500 year old pub near
to Chipping Hill Church, with a
very varied clientele. The collection of pump-clips shows the
very varied range of guest beers.
Occasional Real Cider. Rolls and
sandwiches available until the
bread runs out! Limited parking.
Note a cask breather is
occasionally used on the Greene
King IPA.

Wivenhoe E2

11.30-2.30 (or later); 6-11 (12-3;
7-10.30 Sun)
Black Buoy
Black Buoy Hill (nr B1028)
Tel: (01206) 822425
Whitbread Boddingtons Bitter,
Flowers IPA, Original; **Guest
Beer H**
❶ 🇩 🌼 🚬
Quaint, traditional, nautical and
friendly family pub, very popular
for its food. Lunchtime specials,
Sunday roasts, evening meals
(set menu) Tuesdays to
Saturdays only.
Children allowed when dining.
No juke boxes. Hard to find.
Small car park.

11-3; 6-11 (12-3; 7-10.30 Sun)
Flag Inn
Colchester Road (B1028)
OS: TM041232
Tel: (01206) 822830
S&N Courage Best, Directors;
Guest Beers H
❶ 🇩 🍺 🌼
Family, village pub north of the
town, with emphasis on fresh
food. Full choice of meals avail-
able - including Sundays.
Football teams, darts teams.
Popular with staff and students
at nearby Essex University.
Beware 'sparklers' used.

12-11 (12-3; 7-10.30 Sun)
Greyhound
62 High Street (B1028)
Tel: (01206) 825573
Ind Coope Benskins BB; **Tetley**
Imperial; **Whitbread** Flowers
IPA **H**
❶ 🍺 🍴 🐾 🌼 🚬
Friendly and noisy bar, calm and
cosy saloon with open fire.
Popular with families - particularly in summer. Specials every
day. Two darts teams. Public car
park opposite.

10.30-3; 5.30 (6 Sat)-11 (12-3.30;
7-10.30 Sun)
Horse & Groom
55 The Cross (B1028)
OS: TM040228
Tel: (01206) 824928
Adnams Bitter, Old (Winter),
seasonal beers; **Mansfield**
Riding Mild (occasional) **H**
❶ 🇩 ❶ 🍺 🌼 ♿ 🚬
Excellent locals pub with
consistently good beer and
good, home-cooked food. Five
darts teams.

11-11 (12-3 (or later); 7-20.30
Sun)
Park Hotel
140 High Street/The Avenue
(B1028)
Tel: (01206) 822424
Ind Coope Benskins BB;
Guest Beer H
❶ 🇩 🍺 🍴 ♿ 🚬
Friendly local with three darts
teams, quiz team and pool table.
Snacks available until 8pm only.

11-2.30 (3 Sat); 6-11 (12-3; 7-
10.30 Sun)
Rose & Crown
The Quay (nr B1028)
Tel: (01206) 826371
Adnams Bitter; **Fullers** London
Pride; **Ind Coope** Friary Meux
BB, Burton Ale; **Guest Beer H**
❶ ❶ 🌼 🚬
Traditional, 18th century pub
with an open fire and riverside
terrace - don't fall in!!
Popular with sailors, one darts
team. Evening meals available
Mondays, Tuesdays, Thursdays
and Fridays. Parking difficult.

12-11 (12-3 (or later); 7-10.30
Sun)
Station Hotel
27 Station Road (B1028)
Tel: (01206) 822991
Greene King IPA; **Tetley** Bitter,
Imperial; **Tolly Cobbold**
Original **H**
🍺 🌼 🚬
Friendly local near the station,
with mixed memorabilia, domi-
noes and two darts teams.
Beware 'sparklers' used.

Wix F2

11-11 (12-10.30 Sun)
Waggon At Wix
Rectory Hill, Wix Cross (nr A120)
Tel: (01255) 870279
Greene King IPA, Abbot Ale;
Guest Beers H
❶ 🇩 ❶ 🍺 🍴 🐾 🚬
Family-run local with live music
- rock, blues and folk - at week-
ends. One of the guest beers is
usually on 'special offer'.

11-11 (12-10.30 Sun)
White Hart
Harwich Road (nr A120)
Tel: (01255) 870368
Greene King IPA, Abbot Ale **H**
❶ 🇩 ❶ 🇷 🌼
Fine 17th century, weather-
boarded inn with genuine
beams, overlooking the A120.
Narrowly avoided closure.

Woodford
Bridge A4

11-11 (12-10.30 Sun)
Three Jolly Wheelers
735 Chigwell Road (A113)
Tel: (0181) 504 0591
Bass Brew XI, Draught Bass **H**
❶ 🇩 ❶ 🇷 🌼 ♿
Attractive and welcoming, but
totally beer-dominated. Even the
tables in the beer garden have
cutlery, serviettes and menus!
Sadly, the previous guest beer
policy has been discontinued.
Good disabled facilities. Beware
keg cider on fake handpump.

11-11 (12-10.30 Sun)
Crown & Crooked Billet
13 Cross Road (by B173)
Tel: (0181) 505 3570
Bass Brew XI, Draught Bass **H**
❶ 🇩 ❶ 🇷 🌼
Pleasant, comfortable local with
a distinct dining area and a large
bar. Secluded garden only spoilt
by traffic noise. Weekly quiz
nights and functions.

White Hart
692 Chigwell Road (A113)
Tel: (0181) 505 2254
Allied - No Real Ale.

Woodford
Green A4

An area of fine open spaces.

11-11 (12-10.30 Sun)
Castle
393 High Road (A104)
Tel: (0181) 504 0025
Bass Toby Light, Draught Bass **H**
❶ ❶ 🇷 🍴 🚬
Massive, expensively-refur-
bished, showpiece pub, with
stone pillars, almost opposite
the green. Mainly catering for
the younger generation - the
music can be loud. 'Bouncers'
some sessions.

11-3; 5.30-11 (11-11 Sat: 12-10.30
Sun)
Cricketers
299/301 High Road (A11)
Tel: (0181) 504 2734
McMullens Original AK,
Country, Gladstone,
seasonal ales **H**
❶ ❶ 🍺 🚬
Pleasant, traditional local with
consistently good, reasonably-
priced beer. Note the wood panelling. No food on Sundays.

12-3; 5.30-11 (12-11 Sat: 12-10.30 Sun)

Horse & Well
566 High Road (A104)
Tel:
Tetley Bitter; **Youngs** Bitter H
◑ ◖ ❀

Large, attractive pub by Woodford Wells, with garden, play area and seafood stall. Frequented by the younger generation. No food Sundays. Limited parking.

11-11 (12-10.30 Sun)

Railway Tavern
126 Snakes Lane East / West Grove
Tel: (0181) 506 2286
S&N Theakstons XB, Websters Yorkshire Bitter H
◑ D ⊞ 🛒

Large, traditional, restored urban pub with darts and big screen TV for sports. Limited parking.

11-11 (12-10.30 Sun)

Rose & Crown
31 Mill Lane (nr A104)
Tel: (0181) 504 0420
Marstons Pedigree; **Whitbread** Boddingtons Bitter, Flowers Original; **Wadworths** 6X; **Guest Beers** H
◑ D ◖ ◗ R ⊞ ❀

Popular, cosy and friendly, split-level, back-street local with extended upper level bar. A good range of beers, families welcome in restaurant. Barbecues, live music. Limited parking.

11-11 (12-10.30 Sun)

Travellers Friend
496/498 High Road (A104)
Tel: (0181) 504 2435
S&N Courage Best Bitter, Directors; **Ridleys** IPA; **Wells** Fargo; **Guest Beers** H
◑ ◖ ▐━ 🛒

Small, friendly traditional pub with wood panelling and 'snob screens'. No music or machines. No food Sundays and snacks only on Saturdays. Has never sold keg bitter. A gem!

11-11 (12-10.30 Sun)

Woodford Moat House
30 Oak Hill (nr A104)
Tel: (0181) 787 9988
Queens Moat House - No Real Ale.

11-11 (12-10.30 Sun)

Woodman
156 Snakes Lane East / Ray Lodge Road (nr A113)
Tel: (0181) 504 8006
Greene King IPA; **Guest Beer** H
🛒

Light, airy, comfortable locals pub with new patio drinking area. Look for the carved woodman scene at the front of the pub. Different guest beer each week, including independent breweries. Formerly "Double L", the "Viper" & "Mr Woods".

Woodham Ferrers   C4

On high ground aloof from South Woodham Ferrers new town.

11-3; 6-11 (12-3; 7-10.30 Sun)

Bell Inn
Main Road (B1418)
Tel: (01245) 320443
Adnams Bitter; **Nethergate** Old Growler; **Ridleys** IPA; **Taylors** Landlord; **Guest Beers** H
◑ D ◖ ◗ ⊞ ❀

Much-enlarged free-house, with six to eight fine ales usually available. A good base for walkers. Story-telling group meet monthly. Large garden, giving views of the surrounding area.

Woodham Mortimer   D3

11-3; 6-11 (12-3; 7-10.30 Sun)

Hurdlemakers Arms
Post Office Road (between A414 & B1010)
OS: TL813045
Tel: (01245) 225169
Greene King IPA, Abbot Ale H
◑ D ◖ ◗ ⊞ 🍴 ❀ ♿

Superb 'Grays' outlet, run to the highest standards, with olde worlde charm and fine garden. Darts, 'Shut the Box' and 'Devil Amongst the Tailors' played. No meals Friday evenings, and no fried food of any nature! Barbecues on Sunday lunchtimes.

11-3; 5.30-11 (11-11 Sat: 12-10.30 Sun)

Royal Oak
Chelmsford Road (A414)
OS: TL804049
Tel: (01245) 352184
Ind Coope Benskins BB, Burton Ale; **Tetley** Bitter H
◑ D ◖ R 🛒

Unpretentious roadhouse, focusing on food.

Woodham Walter   C3

Pretty village near Chelmer-Blackwater canal.

12-3; 6-11 (12-3; 7-10.30 Sun)

Bell
The Street
Tel: (01245) 223437
Adnams Bitter; **Ind Coope** Friary Meux BB; **Guest Beers** H
◑ D ◖ ◗ R ▐━ ❀

Cosy and beautiful oak-beamed pub, built in 1563, with open fires and plenty of atmosphere.

Cats
Blue Mill Lane
OS: TL815076
Tel:
Greene King IPA, Abbot Ale; **Guest Beers** H
◑ ❀ ♿

Cosy, country local with tranquil views, low beams and open fires. Hard to find - nearly a mile from the village. Ploughmans lunches. Guest beers include Mauldons.
The landlord is not interested in being in any beer guides - but benefits from the extra customers that they can bring!

12-3; 7-11 (12-3; 7-10.30 Sun)

Queen Victoria
Top Road
Tel: (01245) 222176
Greene King IPA; **Shepherd Neame** Masterbrew (Winter) H
◑ D ⊞ 🐾 ❀

Basic Grays local.

Wormingford   D2

A former WW2 airfield here is now used for gliding.

11.30-3; 6-11 (12-3; 7-10.30 Sun)

Crown Inn
Colchester Road (B1508)
OS: TL930316
Tel: (01787) 227405
Greene King IPA H, Abbot Ale G
◑ D ◖ ◗ R ⊞ ❀

17th century 'beamed' pub, with real fires in both bars, superb beer and a good range of snacks and full meals (specials). Framed sets of aircraft cigarette cards adorn the walls.
The comfortable lounge contrasts with the basic public bar, which has a darts board, pool table and fruit machine.

Queens Head
Bures Road (B1508)
OS: TL934315
Free-house - Pub closed and converted to a private house.

Wrabness   F2

Idyllic part of the Tendring Peninsula - the Stour estuary and wood-nature reserves.

Black Boy Inn
Black Boy Lane (nr B1352)
Pubmaster - Pub closed, and for sale as a private house.

11-11 (12-4; 7-10.30 Sun)

Wheatsheaf
Harwich Road (B1352)
Tel: (01255) 870200
Fullers London Pride; **Marstons** Pedigree H
◑ D ◖ ◗ R ⊞ 🛏 ❀

Attractive, isolated and friendly with open fires and relaxed atmosphere.
The spacious, comfortable lounge and dining room contrast with bare boards and wooden settles in the snug public bar. Pool played. Formerly the "Drunken Duck".

Writtle C3

Unspoilt village with triangular green, church, many fine 16th & 17th century houses and an agricultural college. Much relieved by its bypass.

11-3; 6.30-11 (12-3; 7-10.30 Sun)

Chequers
11 Chequers Road, Oxney Green (nr A414)
OS: TL668061
Tel: (01245) 422515
Greene King IPA **H**
🍴 ❀
Catering mainly for the lager trade - Real Ale not always available.

11-3; 6.30-11 (12-3; 7-10.30 Sun)

Cock & Bell
1 Bridge Street
Tel: (01245) 421139
Greene King IPA; **S&N** Courage Directors, John Smiths Bitter; Websters Yorkshire Bitter **H**
🍺 🍷 (Fri/Sat) 🍴 🎯 🍴 ❀
Basic local with Sky TV in large public bar. Occasional quiz nights.

11-11 (12-10.30 Sun)

Horse & Groom
Roxwell Road (A1060)
OS: TL682075
Tel: (01245) 420245
S&N John Smiths Bitter, Theakstons BB, XB;
Guest Beers H
🍺 🍷 🍷 **R** 🍴 ❀ ♿
Smart, roadside pub, tidily-kept after major refurbishment. Extensive menu - food available all sessions.

11-3; 6-11 (11-11 Wed-Sat; 12-10.30 Sun)

Inn On The Green
57 The Green
Tel: (01245) 420266
Adnams Broadside; **Mighty Oak** Burntwood Bitter; **Nethergate** IPA; **S&N** Courage Directors;
Guest Beer H
🍺 🍷 🍷 **R** 🍴 ❀
Large Victorian pub, by the village green, tastefully refurbished with 'olde-worlde' bric-a-brac. Popular with Writtle College students. Extensive menu, including 'A-la-Carte'. The upstairs restaurant is open Friday and Saturday evenings and Sunday lunch. Varying range of guest beers from the region. Formerly the "Rose & Crown".

11-11 (12-10.30 Sun)

Victoria
76 Victoria Road (nr A414)
Tel: (01245) 420535
Greene King IPA; **Ridleys** IPA (Summer); **Guest Beers** (Summer) **H**
🍺 🍷 🎯 🍼 ❀ ♿
Basic public bar with occasional family discos / live country music, pool and darts. Comfortable lounge, suitable for families and popular with locals. Bar snacks only.

11-2.30; 5.30-11 (11-11 Sat; 12-10.30 Sun)

Wheatsheaf
70 The Green (nr A1060)
Tel: (01245) 420695
Greene King IPA, Abbot Ale;
Guest Beers H
🍺 🍷 🎯 🚃
Small, friendly and unspoilt village local, retaining separate public bar. Popular with locals, bell ringers and morris dancers. Limited parking.

Youngs End C2

11.30-3; 6-11 (11.30-11 Sat; 12-10.30 Sun)

Green Dragon
London Road (A131)
OS: TL739196
Tel: (01245) 361030
Greene King IPA, Abbot Ale, seasonal beers (occasional)
🍺 🍷 🍷 **R** 🎯 ❀ ♿
Sympathetic restoration, retaining public bar. Extensive and interesting menu available seven days a week.
Very popular restaurant in former barn. The garden is well-equipped for children.

"The Green Dragon", Youngs End

THE BREWERIES AND BEERS

Breweries and those beers listed in the pub section of this guide are shown below in alphabetical order of brewery.

Their approximate Original Gravities and strength (ABV) - see page 4 - are given, together with brief descriptions. This is not a comprehensive list of the beers brewed by these breweries, but covers those you are most likely to see in Essex at the present time.

For fuller descriptions of these, and other beers and breweries, see CAMRA's annual "Good Beer Guide".

ADNAMS

Adnams & Co PLC, Sole Bay Brewery, East Green, Southwold, Suffolk IP18 6JW.
Tel: (01502) 727200 Fax: (01502) 727201
Family brewery established in 1890, with Real Ale in all its tied estate of around 80 pubs.
Available widely in the free trade and as a Guest Beer in many Big 5 outlets.

Mild	1035 (3.2%) -	A fine dark mild with a faint aroma of both malt and hops, and a slightly sweet finish. Now available only in February
Bitter	1036 (3.7%) -	distinctive, dry, hoppy session beer
Old	1043 (4.1%) -	dark malty winter ale
Extra	1042 (4.3%) -	pale with an abundant hoppy aroma and flavour
Regatta	1042 (4.3%) -	pleasant and malty summer ale
Oyster Stout	1047 (4.3%) -	
Broadside	1048 (4.7%) -	well-balanced copper-red beer
Tally Ho	1075 (7.0%) -	delicious Christmas barley wine

B&T

B&T Brewery Ltd, The Brewery, Shefford, Beds SG17 5DZ
Tel: (01462) 815080 Fax: (01462) 850841
Banks and Taylor were founded in 1981, and were rescued from receivership in 1994 as "B&T".
They produce an extensive range of beers including monthly specials.

Shefford Bitter   1038 (3.8%) - pleasant, well-hopped session beer

BASS

Bass Brewers Ltd, 137 High Street, Burton upon Trent, Staffordshire DE14 1JZ
Tel: (01283) 511000 Fax: (01283) 513256
Founded in 1777, Bass is the second-largest of the national brewers, and has its original brewing home in Burton upon Trent.
It has recently bought the adjacent Ind Coope brewery, and plans to close its "Hancock's" plant in Cardiff, and its "Cannon" plant in Sheffield.

Stones Bitter	1037 (3.7%)	-	reduced in strength from 3.9%
Hancock's HB	1037 (3.6%)	-	pale brown and slightly malty
Worthington BB	1038 (3.6%)	-	pale brown bitter of thin and unremarkable character.
M&B Brew XI	1039 (3.6%)	-	Sweet and malty with a hoppy aftertaste
Draught Bass	1043 (4.4%)	-	a classic pale brown beer which can vary greatly in character depending on its age - it needs to be allowed to mature.

BATEMANS

George Bateman & Son Ltd, Salem Bridge Brewery, Mill Lane, Wainfleet, Lincolnshire PE24 4JE
Tel: (01754) 880317 Fax: (01754) 880939
A family-owned brewery established in 1874 and specialising in "Good Honest Ales", to its own 59 tied houses and free trade outlets. Two seasonal ranges of beers are produced - "Jolly's Jaunts" and "Mystic Brews".

Dark Mild	1033 (3.0%)	-	ruby/black mild with a creamy brown head,with a complex mix of malt, hop and fruit taste.
XB	1037 (3.7%)	-	distinctive well-balanced bitter with refreshing hoppy "bite"
XXXB	1048 (5.0%)	-	excellent, fruity, darker bitter with strong taste of hops and malt

BENSKINS - See Ind Coope
BODDINGTONS - See Whitbread

BRAKSPEAR

WH Brakspear & Sons PLC, The Brewery, New Street, Henley-on-Thames, Oxfordshire RG9 2BU
Tel: (01491) 570200 Fax: (01491) 410254
The Brakspear family have been brewing in Henley since 1799, and have some lovely unspoilt pubs to the west of London.
In addition to their normal range, they also brew several seasonal specials.

Bitter	1035 (3.4%)	-	distinctive, hoppy mid-brown bitter
Special Bitter	1043 (4.3%)	-	honey-coloured, well-balanced, hoppy and bitter
XXXX Old Ale	1043 (4.0%)	-	strong roast malt and caramel flavoured, red/brown ale

CASTLE EDEN - See Whitbread
CHARRINGTON - See Bass (NB: Charrington IPA is no longer brewed)

COTLEIGH

Cotleigh Brewery, Ford Road, Wiveliscombe, Somerset TA4 2RE
Tel: (01984) 624086 Fax: (01984) 624365
Cotleigh have been brewing since 1979, and their beer is now widely available.

Tawny Bitter   1038 (3.8%) - a classic, hoppy, mid-brown bitter

COURAGE - See S&N

CROUCH VALE

Crouch Vale Brewery Ltd, 12 Redhills Road, South Woodham Ferrers,
Chelmsford, Essex CM3 5UP
Tel: (01245) 322744 Fax: (01245) 329082
Crouch Vale were established in 1981, and have one tied house - the "Cap &
Feathers" in Tillingham, which became CAMRA's "National Pub of the Year"
in 1989. Their beers are available in many pubs in Essex and beyond and
numerous special and seasonal beers are produced. Crouch Vale are also
beer wholesalers supplying a wide range of beers from independent
breweries.

Best Dark Ale	1036 (3.6%) -	a smooth, malty mild
Woodham IPA	1036 (3.6%) -	amber-coloured, hoppy, session bitter, with a dry finish
Golden Duck	1038 (3.8%) -	seasonal beer
Best Bitter	1040 (4.0%) -	copper-coloured, full-flavoured bitter, with a hoppy, malty finish
Millenium Gold	1042 (4.2%) -	golden, hoppy and fruity, easy-drinking bitter
Kursall Flyer	1045 (4.5%) -	seasonal brew
SAS	1050 (5.0%) -	full-bodied, with malty yet robust bitterness
Essex Porter	1051 (5.1%) -	occasional/seasonal brew
Fine Pale Ale	1057 (5.9%) -	occasional/seasonal brew
Willie Warmer	1060 (6.4%) -	a meal in a mug! fruity and strong ale

ELDRIDGE POPE - See Hardy's

EXMOOR

Exmoor Ales Ltd, Golden Hill Brewery, Wiveliscombe, Somerset TA4 2NY
Tel: (01984) 623798 Fax: (01984) 624572
Founded in 1980, and within a few months it won the "Best Bitter" Award at
that year's Great British Beer Festival.

Exmoor Ale	1039 (3.8%) -	a pale-brown malty, well-balanced beer.
Exmoor Gold	1045 (4.5%) -	yellow-golden bitter, with a malty aroma and flavour.

FORD & FIRKIN

Ford & Firkin, 15 High Street, Romford, Essex RM1 1JU
Tel: (01708)

There are some 185 pubs in the Firkin chain, but only 51 brew on site and
these supply beer to the others. All 51 brew the same basic 3 beers which
are sold under various local names. (Ford does not brew Dogbolter).

River Ale	1036 (3.5%)	-
Ford Ale	1045 (4.5%)	-
Flash Flood Bitter	1050 (5.0%)	-

FLOWERS - See Whitbread

FREMLINS - See Whitbread

FRIARY MEUX - See Ind Coope

FULLERS

Fuller, Smith & Turner PLC, Griffin Brewery, Chiswick Lane South,
Chiswick, London W4 2QB

Popular London independent brewery. Brewing has taken place on this site
for over 325 years and the Fuller, Smith and Turner partnership was formed
in 1845.

Tel: (0181) 996 2000 Fax: (0181) 995 0279

Chiswick Bitter	1034 (3.5%)	-	distinctive, hoppy and refreshing
Summer Ale	1037 (3.9%)	-	refreshing, golden and hoppy bitter
London Pride	1040 (4.1%)	-	awarding-winning, malty, hoppy bitter
ESB	1055 (5.5%)	-	copper red, fruity, potent bitter

GREENE KING

Greene King PLC, Westgate Brewery, Westgate Street, Bury St Edmunds,
Suffolk IP33 1QT
Tel: (01284) 763222 Fax: (01284) 723803.

This large regional brewer closed its Rayments subsidiary in 1987 and
transferred production of BBA to Bury.

Unfortunately it was a shadow of its former self and was phased out
early in 1991.

Their other brewery at Biggleswade was also closed in 1997 and their
maltings and bottling line are also due to close. However the good news is
that the company remain strongly committed to cask beer and this is backed
by national press and TV advertising.

A range of twelve "King's Court" seasonal beers run through the year.

XX Mild	1032 (3.0%)	-	dark russet brown ale, drink it or lose it
Martha Greene's			
Bitter	1031 (3.1%)	-	A session bitter
IPA	1036 (3.6%)	-	widely available, but unfortunately not as good as it was, a bland beer
Rayments Special	1040 (4.0%)	-	excellent, mid-range bitter

| **Abbot Ale** | 1049 (5.0%) - | a veritable explosion of flavours, but this beer needs ample time to mature in the cellar before serving. Much improved in recent years, following the phasing out of the use of hop oil. |

HANCOCK'S - See Bass

HARDY, THOMAS

Thomas Hardy Brewing Ltd. Weymouth Avenue, Dorchester,
Dorset DT1 1QT
Tel: (01305) 250255 Fax: (01305)258381
Now brews Eldridge Pope's beers under contract.

Popes Traditional	1036 (3.8%) -	A mixture of malt and hop with a hint of fruit
Hardy Country	1040 (4.2%) -	A dry, hoppy beer
Royal Oak	1048 (5.0%) -	classic west country premium strong Ale.

HOOK NORTON

Hook Norton Brewery Co. Ltd., Hook Norton, Banbury,
Oxfordshire OX15 5NY
Tel: (01608) 737210 Fax: (01608) 730294
A delightful Victorian tower brewery, still family owned.

| **Old Hooky** | 1049 (4.3%) - | sweetish, malty ale with bitter finish |

IND COOPE (CARLSBERG-TETLEY)

Carlsberg Tetley Burton Brewery, 107 Station Street, Burton-on-Trent,
Staffordshire DE14 1BZ
Tel: (01283) 531111
Ind Coope is part of the national brewing company Carlsberg-Tetley, the result of a long and sorry tale of mergers, takeovers and brewery closures. See the Good Beer Guide for the full story so far!

House Bitter	1033 (3.3%) -	A low gravity, low priced bitter
ABC Best Bitter	1035 (3.7%) -	light and refreshing
Benskins BB	1037 (3.5%) -	pleasant and hoppy
Friary Meux BB	1037 (3.5%) -	unremarkable darkish bitter
Burton Ale	1048 (4.9%) -	strong, full-bodied and fruity, CAMRA Champion beer of Britain 1990. A Classic beer but increasingly hard to find.
Greenall's Original	(4.6%) -	Fruity with a hint of sweetness.

JOHN SMITH'S - See S&N

McMULLEN

McMullen & Sons Ltd., The Hertford Brewery, 26 Old Cross, Hertford,
Herts SG14 1RD
Tel: (01992) 584911 Fax: (01992) 500729
Hertfordshire's oldest independent brewery. Seasonal 'Special Reserve'
Beers.

Original AK	1034 (3.7%) -	well attenuated, hoppy beer
Country BB	1041 (4.3%) -	full-bodied, malty bitter
Gladstone	1041 (4.3%) -	hoppy and fruity. Sweetish aftertaste
Strongheart	1070 (7.0%) -	rich, dark winter ale

MARSTONS

Marston, Thompson & Evershead PLC, The Brewery, Shobnall Road,
Burton-upon-Trent,
Staffordshire DE14 2BW. Tel: (01283) 531131 Fax: (01283) 510378
The only brewery still using the unique Burton Union system of fermenta-
tion for its stronger ales.

Bitter	1037 (3.8%) -	an amber/tawny session beer. Can be excellent
Pedigree	1043 (4.5%) -	widely available in the portfolios of the large brewers and pub chains. Hoppy and fruity with a bitter aftertaste

MAULDONS

Mauldons Brewery, 7 Addison Road, Chilton Industrial Estate, Sudbury,
Suffolk CO10 6YW
Tel/Fax: (01787) 311055
Many of the beers are blends ie not separately brewed. Provides house
beers for local pubs, look out for these. The extensive beer list changes fre-
quently and numerous seasonal beers are brewed.

Best Bitter	1037 (3.8%) -	now known as Moletrap bitter refreshingly malty ale with hoppy finish
Original Porter	1042 (3.8%) -	smooth chocolatey, dark ale
Squires Bitter	1044 (4.2%) -	russet coloured ale, well bittered
Black Adder	1055 (5.3%) -	quite like a stout, dangerously drinkable
White Adder	1055 (5.3%) -	a pale brown, almost golden, strong ale

MIGHTY OAK

Mighty Oak Brewing Company, 9 Prospect Way, Hutton Industrial Estate, Brentwood, Essex CM13 1XA
Tel/Fax: (01277) 263007
Launched in 1996 supplying some 80 outlets mainly in Essex. Several seasonal ales are also produced.

Barrackwood IPA	1038 (3.6%)	-	a golden, predominantly malty beer
Burntwood Bitter	1041 (4.0%)	-	well-balanced hops, malt and fruit
Twenty Thirst	1044 (4.4%)	-	initially brewed for S.W. Essex CAMRA's 21st anniversary
Mighty Oak Bitter	1047 (4.8%)	-	red-brown, full-bodied and malty

MORLAND

Morland PLC, The Brewery, Ock Street, Abingdon, Oxfordshire OX14 5BZ
Tel: (01235) 553377 Fax: (01235) 540508 Established in 1711, it survived a takeover bid by Greene King in 1992 and has now itself acquired the once revered Ruddles brewery, deciding sadly to close the brewery in Langham and produce the Ruddles brands in Abingdon.

Independents IPA	1036 (3.4%)		
Ruddles Best	1037 (3.7%)		
Ruddles County	1049 (4.9%)		
Old Speckled Hen	1051 (5.2%)	-	A malty, fruity beer that has become somewhat blander as it became more widely available

NETHERGATE

Nethergate Brewery Co. Ltd., 11-13 High Street, Clare, Suffolk CO10 8NY
Tel: (01787) 277244 Fax: (01787) 277123
A small brewery on the Essex/Suffolk border, brewing to the highest of standards. No artificial colourings used. The Umbel beers are infused with coriander seeds.

IPA	1036 (3.6%)	-	crisp, refreshing and hoppy
Umbel Ale	1039 (3.8%)	-	spicey and fruity
Bitter	1039 (4.0%)	-	hoppy aroma, fairly dark, dry bitter
Golden Gate	1045 (4.5%)	-	a golden bitter using 3 hop varieties
Old Growler	1055 (5.5%)	-	naturally dark, wonderfully complex, based on an old porter recipe
Umbel Magna	1055 (5.5%)	-	distinctive, spicey, dark beer

Brewed for Martin Elms Wines:
Porters Suffolk bitter (3.5%)

RAYMENTS

This small village brewery was closed by Greene King in 1987.

RIDLEYS

TD Ridley & Sons, Hartford End Brewery, Felsted, Chelmsford,
Essex CM3 1JZ
Tel: (01371) 820316 Fax: (01371) 820316
Traditional brewery established in 1842 in a picturesque riverside setting
next to the family owned mill in the hamlet of Hartford End, 6 miles north of
Chelmsford

Champion Mild	1034 (3.5%) -	darker version of the bitter - artificially coloured
IPA Bitter	1034 (3.5%) -	balanced, with lingering bitterness
ESX Best	1043 (4.3%) -	malty and hoppy best bitter
Witchfinder Porter	1045 (4.3%) -	bittersweet winter beer
Rumpus	1045 (4.5%) -	a tawny, malty beer
Spectacular Ale	1047 (4.6%) -	pale malty beer. Bitter aftertaste

RUDDLES - See Morlands

S&N

Scottish & Newcastle PLC, 111 Holyrood Road, Edinburgh, Lothian, EH8 8YS
Tel: (0131) 556 2591 Fax: (0131) 558 1165
Scottish & Newcastle recently took over the Courage brewers and became
Scottish-Courage! They have decided to close both their Home brewery in
Nottingham and the Websters brewery in Halifax.
Note that a small proportion of the beers sold under the Theakston name are
still brewed at the Masham brewery in North Yorkshire. However, S & N
don't tell you where your pint is actually brewed, and there is very little
chance of finding the 'proper' Theakston ales in Essex, except for "Old
Peculier", which is now only brewed at Masham.

Bristol Brewery, Counterslip, Victoria Street, Bristol, Avon BS1 6EX
Tel: (0117) 929 7222
Courage was founded in 1787 and has recently been taken over by S & N, to
form Scottish-Courage.

John Smith's Tadcaster Brewery Ltd., Tadcaster, North Yorkshire LS24 9SA
Tel: (01937) 832091
For many years John Smith's had ignored customer demand and refused to
brew Real Ale, then suddenly in 1984 they gave in and returned to the fold
with an extensive advertising campaign for their traditional Yorkshire Bitter
but as part of S&N the brand is now heavily promoted in its nitrokeg form.

T&R Theakston, Masham/ Tyne Brewery, Newcastle-upon-Tyne

**Websters Green
Label Best**   1032 (3.2%)
**Websters Yorkshire
Bitter**   1035 (3.5%) - undistinguished

John Smiths Bitter 1036 (3.8%) - copper coloured, with no dominant
                                       features

Courage Best   1038 (4.0%) - Medium bodied, dry and bitter
Theakstons BB   1039 (3.8%) - a pale,dry bitter

Theakstons XB   1044 (4.5%) - a sweet tasting bitter with a malty
                                       dominance
Courage Directors 1045 (4.8%) - originally brewed for the brewery's own
                                       directors, full-bodied and malty

**Theakstons Old
Peculier**   1057 (5.6%) - notorious, rich and heavy

SHEPHERD NEAME

Shepherd Neame Ltd., 17 Court Street, Faversham, Kent ME13 7AX
Tel: (01795) 532206 Fax: (01795) 538907
Faversham's only brewery - following the closure of Fremlins - and now
Britain's oldest - since 1698. It has a wide trading area in Kent plus a few
tied houses in London, and three in Essex, with more expected. Sadly, tight
sparklers and swan necks are common in their pubs. A number of seasonal
beers are produced.

Master Brew Bitter 1037 (3.7%) - very distinctive with a hoppy aroma
Spitfire Ale   1047 (4.7%) - brewed to mark the 50th and 51st
                                       anniversary of the Battle of Britain
Bishops Finger   1049 (5.2%) -

TAYLOR

Timothy Taylor & Co. Ltd., Knowle Spring Brewery, Keighley,
West Yorkshire BD21 1AW
Tel: (01535) 603139 Fax: (01535) 691167
Independent Yorkshire brewery whose ales have won many awards

Landlord   1042 (4.3%) - highly regarded, full-flavoured bitter

TETLEY

Joshua Tetley & Son Ltd., PO Box 142, The Brewery, Hunslet Road, Leeds, West Yorkshire LS1 1QG
Tel: (0113) 2594594

Carlsberg-Tetley's Yorkshire brewery, Tetley Bitter is widely available in Essex. Getting a full pint measure is a rarity though - owing to the use of the sparklers and swan-necks used to dispense the beer. These agitate the beer, resulting in an unacceptably large head on the pint. Up north oversize glasses are used to contain the head, but around here you'll just have to insist on a top-up! The nitrokeg version of the bitter is increasingly being seen on the bar, so if the pub serves both make sure you get the handpumped beer.

Bitter	1036 (3.7%) -	creamy! Light bitter with dry aftertaste
Imperial	1042 (4.3%) -	a creamy, copper-coloured beer

THEAKSTONS - See S&N

TOLLY COBBOLD

Tollemache & Cobbold Brewery Ltd., Cliff Brewery, Ipswich, Suffolk. IP3 0AZ
Tel: (01473) 231723 Fax: (01473) 280045

Suffolk regional brewery taken over and closed by Brent Walker, then saved and reopened following a management buyout which was aided by the efforts of CAMRA and Ipswich Council. Brewery tours for groups are a major attraction. Introduces a new bottled (and draught) beer annually.

Mild	1032 (3.2%) -	sweet and malty with a ruddy tinge
Bitter	1035 (3.5%) -	subtle and pleasantly dry, rather thin
Original	1038 (3.8%) -	well-hopped flavoursome bitter
Old Strong	1050 (5.0%) -	unusual, fruity winter brew
Tollyshooter	1050 (5.0%) -	a reddish premium bitter

USHERS

Ushers of Trowbridge PLC, Directors house, 68 Fore Street, Trowbridge, Wiltshire, BA14 8JF
Tel: (01225) 763171 Fax: (01225) 774289

A brewery which has seen many changes. Brews for Enterprise Inns (Gibbs Mew).

Salisbury BB	1042 (4.1%) -	a pleasant beer, lacking in bitterness

WADWORTHS

Northgate Brewery, Northgate, Devizes, Wiltshire SN10 1JW
Tel: (01380) 723361 Fax: (01380) 724342

Delightful traditional market-town brewery supplying a wide-ranging free trade

6X	1040 (4.3%) -	a splendid, malty bitter, slightly sweet

WEBSTERS - See S&N

WELLS

Charles Wells Ltd., The Eagle Brewery, Havelock Street, Bedford,
Beds MK40 4LU
Tel: (01234) 272766 Fax: (01234) 279000

Bombardier	1042 (4.3%) -	well balanced best bitter
Fargo	1050 (5.0%) -	a winter beer with a balance of hops and fruit

WHITBREAD

Whitbread PLC, Porter Tun House, Capability Green, Luton,
Bedfordshire, LU1 3LS
Tel: (01582) 391166 Fax: (01582) 397397
A national brewing company which has a long (and still continuing) history
of destroying breweries. Until recently they at least showed commitment to
cask ales by producing a wide range of brands based on the products of
defunct breweries but that policy now seems to have changed with beers
being axed in favour of Boddingtons bitter - a national "bland".

Boddingtons, Strangeways Brewery, PO Box 23, Strangeways,
Manchester M60 3EL
Tel: (0161) 828 2000 Fax: (0161) 828 2213
Once a proud independent, which sold its soul to Whitbread.

Castle Eden, PO Box 13, Castle Eden, Hartlepool, Cleveland TS27 4SX
Tel: (01429) 836007
Traditional north-eastern brewery, which has produced many one-off beers
for the Whitbread Cask Collection. Threatened with closure in 1998, but
saved by a couple of local businessmen.

Flowers Brewery, Monson Avenue, Cheltenham, Gloucestershire GL50 4EL
Closed in 1998 - beers to be produced at Strangeways

Boddingtons Bitter	1035 (3.8%) -	bland and sweet, served with a thick head of foam
Flowers IPA	1036 (3.6%) -	faintly malty, little hoppiness
Whitbread BB	1036 (3.6%) -	previously a keg only beer now available on draught
Castle Eden Ale	1042(4.2%) -	rich and sweetish bitter with hoppy aroma and nutty flavour. Probably the best of the remaining Whitbread ales
Flowers Original	1045 (4.5%) -	full-bodied and well-hopped

WOODFORDES

Woodfordes Norfolk Ales, Broadland Brewery, Woodbastwick,
Norwich, NR13 6SW
Tel: (01603) 720353 Fax:(01603) 721806
Founded in 1980, now brews an extensive range of beers and runs three
tied houses. Also produces its own home brew kits

Wherry Best Bitter 1039 (3.8%) - an award winning distinctively hoppy
beer with a long-lasting bitter aftertaste

Great Eastern Ale 1043 (4.3%) - pale and well-balanced

Headcracker 1069 (7.0%) - dangerous!

WORTHINGTON - See Bass

YOUNG'S

Ram Brewery, High Street, Wandsworth, London SW18 4JD
Tel: (0181) 875 7000 Fax: (0181) 875 7100
One of the most popular breweries around. It stood alone in the London
area when Keg was the fashion, all its pubs sell Real Ale and its tied estate
is growing, now including several pubs in Essex.

Bitter 1036 (3.7%) - light, bitter and distinctive.
Commonly known as "ordinary" but in
fact far from it.

Special 1046 (4.6%) - full-flavoured and distinctive, hoppy dry
finish

Ram Rod 1050 (5.0%) - malty and slightly sweet

Winter Warmer 1055 (5.0%) - strong old winter brew, sweet and
Satisfying. A good reason to look
forward to October.

YOUNGERS - See S&N

CAMRA MEMBERSHIP APPLICATION

I/We wish to join the Campaign for Real Ale and agree to abide by its rules.

Title _____ Surname _____

Forename(s) _____

Date of birth _____

(Partner's name) _____

(Partner's date of birth) _____

Address _____

_____

_____

Postcode_____ Date _____

Telephone number(s) _____

		Tick
Single Membership	£14	_____
Under 26 or over 60 (retired)	£8	_____
Residents outside the E.U.	£18	_____
Partner at same address Add	£3	_____
		_____
Total £		_____

Please charge my Access / Master Card / Visa / Delta / Switch

Number_____

Name on card _____

Expiry date _____ Issue number for Switch cards _____

Signature _____

Or phone 01727 867201 with your card details.

If you wish to pay by cheque please post this form and your cheque made payable to CAMRA to: CAMRA, 230 Hatfield Road, St Albans, Hertfordshire, AL1 4ZA.

For details of life membership, please phone 01727 867201.

THREE MONTHS FREE MEMBERSHIP WHEN PAYING BY DIRECT DEBIT - PLEASE PHONE FOR A FORM.

NOTES

NOTES